Multichannel Image Detectors

Multichannel Image Detectors

Yair Talmi, EDITOR
EG&G Princeton Applied Research Corporation

Based on a symposium
jointly sponsored by the
ACS Divisions of
Analytical and Physical Chemistry
at the 176th Meeting of the
American Chemical Society,
Miami Beach, Florida,
September 11–12, 1978.

ACS SYMPOSIUM SERIES 102

AMERICAN CHEMICAL SOCIETY
WASHINGTON, D. C. 1979

Library of Congress CIP Data

Multichannel image detectors
(ACS symposium series; 102 ISSN 0097-6156)

Includes bibliographies and index.

1. Spectrum analysis—Congresses. 2. Spectrum analysis—Instruments—Congresses. 3. Image processing—Equipment and supplies—Congresses.
I. Talmi, Yair, 1942- . II. American Chemical Society. Division of Analytical Chemistry. III. Series: American Chemical Society. ACS symposium series; 102.

QD95.M975 543'.085 79-12441
ISBN 0-8412-0504-3 ACSMC8 102 1-351 1979

PRINTED IN THE UNITED STATES OF AMERICA

ACS Symposium Series

FOREWORD

The ACS SYMPOSIUM SERIES was founded in 1974 to provide a medium for publishing symposia quickly in book form. The format of the Series parallels that of the continuing ADVANCES IN CHEMISTRY SERIES except that in order to save time the papers are not typeset but are reproduced as they are submitted by the authors in camera-ready form. Papers are reviewed under the supervision of the Editors with the assistance of the Series Advisory Board and are selected to maintain the integrity of the symposia; however, verbatim reproductions of previously published papers are not accepted. Both reviews and reports of research are acceptable since symposia may embrace both types of presentation.

CONTENTS

UNCONVENTIONAL APPLICATIONS

PREFACE

Progress in scientific research, particularly in the physical sciences, has become increasingly dependent on the concurrent development of the appropriate instrumentation necessary to execute experiments of an increasingly complex nature.

Spectrometric measurements can produce copious scientific data. Such data is often adequate to unambiguously characterize a sought-after entity, whether it is related to a study of a stellar object, a high-temperature plasma, or a chemical compound. Unfortunately, the extraction of such information is frequently hampered by the lack of measurement signals with adequate signal-to-noise ratios (SNR), for example when very low light level signals are buried in a noisy background or when a very limited quantity of sample is available for examination. Other times the signal magnitude is ample but its transient nature does not lend itself to sufficiently long observation periods.

It has been long recognized that the panacea for these inadequacies lies with the development of more efficient detection systems that allow simultaneous monitoring of an entire spectral region (window).

In the IR spectral region the noise characteristics, typical of the measurement system, have led to the development of multiplex detectors whose operation is based on the use of mathematical transformations such as the Fourier and the Hadamad. With these detection systems, an appropriate encoding (transformation) of the raw spectral signal is performed, which permits simultaneous monitoring of a wide spectral window with a single-channel sensor. A SNR (multiplex) advantage is achieved that is typically proportional to the square root of either the observation time or the number of spectral-resolution elements contained in that spectral window.

In the UV–NIR spectral region, an alternative approach has been shown to be advantageous; parallel multichannel detection, whereby an array of individual detectors is placed at the exit focal plane of a spectrometer, allows simultaneous monitoring of a side spectral window without resorting to signal encoding. Of course the dispersion spectrometer, by its very nature, is an encoding device capable of transforming a spectral information record into a corresponding spatial one.

With the advancement of television technology and the development of commercially available miniaturized image devices, the necessary "parallel" optical multichannel detector has become a reality. These devices, often referred to as optoelectronic image devices (OID), are typically constructed on a single monolithic silicon crystal wafer, using well established LSI manufacturing techniques. Linear detectors (25 nm long) with up to 2000 discrete light sensors and two-dimensional image devices with a few hundred thousand sensors are now commercially available.

These devices have proved their capability to actually achieve the theoretical multiplex (SNR) advantage. This makes them very attractive for studies of light phenomena that have ultra-short (μsec to psec) lifetimes or that involve measurements of very low SNR.

State-of-the-art optical parallel detectors conform very well to most criteria of "ideal" detectors. They are reliably manufactured at a reasonable cost. They can be made immune to sudden "light-shocks." They are mechanically rugged, compact and easily cooled, and consume little electrical power. They can be constructed with exceptionally high geometric accuracy and thus provide an equally excellent wavelength accuracy (wavelength-to-sensor position registration across the focal plane of the spectrometer). Some of these detectors provide high flexibility in addressing their individual sensors, including random access. The silicon-type detectors, particularly the self-scanned photodiode arrays, have a remarkably high spectral response with relatively uniform characteristics across a very wide spectral range: 190–1060 nm. Most significantly, their dynamic range (real-time) can be as high as 10^5:1 with highly linear transfer characteristics (gamma of 1).

The performance of these detectors, vis-a-vis that of single channel detectors, has been rapidly and steadily growing and in a few cases actually has shown distinct superiority. Particularly in such cases (some of which are discussed in this manuscript) the parallel detector has gained wide acceptance and currently is often used as a viable component in many measurement systems of very complex natures.

Unfortunately (alas, not uncommonly), the significance of the optical multichannel detector has as yet escaped most potential users, who erroneously consider it a mere curiosity still emerging from its embryonic stage. This manuscript is another attempt to demonstrate the maturity and viability of the optical-multichannel detection approach. No longer is the technique a novelty toyed with by a handful of curious instrumentalists, but rather a readily available scientific tool whose performance characteristics and spectrometric applicability are relatively well understood.

It is hoped that the few examples described in this manuscript, which in no way represent the exhaustive list of current uses, will convince the reader of the validity of the above statements. Perhaps this time the undesirable time gap between the availability of a new technology and its widespread use and acceptance can be shortened.

E G & G Princeton Applied Research Corporation YAIR TALMI
Princeton, New Jersey
February 1, 1979

SPECTROSCOPIC APPLICATIONS

1

Optoelectronic Image Detectors in Chemistry, An Overview

YAIR TALMI

EG&G Princeton Applied Research Corporation, Princeton, NJ 08540

Spectrometric information can be obtained either by scanning across the spectral region of interest or by simultaneously monitoring this region in its entirety. Two instrumentation approaches to simultaneous spectrometric detection, that have evolved in the last two decades are multiplex and multichannel techniques. The former, utilizes transform methods based upon either Hadamand or Fourier mathematics. This approach has been rigorously studied both theoretically and experimentally and has been proven commercially feasible. However, its simultaneous (multiplex) advantage has been realized only for the IR region, where the spectrometric system is typically detector-noise limited. The multiplex advantage has been only partially realized with VUV to near IR-, electron- and ion-spectrometers, where the overall performance of the detector system is rarely limited by the detector noise itself. In fact, in a few cases, where "dense" spectra were studied, a "multiplex-disadvantage" has been actually observed (1,2). The alternative approach is "parallel-detection"; an array of detectors is placed across the focal plane of a polychromator and the dispersed radiation is simultaneously measured.

By far, the most widely used and commonly available parallel detector is the photographic emulsion. It has a fixed and accurate geometric registration that allows for reliable wavelength calibration. Its operation is methodically and practically simple, its cost is affordable and its physical dimensions, and therefore spectral resolution, practically unlimited, depending only on the design of the polychromator. Unfortunately, the sensitivity (quantum efficiency) of these detectors is poor, their transfer characteristics non-linear (gamma $\neq 1$), their accuracy and precision are marginal and require tedious and time consuming calibration procedures and worse yet, the validity and usefulness of the spectral data gathered can be verified only after the "plate-development" process, thus, often resulting in a loss of invaluable, and at times, irreproducible experimental data.

Because of its wide acceptance as a VUV-near IR spectrometric detector, the PMT has emerged as the natural electro-optical parallel detector. This has been accomplished by placing an array of

0-8412-0504-3/79/47-102-003$05.75/0

mini-PMTs in predetermined positions (corresponding to spectral regions of interest) across the focal plane of a polychromator, each with its associated readout electronics. Such detection systems, despite their clumsiness have been proven very useful in various routine spectrometric studies, where the same few spectral features (10-40) are repeatedly interrogated, where absolute (spectroradiometric) spectral data is not required and where the most critical and desirable performance features are; a very wide dynamic range, high sensitivity and low stray light, rather than optimal flexibility in the interaction between the spectroscopist and his experiment. A typical example of this design approach is the "direct-reader"; a rather expensive, and dedicated, "factory-tuned" multichannel spectrometer that is capable of monitoring up to forty spectral lines simultaneously and is used almost exclusively in conjunction with arcs, sparks and plasmas for routine elemental analysis.

In the last decade, as the state-of-the-art TV cameras have adequately matured, their use as spectrometric parallel detectors has been demonstrated and gradually gained acceptance among spectroscopists. All TV-detectors, and more generally optoelectronic image detectors (OID) including image-orthicon and isocon, silicon, lead-oxide and KCl vidicons and a variety of solid-state imagers, such as self-scanned photodiode arrays, charge-coupled and charge-injection devices, are by their very nature, multichannel parallel photon detectors which can accurately transform optical images into their corresponding electronic images. All OIDs comprise three basic components; a transducer to convert photon images to their electrical analogs, a device for storing these "latent" electrical images and a readout (video) mechanism to reconstruct the stored images and transmit them (in real-time) to a display monitor or via the use of an A/D converter to store them in a digital memory for further data processing and manipulation. Historically, the trend in the TV-detector industry has been toward simplification via consolidation of these components. Thus, in first generation imagers, e.g., charge-coupled devices, all three components including the video preamplifier itself are combined on a single monolithic silicon crystal wafer (3).

Although most experts predict that third generation self-scanned solid state imagers will eventually become the OIDs of choice, at the present time, their compromised performance, low manufacture yield and therefore, limited commercial availability, greatly limit their use as spectrometric detectors. An exception to that are self-scanned photodiode arrays.

Because vidicon imagers and particularly the silicon vidicon with its various image-intensified derivatives are much more readily available and their behavior and performance are better controlled (even if not always fully understood), a brief description of their principles of operation may be necessary if their spectrometric performance (and that of other imagers as well) is to be properly and intelligently interpreted.

The heart of the SV is a single monolithic silicon crystal

wafer with a microscopic array of a few million diode junctions grown on it (Figure 1). All diodes have a common cathode and isolated anodes selectively addressed by a scanning (readout) electron beam. The diodes function as photodiodes, generating the production and storage of electron-hole pairs upon incidence of UV to near-IR photons.

A continuously scanning electron beam recharges all photodiodes to an equal and preset reversed-bias potential. Exposure of the target to photons or electrons causes production of electron-hole pairs that combine to deplete the surface charge. When the beam scans again, this time a partially depleted region, a recharging current flows. This current is proportional to the depleted charge and likewise to the density of the electron-hole pairs. It therefore, is proportional also to the number of photons (or photoelectrons) incident on each diode.

The imaging (and spectral) resolution of the SV is limited by the diameter of the scanning electron beam, typically 25 μm. However, any number of diodes can be grouped together (by a computer-pre-programmed addressing manipulation of the readout beam) and their combined signal stored in the same memory cell. Thus, a trade-off between resolution and signal-to-noise ratio (SNR) can be accomplished, in a manner analogous to that achieved by varying the slit width of a spectrometer. Because the readout noise of silicon vidicons (SV) is approximately 2000 electron rms, the smallest signals that can be detected (in each resolution element) are a few thousand photons in magnitude; typical quantum efficiency (QE) of silicon is 10% to 80% in the UV to near-IR region. To detect single photoelectrons, an image intensification section is added to the silicon vidicon. The resultant imager, a silicon-intensified target (SIT) vidicon, has a photocathode (transducer) that converts the photon image into a corresponding photoelectron image. The generated electron image is accelerated (typically 7 - 9 kv) and focused onto the silicon target. Since the number of electron-hole charge pairs produced on the target is proportional to the potential of the incident electrons (approximately one charge pair per 3.6 ev) an internal gain of approximately 1500 is typically achieved, i.e., this is the number of electrons produced from each photoelectron emitted from the photocathode (the electron energy is partially absorbed by the silicon oxide overcoat). With this gain, the signal is sufficiently enhanced (compared to the readout noise) to allow the detection of very weak signals. Further gain, if necessary, can be obtained by adding another image intensification stage; the intensified silicon intensified target (ISIT) detector. In fact, the ISIT is capable of detecting a single photoelectron per resolution element (500 channels in the linear mode and a few thousands of resolution elements in the two-dimensional or random-access mode of operation).

OIDs are now available which can be used as parallel light detectors with up to 2000 channels in the linear mode of operation and many tens of thousands in the two-dimensional mode of

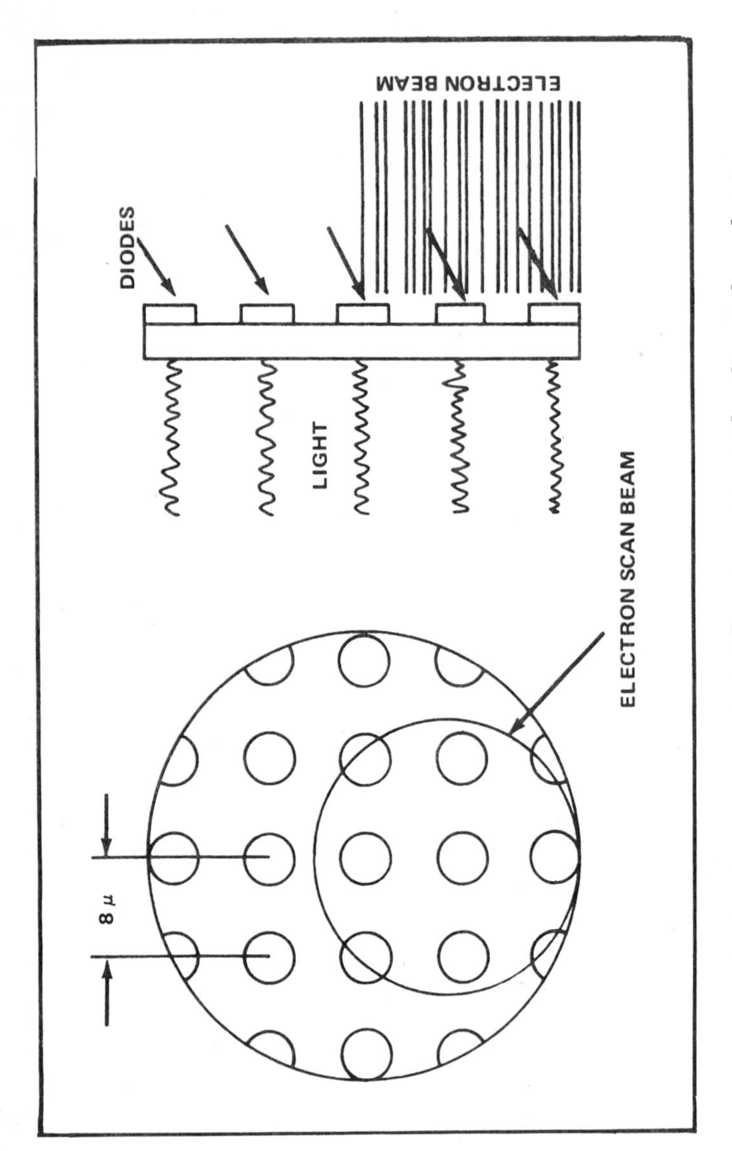

Figure 1. Diode structure and principles of operation of the silicon vidicon detector

Table 1

Advantages of multichannel (parallel) TV detectors

Applications	**SNR advantage (F)[a] or time saving advantage (TS)**
Low light illumination Photon shot-noise or preamplifier shot-noise limitations, or source-flicker-noise limitations but utilizing "source compensation" techniques	*Single readout or continuous read-and-store-in-memory accumulation* $F \propto (N)^{1/2}$; N = number of individual spectral resolution elements simultaneously monitored by the TV detector $TS \propto (N)^{1/2}$ *also* $F \propto (t)^{-1/2}$; $t = T/N$; T = time required for a complete scan of a spectrum, using a scanning monochromator $F \propto (\Delta\lambda)^{-1/2}$; $\Delta\lambda$, spectral coverage of a single resolution element (during time t)
Medium to high light level illumination Sampling or analysis-time limitations, e.g., insufficient amounts of samples for a destructive spectrometric analysis	*Single readout or continuous read-and-store-in-memory accumulation* $F \propto N$; *also* $TS \propto t^{-1}$ $TS \propto N$; *also* $TS \propto (\Delta\lambda)^{-1}$
Ultralow light level illumination Preamplifier shot-noise limitation, e.g., astronomical and some luminescence measurements	*Uninterrupted long exposure of the target to the signal (signal buildup on target) followed by a single readout-integration* F and $TS \propto N$ F and $TS \propto t^{-1}$ F and $TS \propto (\Delta\lambda)^{-1}$
Ultrarapid light phenomena Submicrosecond to picosecond temporal range	*Measurements impossible to perform with a single-channel, scanning spectrometer* $F \propto \infty$

[a] $F = \dfrac{\text{(SNR) TV detector}}{\text{(SNR) single channel detector}}$

operation.

The relative merits of OIDs (parallel detectors), compared to single-channel spectrometric detectors, are derived from the simultaneity (multiplex advantage) at which whole spectral regions are detected. This feature results in a significant improvement in the measured SNR or in a proportional reduction in the observation time required for the measurement. A summary of these advantages is given in Table I. The third mode of detector operation described in this Table, the "integration" mode, is very unique to OIDs. At low temperatures, e.g., -50°C, the detector can be exposed to ultra-low-light level signals for long periods of time (with the readout beam turned off) until the "latent" electrical, on-target-"developed", signal is sufficiently high to be read-off the storage device (target) with an adequate S/N ratio. In this mode of detection, subphoton-per-second light signals can be measured quantitively, Fig.2. Moreover, because entire spectra are simultaneously monitored, any source fluctuation can be readily compensated for (vide infra).

Because of their accurate geometric registration, i.e., spectral-to-spatial (channel position) transformation, their integration and storage features, i.e., OIDs are <u>energy</u> rather than <u>power</u> detectors, and because of their two-dimensional characteristics (area array), OIDs are particularly suited for numerous computer-data handling and data processing techniques which can greatly facilitate the interpretation of raw spectrometric data. These techniques have been previously discussed elsewhere (<u>4</u>) and will be only briefly summarized here.

Because the EG&G PARC optical-multichannel analyzer (OMA) has been specifically designed to operate with OIDs, it will be frequently referred to in the following discussion, where various computer manipulations are described and assessed.

<u>Background and blank subtraction:</u> Since the OMA is a curve (spectrum) manipulator, it easily lends itself to subtraction of a background dark-charge (and "pattern") spectrum and/or a blank spectrum from each acquired analyte spectrum. The resultant analyte spectrum. The resultant analyte spectrum is thus free of any detector or blank e.g., solvent, distortions, Fig. 3.

<u>Channel-to-channel spectral response correction:</u> Normalization factors necessary to correct for channel-to-channel spectral response variations and variations in the spectral transfer effi- of the optical system, e.g., grating efficiency, can be stored in memory and thus provide the means for an automatic spectrum correction, Fig. 4.

<u>Spectral Stripping</u>: Mathematical curve-fitting manipulations (5), requiring highly accurate geometric (wavelength) registration, can be performed in order to quantitatively deconvolute mixtures of known individual components. Such techniques, successfully implemented with the OMA, can significantly reduce the number and

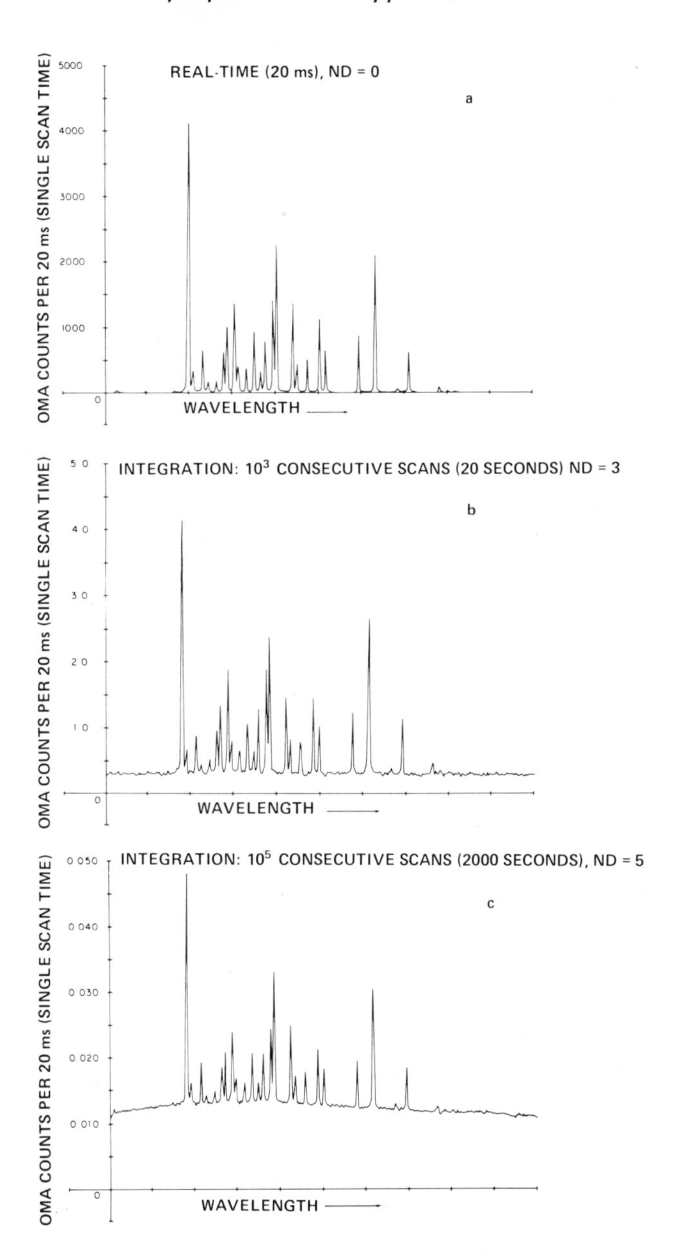

Figure 2. Neon spectra (hollow cathode emission) acquired with an SIT detector cooled to −50°C. (a) Real-time detection, 20 ms/scan, neutral density filter (ND) = 0; (b) Readout, after signal integration for 20 seconds; (c) Integration equivalent to 10^5 scan periods. ND filter = 5 (0.001% transmission) was used to attenuate the signal. Equivalent "dark" spectra were subtracted from each neon spectrum.

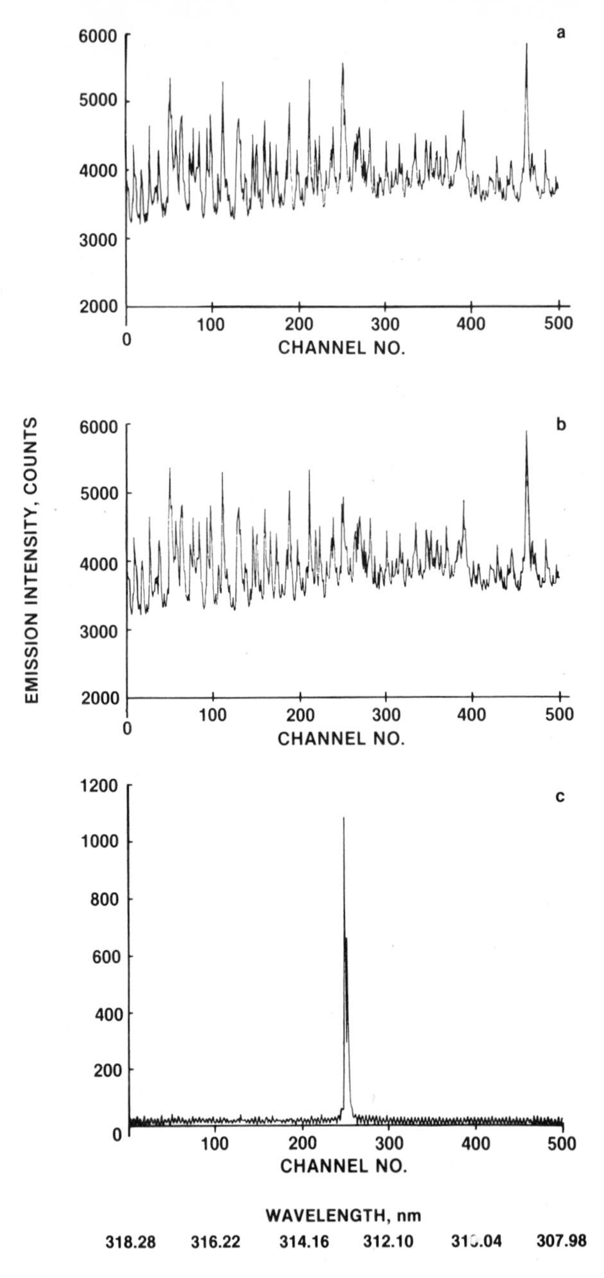

Figure 3. Emission spectra obtained from an induction coupled plasma with an ultrasonic nebulizer (for sample introduction). A 1 m spectrometer, JACO model with a diffraction grating blazed at 250 nm, and a slit width of 20 μm, was used. The spectral resolution was 10.3 nm/500 channels = 0.0206 nm/channel. (a) Emission spectrum of a 1 μg/l beryllium, 1% HNO_3 solution. (b) Emission spectrum of a 1% HNO_3 blank solution. (c) Difference spectrum obtained by subtracting spectrum (b) from (a). Spectra were obtained after an on-target integration for 8 sec.

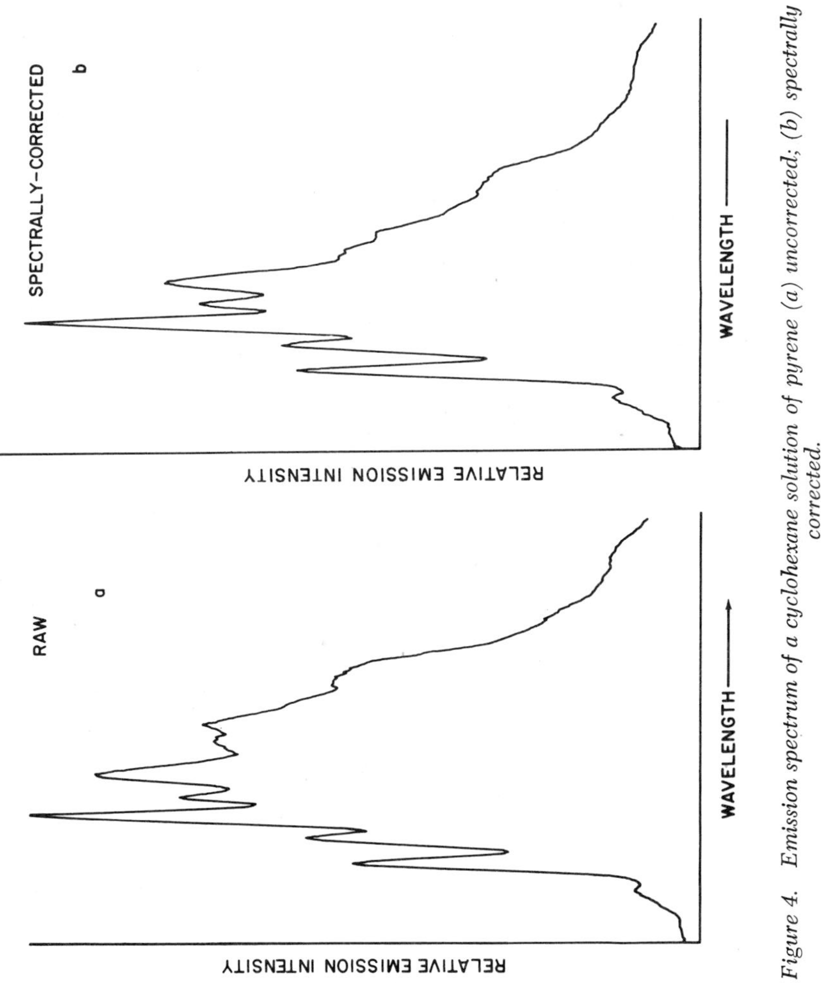

Figure 4. Emission spectrum of a cyclohexane solution of pyrene (a) uncorrected; (b) spectrally corrected.

extent of chemical separation steps required for analyzing such mixtures (6,7,8), Fig. 5.

Smoothing and differentiation of spectral data: The high geometric accuracy of OIDs provides the means for an accurate, software-preformed, smoothing (low-pass filtering) and differentiation (high-pass filtering) of raw spectral data. These manipulations facilitate the interpretation and identification of acquired spectra, Fig. 6 and 7.

Source compensation: Pulse-to-pulse intensity variations and intensity fluctuations in the spectrometric excitation source are often the dominant noise source affecting the performance of the detection system. However, since OIDs are parallel multichannel detectors, these intensity variations do equally and simultaneously affect the entire spectral distribution as a whole. Thus, with the aid of a single-channel reference detector, monitoring a portion of the source's light flux, it is possible to accurately normalize for spectrum-to-spectrum variations and practically eliminate these and any other source flicker noise related effects.

Two-dimensional (2D) spectroscopy: The silicon vidicon is a two-dimensional OID with an area-array target comprising a few hundred thousands dicrete photodiodes. Since these diodes can be randomly read out by the scanning beam, the detector is capable of performing some very useful spectrometric tasks:

1. Random-access readout of the imager is useful for conservation of time and computer memory space since only relevant data is digitized and stored.

2. The adverse effects of blooming (channel-to-channel cross-talk due to "overspill" of photon-generated charge) and spectral interference, whereby minor spectral features are masked by dominant neighboring features, can be largely reduced. The intense features are more frequently read-out (erased) by the scanning beam while the weak feature is allowed to integrate (on target) in order to improve its readout SNR.

3. 2D spectral contours, such as obtained in "total-luminescence spectroscopy" (excitation vs. emission)(8-10) can be simultaneously acquired, and actually monitored in real-time, by the OMA.

4. When the image of elongated excitation sources, e.g., arcs, flames, plasmas, etc., is focused along the slit height of a polychromator, the spatial intensity information (vertical axis) is accurately relayed to the exit focal plane, concurrently with the horizontal spectral dispersion. Thus, by (electronically) dividing the target into a few tens of tracks, the entire spectral profile of these sources can be simultaneously observed and quantitatively studied.

5. The electronic division of the target into a large number of individual tracks, each of which has 500 channels, provides the means for a rather unique dual-beam and more generally

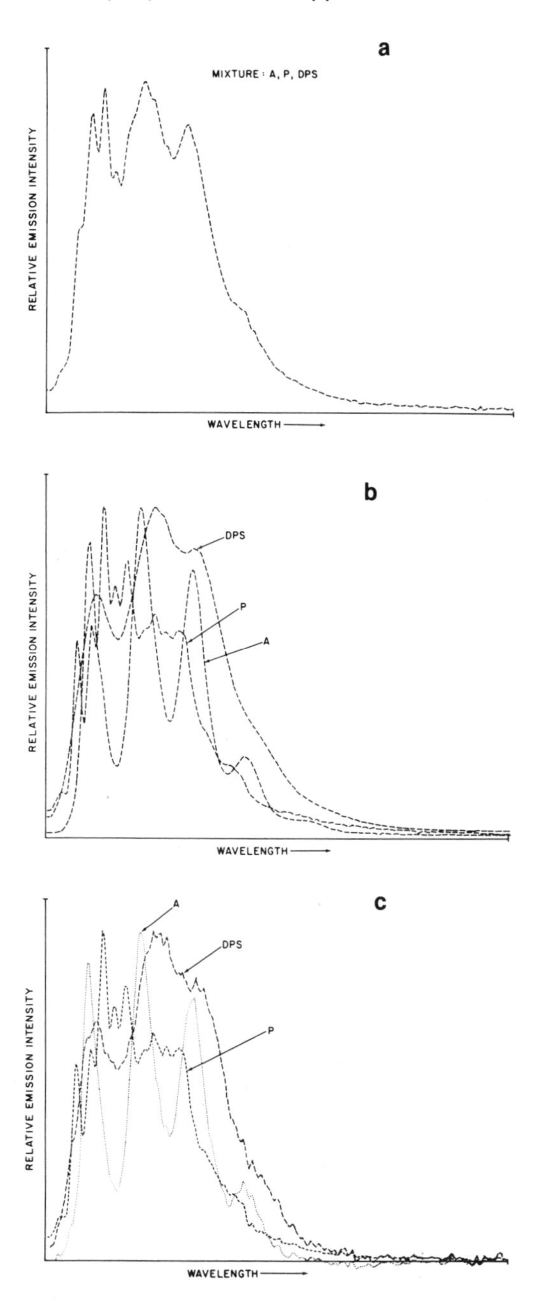

Figure 5. Emission spectra of anthracene, pyrene, and diphenylstilbene. (a) 1 μg/ml solution of the three compounds. Experimental conditions: excitation wavelength, 340 nm; 400 scans; spectral bandpass, 3 nm (b) individual emission spectra of same three compounds (c) Computer-deconvoluted emission spectra of same compounds.

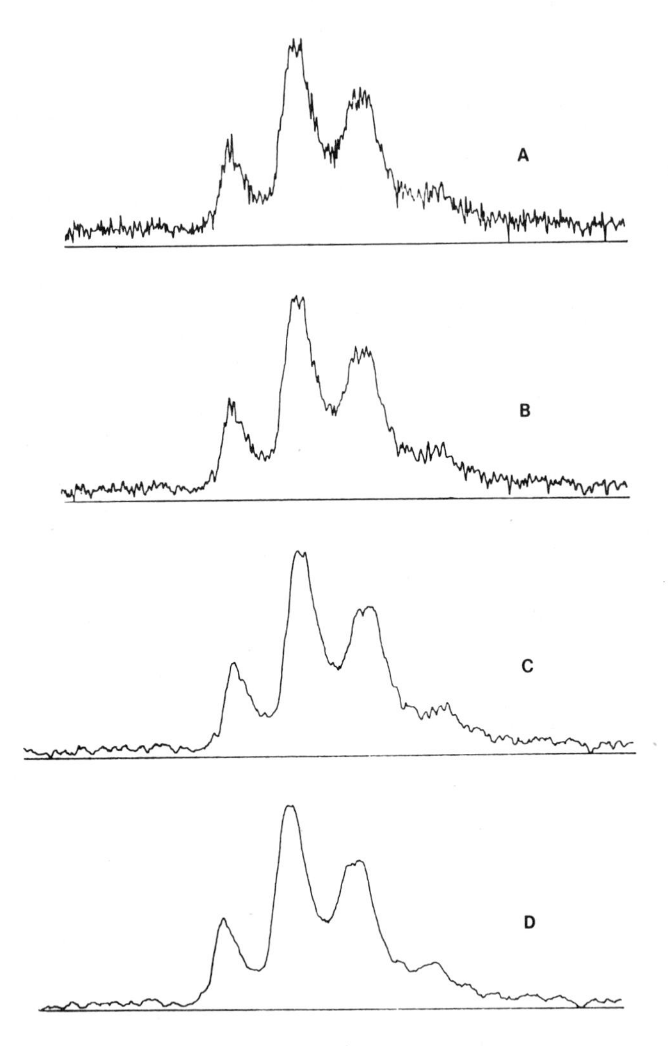

Figure 6. The effect of digital data smoothing on the emission spectra of anthracene. (a) Raw data; (b) With a quadratic fit, 7-point Savitzky-Golay smoothing; (c) Same, but 11-point; (d) Same, but 17-point smoothing.

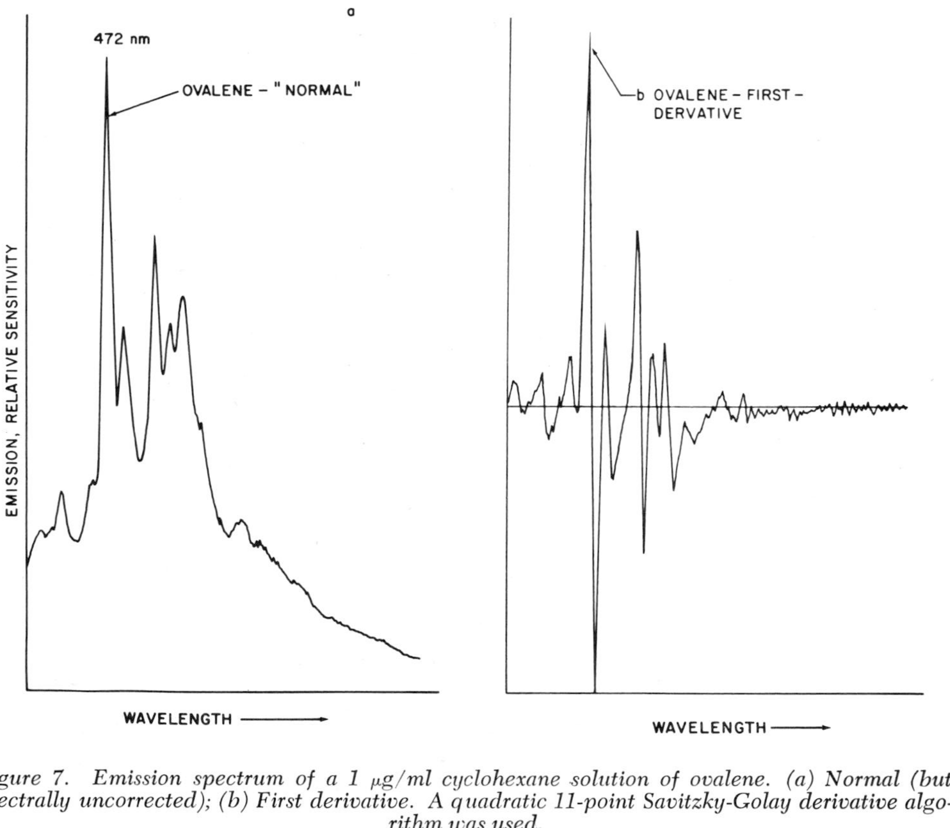

Figure 7. Emission spectrum of a 1 μg/ml cyclohexane solution of ovalene. (a) Normal (but spectrally uncorrected); (b) First derivative. A quadratic 11-point Savitzky-Golay derivative algorithm was used.

poly-beam spectroscopy. The light beams transmitted through or emitted by a few sample cells are focused at different locations along the entrance slit of a polychromator. The resultant spectra are simultaneously detected, each on a track, whose position corresponds to that of the beam position on the slit. This eliminates the need for laborious pulse-to-pulse normalization procedures and long experimental observation times, typically required in many pulse spectroscopy studies. Furthermore, since all beams are detected by the same target (single crystal, silicon wafer), both detector and source flicker noise are practically eliminated.

Transient Spectroscopy

Parallel optoelectronic detectors are ideal for transient spectroscopy studies. In the following discussion this field will be categorized into a few time domains related to the measurement instrumentation required, Fig. 8.

1. Seconds to ms: In this temporal range use is made of the scanning mechanism of the OID. Silicon vidicons can complete a full scan (500 channels) in 10 ms. Faster scans are prohibited by the inherent discharge lag, i.e., incomplete readout of signal, characteristic of all electron-beam-readout OIDs. For temporal resolution in the millisecond time range, the self-scanned array detector, e.g., photodiode array, is the imager of choice. The OMA is particularly suited for ms kinetics studies with photodiode arrays. A complete scan of all 1024 channels can be accomplished within 16 ms. However, channels that don't contain relevant information can be skipped at the rate of 0.5 μsec per channel, a process called, "fast access". Moreover, temporal resolution can be further improved by summing neighboring channels, a process called, "grouping". The reduction in frame scan time is practically linearly inverse to group size (for group sizes above two). Thus, using the fast access and grouping procedures, a useful compromise between temporal and spectral resolution can be achieved.

In the second-to-millisecond temporal range, the OMA is very useful for studies of liquid-phase chemical reactions, including stop-flow. The OMA can also serve as a very efficient (real-time) spectroscopic detector, absorption or fluorescence, for liquid-chromatographic effluents. Because the entire spectral region of interest is simultaneously monitored, no compromise concerning the selection of optimized wavelengths is necessary and sufficient chemical characterization data is provided for each effluent to allow pattern-recognition and "finger-printing" of complex mixtures, e.g., oil and smoke extracts, etc. (11).

2. Milliseconds-to-microseconds: This time domain is covered with either gated image devices or with the rotating optical slit, a recent EG&G-PARC development,(12). The intensified OIDs, e.g., SIT and ISIT, have a triode-structured image section

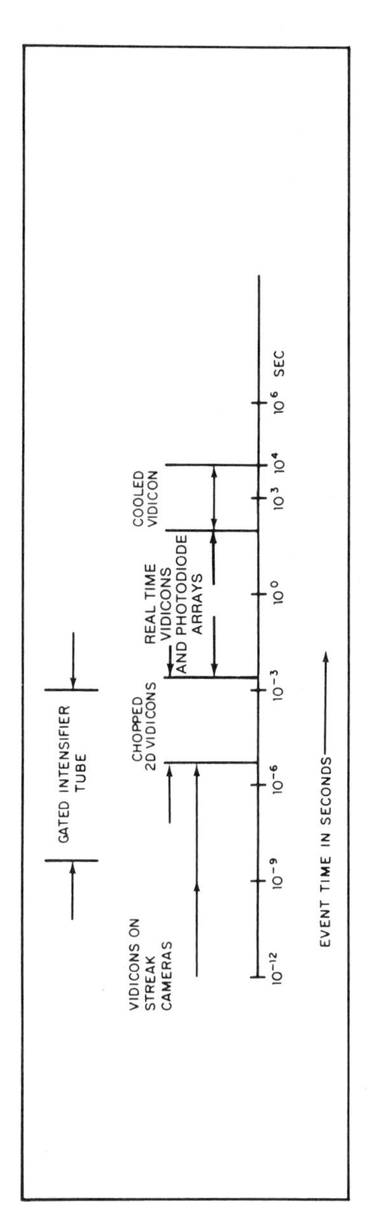

Figure 8. The use of optical multichannel detectors in studies of optical phenomena with various time durations

that can be electronically shuttered after a precisely preset delay time. Temporal resolution as low as 40 nsec can be accomplished with minimal image distortion. Gating is also a very valuable tool in discriminating against a relatively high-luminousity background that is virtually a continuous wave (cw) in nature. An excellent example is the monitoring of a Thompson-scattered low-light level signal, superimposed on a super-hot and intensely emitting plasma (13). Another example is the real-time detection of oil spills (contamination) in sea water (14). The backscattered fluorescence spectrum of the oil is detected (in real-time) from an airplane. Since the SIT can be synchronously gated (and externally triggered) with the firing of the exciting laser beam, the sampling time of the background light, i.e., reflection of sunlight from the water, is limited to the gating pulse-width time period and is thus sufficiently reduced to allow day-light monitoring. Gating, however, can produce only a single time datum per pulse, because of the relatively long readout time ($t \geq 10$ msec) of the target. To obtain the complete time and spectral information contained in a single event, e.g., flash photolysis, the rotating optical slit, Fig. 9,10 , is used. A wheel with sixty horizontal slits, equally spaced (10mm apart) is placed in front of the entrance slit (10mm height) of a spectrometer. Rotation of the wheel causes one slit to enter the spectrometer field exactly as the previous one leaves it. Each position of the rotating slit (time axis) corresponds to an OMA track at the focal plane of the spectrometer. The OMA is externally triggered by the event monitored, and data acquisition, along the target tracks begins. When the experiment is ocmpleted, a shift-program is utilized to place the initial track (time zero) at the top of the data set. The temporal resolution (time elapsed between two consecutive tracks) is variable and is practically determined by the width of the choppers' slits (and the corresponding number of tracks on the target) and by its velocity. The performance of the system is limited to events whose persistance is shorter than 1/60th of a wheel revolution-time. Longer events will cause a double exposure. However, with synchronous gating of the detector, double exposure can be prevented (15). At the present time, the temporal resolution range provided by the rotating slit is approximately 8 μs to 3 ms, however, use of other chopping devices, e.g., rotating mirrors, should significantly extend it. The time resolved spectra of a xenon flash (lamp) is shown in Fig. 11 . This system can be applied to medium speed spectrometric kinetic studies including, stop-flow, T-jump, and flash photolysis.

3. Microseconds to nanoseconds: As previously mentioned, gated intensified vidicons can provide temporal resolutions as low as 40 nsec. New intensifiers, e.g., microchannel plates, may extend this range to 1-5 nsec or less. However, by far, the most useful tool for ns to ps spectroscopy is the streak camera, i.e., an ultra-rapid temporal-to-spatial electronic image sweeper (16). Streak cameras convert an optical signal, e.g., a spectrum, into

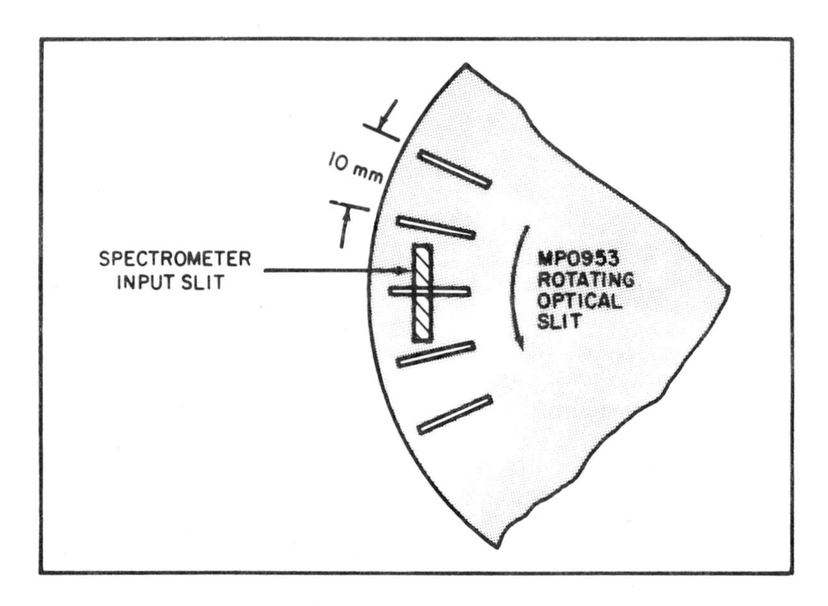

Figure 9. The experimental setup for studies of transient optical phenomena using a rotating optical slit

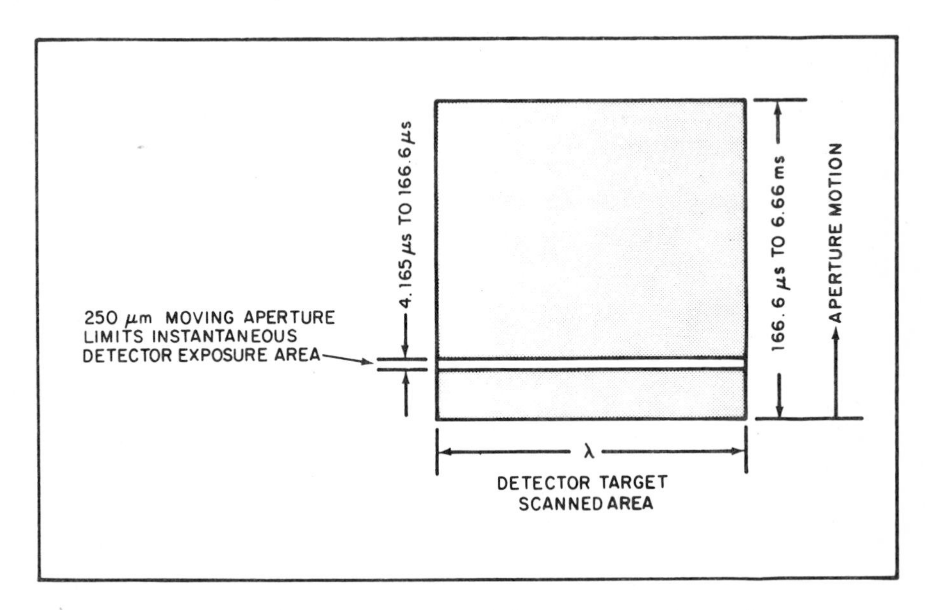

Figure 10. The simultaneous acquisition of the entire spectral record of a transient optical phenomenon, using the rotating optical slit in conjunction with the SIT detector operated in the 2D mode.

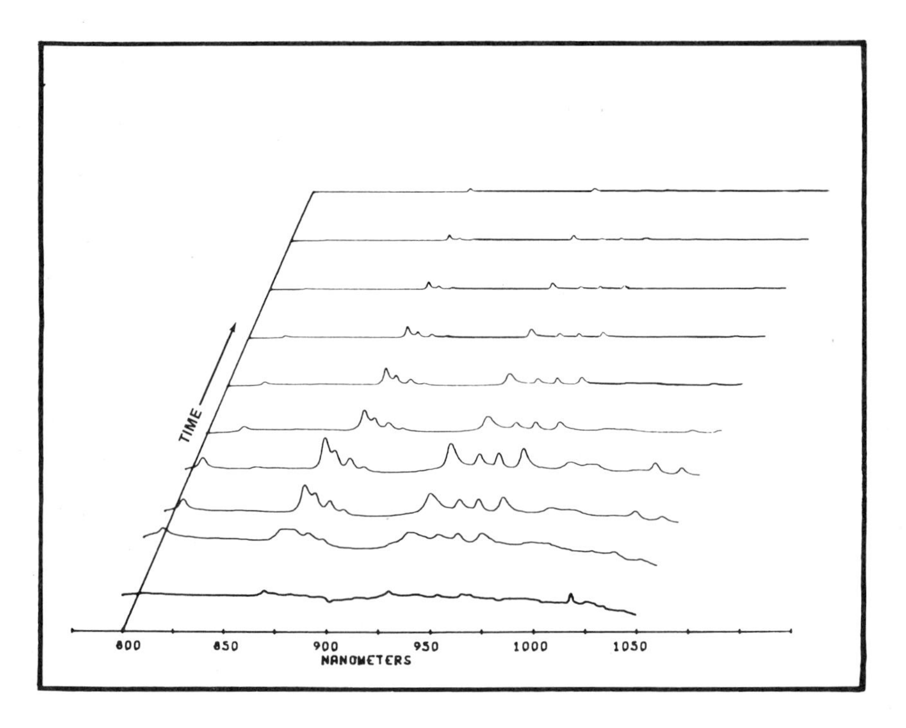

Figure 11. Time resolved spectra obtained from a single flash of a xenon lamp. Total time period (record), 1 msec.

its electron analog (photocathode is used as the transducer) that is then rapidly swept across a phosphor display screen. By optically interfacing the OMA detector to the phosphor-screen output of the streak camera, the entire time-wavelength record can be digitized and stored for further data processing.

4. Picoseconds: Various ingenious techniques have been devised in order to apply the OMA to spectroscopic studies in that time domain, although generally they all utilize either a streak camera or some method of optical delay. Another innovative technique (17) is based on temporal-to-spatial data conversion, with a few psec resolution, via the use of a back aluminized echellon.

Non-photon parallel multichannel detectors

The OMA technology has been recently applied to infra-red spectroscopy (18) as well. A pyroelectric vidicon (utilizing a triglycine sulfate as the sensor element) has been used as a thermal rather than a photon multichannel detector. Simultaneous spectral detection, in the 1-30 um spectral region, was accomplished that has proven to be particularly useful for IR pulse laser applications, Fig.12.

Finally, in the last decade, a new image converter, the microchannel plate (MCP) has been developed and immediately applied to various "non-photon" spectroscopic applications. The MCP (Fig. 13) is a disk-shaped continuous dynode electron multiplier imager. It is made of millions of microscopic (12-14 um diam.) hollow glass (fibers) semi-conducting channels, each acting as an individual electron multiplier, with absolute geometric registration between the input and output plates of the device. The MCP has a typical electron gain of approximately 1000. MCPs have extended the applicability of the OMA to non-optical-spectroscopy because they respond directly to high energy(disperse) radiation; extreme UV, x-rays, electrons, protons, ions, etc. Thus, an imager comprising an MCP multiplier with a phosphor screen output (converting the intensified electron image into a corresponding photon image), when placed at the exit focal plane of a vacuum spectrometer, can serve as an efficient high-energy parallel multichannel detector. The photon-converted spectrum, at the phosphor output, is optically focused onto the faceplate of an OMA light-detector and is therefore read out, digitized and processed as a regular optical spectrum. The MCP imager, operated in that manner, has been successfully used as a VUV, mass-spectrometer and ESCA (electron) detector, Fig. 14 (19-21). The high-gain and low-noise performance of these combined detectors (MCP-OID) has been adequate for "single-event" detection.

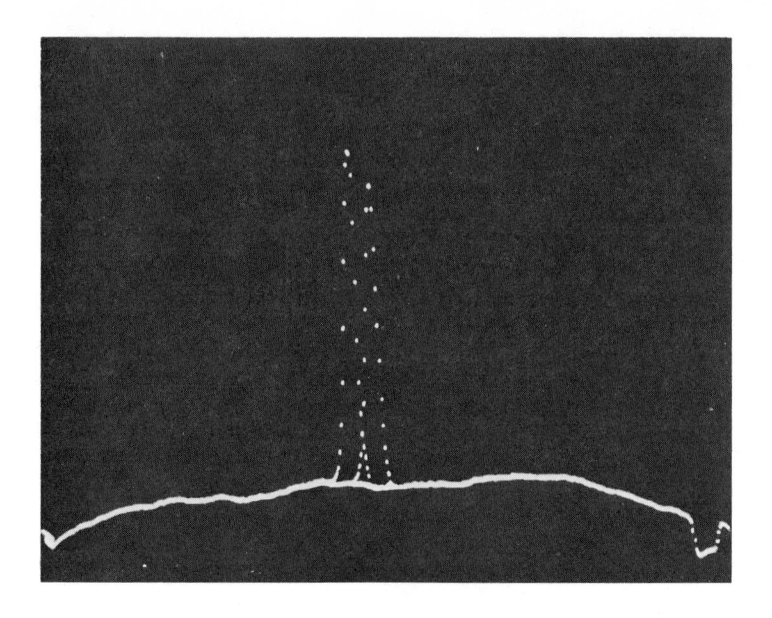

Figure 12. Second order separation of adjacent CO_2 (laser) emission rotation lines [CO_2 transitions P(22) and P(24)]

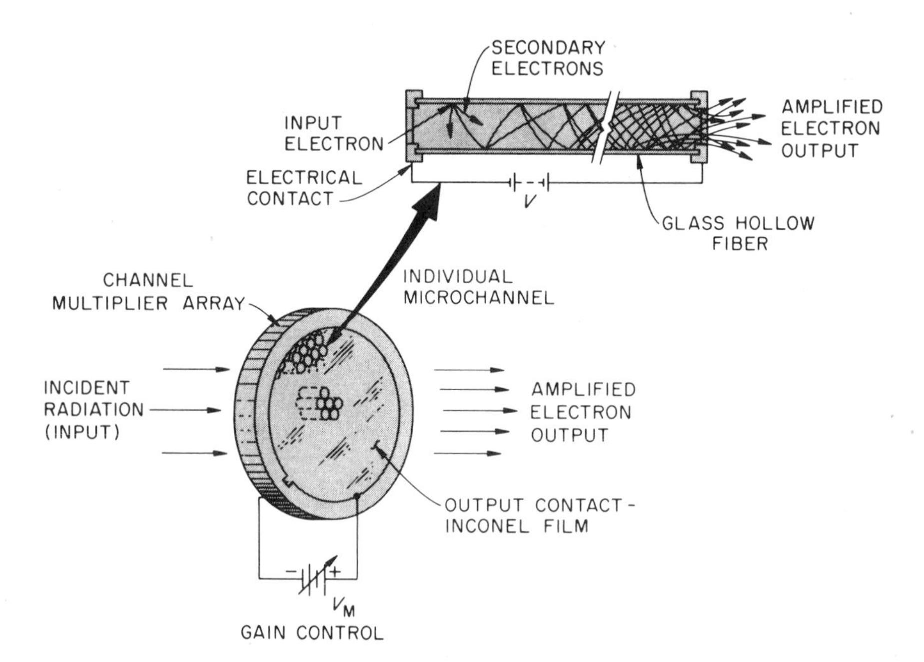

Figure 13. Principles of operation of the microchannel plate (MCP) intensifier

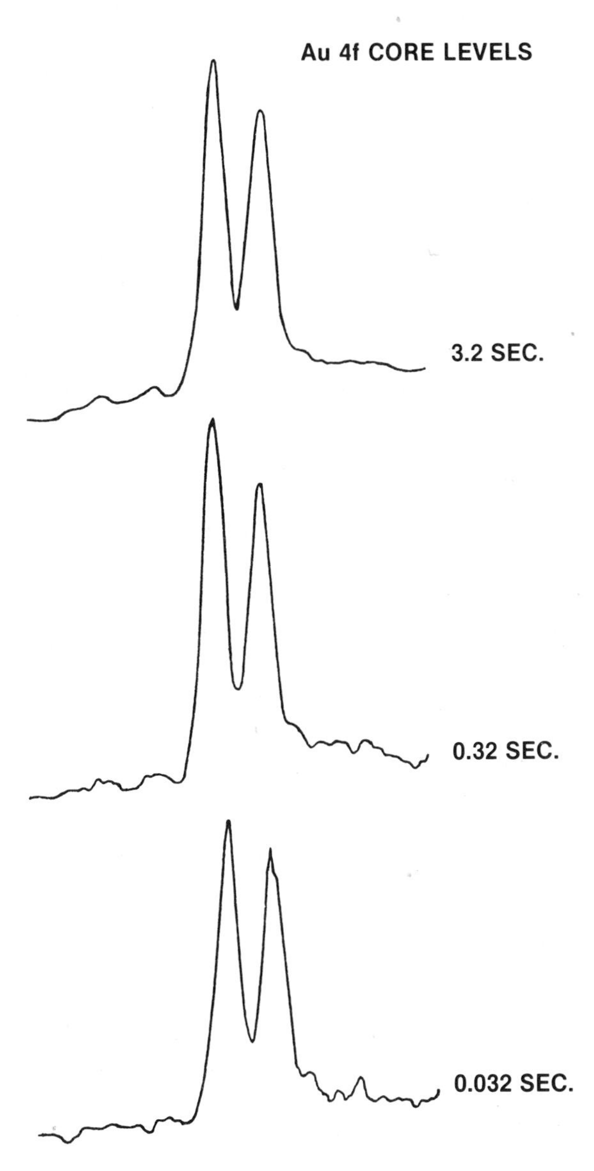

Figure 14. The effect of signal averaging on the SNR of Au 4f spectra (obtained with a McPherson ESCA 36 spectrometer) (21). Spectra were obtained with an MCP intensifier optically coupled to the SIT (OMA) detector. A full (SIT) target scan is completed within 0.032 sec.

Literature cited:

1. F.W. Plankey, T.H. Glen, L.P. Hard, and J.D. Winfordner, Anal. Chem., 46, 1000 (1974)

2. N.M. Larson, R. Crosmum and Y. Talmi, Appl. Opt., 13, 2662 (1974)

3. "Advanced Scanner and Imaging Systems for Earth Observations", NASA, SP-335 Report, 1972.

4. Y. Talmi, American Laboratory, 10(3), 79 (1977).

5. J.C. Sternberg, H.S. Stillo and R.H. Schwendeman, Anal.Chem., 32, 84 (1960)

6. M.J. Milano and K.Y. Kim, Anal. Chem., 49, 555 (1977)

7. A.E. McDowell, R.S. Harner and H.L. Pardue, Clin. Chem. 22, 1862 (1976)

8. Y. Talmi, D.C. Baker, J.E. Jadamec and W.A. Saner, Anal.Chem., 50, 936A (1978)

9. G. Weber, Nature (London), 190, 27 (1961)

10. D.W. Johnson, J.B. Callis and G.D. Christian, Anal. Chem., 49, 747A (1977)

11. D.C. Jadamec, Jr., W.A. Saner, and Y.Talmi, Anal. Chem., 49, 1316 (1977)

12. EG&G PARC, P.O. Box 2565, Princeton, N.J. 08540, Application Note, 1978.

13. N. Bretz, D. Dimock, V. Foote, D. Johnson, D. Long, and E. Tolnas, Appl. Opt. 17(2), 192 (1978)

14. T. Sato, Y. Suzuki, H. Kashiwagi, M. Nanjo and Y. Kakui, IEEE J. Oceanic Eng., OE-3(1), 1 (Jan. 1978)

15. J.L. Weber and J.F. Thompson, Proceedings of the Society of Photo-Optical Instrumentation Engineers, Vol. 148, Aug.1978, in press.

16. G.W. Robinson, T.A. Caughey, R.A. Auerbach and P.J. Harman, "Image Detectors in Chemistry", ACS Symposium Proceeding, June 1979, Editor, Y.Talmi

17. T.L. Metzel, P.M. Rentzepis and J. Leigh, Nature, 182, 238 (1976)

18. Y. Talmi, Appl. Opt. 17(16), 2489 (1978)

19. W.J. Dreyer, A. Kuppermann, H.G. Boettger, C.E. Giffin, D.D. Norris, S.L. Grotch and L.P. Theard, Clin. Chem., 20, 998 (1974)

20. J.H. Beynon, D.O. Jones and R.G. Cooks Anal. Chem. 47, 1735 (1975)

21. G. Ceasar, J.L. Weber and Y. Talmi, Surface and Interface Analysis, (1), Feb. 1979.

RECEIVED January 29, 1979.

2

The Role of Image Devices in Simultaneous Multielement Analysis

K. W. BUSCH and B. MALLOY

Department of Chemistry, Baylor University, Waco, TX 76703

During the past few years, there has been an increasing realization of the need for analytical systems capable of providing quantitative information on many elements in a sample simultaneously. For example, the rising concern in the industrial nations of the impact of man on his environment has prompted numerous investigations on the possible biological hazard of the presence of potentially toxic elements in potable and waste waters. Many of these elements are present at trace and ultra-trace levels, calling for sensitive, sophisticated techniques for their detection and quantification. To provide the maximum amount of information on the composition of a sample, survey analyses may need to quantitatively determine the levels of up to twenty or more elements in a sample. Table I lists some of the currently-available techniques which have been developed by analytical scientists to meet the need for simultaneous multielement analysis (SMA). In particular, analytical spectroscopists have been actively engaged in investigating the multielement capabilities of a variety of novel and ingenious systems. This paper will focus its attention on the role of image devices in SMA.

Characteristics of an Ideal Multielement Spectroscopic System

Before considering the various systems which have been proposed and studied, it is instructive to speculate on the characteristics of the "ideal" spectroscopic system for multielement determinations. Since no system presently available is ideal for multielement analysis, a list of the characteristics of an ideal system would provide a standard toward which all systems should strive. As in any engineering design problem, it may be impossible to design a "real" system which will satisfy all of the design characteristics of an ideal system simultaneously. To facilitate the inevitable compromises which must be made in the design criteria, it is useful to identify certain goals as primary goals and others as secondary goals. Five basic primary

0-8412-0504-3/79/47-102-027$08.00/0

Table I. Multielement Techniques

Technique	No. of elements simultaneously determinable	Analysis time	Sample type
Spark source mass spectrometry	30-50	Photographic detection, slow Electronic detection, fast	Solids
Neutron activation analysis	30-45	Fast to slow depending on element	Solids or liquids
X-ray fluorescence	15-20	Fast	Solids or liquids
Emission spectrometry	20-30	Fast	Solids or liquids

Reprinted from Ref. 69.

goals for a multielement analysis system are speed, flexibility, sensitivity, accuracy, and reliability. Of secondary importance are goals such as compactness and low cost. A goal such as non-destructive analysis is not compatible with atomic spectroscopic procedures.

Speed. For applications where a great number of analyses must be performed on a routine basis, speed is perhaps the most important criterion for a system. Analytical procedures which often take more time than the actual analysis itself include such sample pretreatment procedures as dissolution and digestion. If these pretreatment steps could be kept to a minimum, analysis time would be cut down considerably. Also, mimimum pretreatment reduces the chances of sample contamination by the reagents used, or the loss of volatile elements during pretreatment. Thus the ideal system would require no sample pretreatment at all; real systems should strive for minimum sample pretreatment.

Another factor which influences the speed in performing an analysis is calibration of the instrument. Calibration is especially time-consuming in cases where different elements are run on every analysis; but even in cases where the same elements are determined time after time, the frequency of instrument calibration required to maintain a desired level of accuracy is an important consideration. Since manual data collection is not feasible in multielement determinations, the ideal system would undoubtedly be computerized. The computer would handle all data collection steps, the construction of calibration curves by mathematical curve-fitting methods, and the calculation of concentrations from these curves.

Flexibility. An instrument which can analyze a sample only for a fixed combination of elements is useful for routine analyses, such as clinical analyses, but becomes useless if the combination of elements is to be varied. The ideal multielement spectroscopic system would be able to determine any combination of elements desired, if those elements are amenable to analysis by spectroscopic techniques. Since real samples contain various elements in differing relative concentrations, it is necessary that an ideal multielement spectrometer be able to accept such samples without the need for varying dilutions to accomodate all elements present. Thus the instrument should have a wide dynamic range and be capable of adjustment so that different elements present in major, minor, and trace quantities in the same sample can be simultaneously monitored.

Sensitivity, Accuracy, and Reliability. In order to perform analyses on many real samples with little pretreatment (such as sample preconcentration), detection limits obtained with the ideal system should be as low as possible to permit the direct determination of trace components. Since an analytical technique is of little use unless the results obtained are accurate, it is imperative that all interferences with the ideal system be capable of compensation or elimination. Finally the system should be as rugged and reliable as possible to withstand the rigors of daily usage. In this respect, a system with as few moving mechanical parts as possible is desirable.

The "Best" Real System

The overall performance of any multielement spectroscopic system depends on the performance characteristics of the individual components which make up the system. The actual number of components required depends on the mode of observation chosen to observe the atomic population. For example, once an atomic population has been generated, its presence may be observed by its emission, fluorescence, or absorption.

It is evident that the number of potential configurations for a spectroscopic multielement system is staggering when one considers the number of available options for each component combined with the three complementary modes of observation of the atomic vapor. The question inevitably raised is "Which configuration is the best?" The course of analytical development, however, is very much like the evolutionary development of biological organisms. One cannot point to a single organism and state that this is the best configuration for a living organism. On the contrary, each organism is adapted to the niche which it occupies in nature. Those organisms which cannot adapt to the environment become extinct.

By analogy, analytical systems, to remain viable, must be able to fill some useful role. Thus, the question of which system is the best is academic. By analogy with the evolutionary concept of the survival of the fittest, only those analytical systems which can actually solve "real" analytical problems will survive. Because there are alternative analytical techniques with multielement capability, viable spectroscopic methods must be able to offer real advantages or increased capabilities to compete with these techniques in at least certain analytically-important situations.

Multielement Detection Systems

It is obviously beyond the scope of this paper to discuss the advantages and disadvantages of the various combinations of light sources, atom cells, and detection systems which could be potentially useful in SMA. One point, however, seems certain. In the struggle for supremacy in the area of multielement atomic emission, the recent advent of the induction-coupled plasma (1-9) may result in the eventual extinction of combustion flames as spectroscopic sources. In the area of detection systems, numerous configurations have been proposed, and, at this time, it is not at all certain which of these systems will survive the test of time. This portion of the paper will discuss some of the advantages and disadvantages of these detection systems.

The evolution of detection systems suitable for multielement determinations has proceeded along two basic lines of development as indicated in Figure 1. One line of development is based upon dispersive systems. Dispersive systems are all multichannel devices which may be further classified as temporal or spatial devices. In the temporal approach, the measurement of intensities in different resolution elements is separated in time. The spatial approach uses detectors which are separated in space. Each of these dispersive approaches may be further classified in terms of the type of dispersion employed. Thus, one-dimensional dispersion systems employ a single dispersing device so that the spectral information is spread out as a single band of information dispersed horizontally. Two-dimensional dispersive systems employ an echelle configuration (10) where the spectral information is divided into a rectangular array. Thus, instead of presenting the spectrum for a given wavelength region as a single band of information dispersed horizontally, the echelle system divides the spectrum into segments, and each segment is stacked under the previous one, much like the printed lines of a book are arranged.

The other major line of development is based on multiplex techniques as shown in Figure 1. Multiplex systems refer to those systems capable of transmitting information from several independent sources along the same channel. In spectroscopic terms, the spectral information (i.e., intensities) from different resolution elements is encoded in some manner, and this encoded information is then received by a single detector. Multiplex techniques may be further differentiated (11) into time-division multiplexing and frequency-division multiplexing. Frequency-division multiplexing consists of two classifications known as Hadamard- or Fourier-transform methods depending on the mathematical algorithm employed in the encoding/decoding process. Time-division multiplexing is somewhat simpler in that it does not require complex mathematical transforms to decode the spectral information.

Multiplex Techniques

Frequency-Division Multiplexing. The role of Fourier- and Hadamard-transform methods in simultaneous multielement analysis has been investigated by several research groups (12-22). These techniques have been successfully employed in the infrared region of the spectrum where various factors combine to result in a detector-noise limited spectrometer. Under such conditions, frequency-division multiplexing has resulted in two important benefits, known as Fellgett's advantage and Jacquinot's advantage. Fellgett's advantage (23), sometimes referred to as the

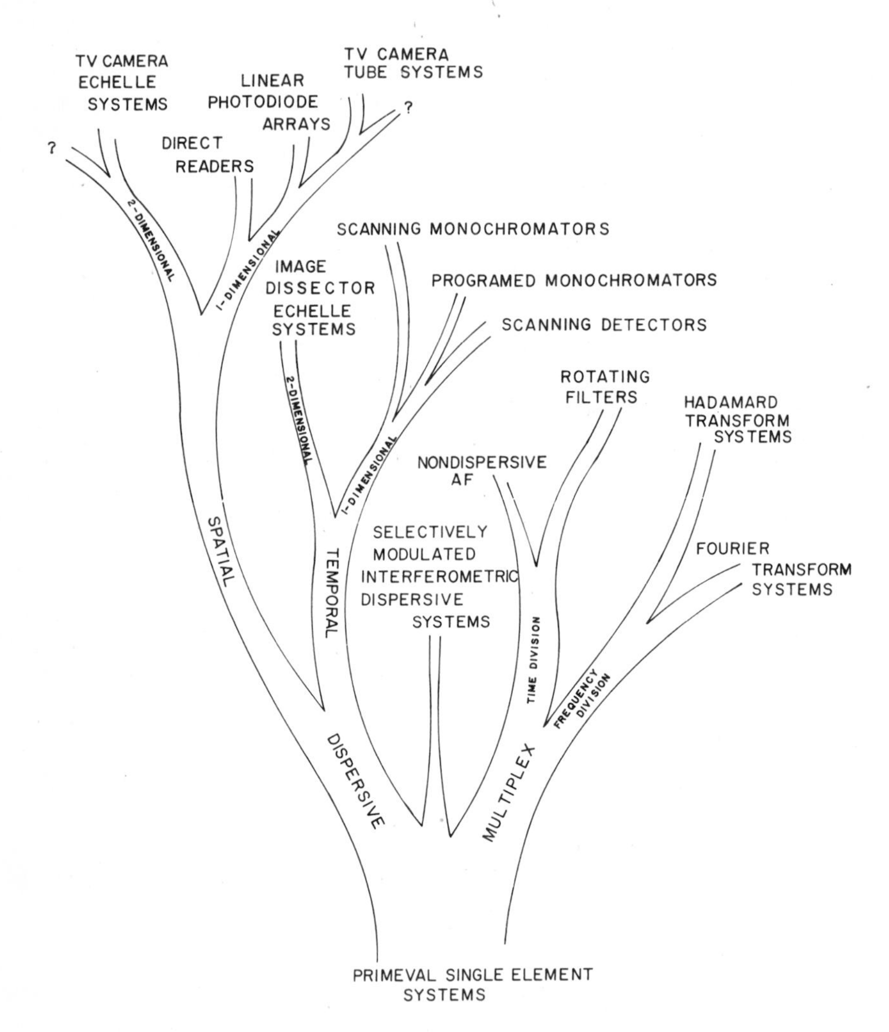

Figure 1. Evolutionary development of multielement detection systems

multiplex advantage, refers to the improvement in the signal-to-noise (S/N) ratio obtained by multiplex systems compared with dispersive scanning systems as a result of the fact that the detector in a frequency-division multiplexed spectrometer monitors all resolution elements simultaneously. In contrast, the detector in a scanning dispersive system monitors a given resolution element only for a short period of the entire scan time, resulting in a poorer S/N ratio compared with multiplex methods. Jacquinot's advantage, sometimes referred to as the throughput advantage, refers to the improvement in the luminosity-resolution product of multiplex systems compared with conventional scanning dispersive systems. Both of these advantages result in substantial improvement in the performance of detector-noise limited systems.

In the UV/VIS region of the spectrum, however, measurements are signal-noise limited, and Fellgett's advantage may not be achieved. In fact, a number of workers (15,16,17,19,20) have studied the signal-to-noise behavior of these systems under photon-noise limited situations, and have concluded that Fourier- and Hadamard-transform methods can be expected to be of limited utility in the UV/VIS region of the spectrum. This is due primarily to the so-called multiplex disadvantage. The multiplex disadvantage arises in photon-noise limited situations because the noise tends to be more or less uniformly distributed throughout the spectrum. Thus, although the S/N ratio of the strong peaks is improved, weak spectral lines are obscured by the noise from strong lines that ends up being uniformly distributed along the baseline of the spectrum. In a study on Hadamard-transform techniques, Plankey, *et al.* (16) observed that a signal 3% of the most intense signal is lost in the baseline noise. In another study, Chester, *et al.* (19) concluded that Fourier-transform spectroscopy will be of limited utility in multielement flame analysis, because most atomization sources in atomic emission and atomic fluorescence have high background levels (due to molecular emission from flame bands and analyte band spectra) and excite lines other than the ones of interest. In atomic absorption, both flame background and unwanted portions of the lamp spectrum are present. The presence of all this extraneous emission striking the detector results in unfavorable S/N characteristics of these systems for multielement analysis in the UV/VIS region of the spectrum.

Despite the potentially poor S/N ratios likely to be achieved with transform procedures in the UV/VIS region, Horlick and Yuen (20) have pointed out that S/N ratio considerations are not the only overriding considerations when carrying out a spectrochemical measurement. These authors cite the following advantages for transform procedures: (1) accurate and precise wavenumber axes for spectra are obtained; (2) high resolution is achieved with a compact system; (3) resolution is easily controlled and manipulated; and (4) wide wavelength coverage is obtained by aliasing. Aliasing refers to the undersampling of modulation frequencies (18,20) in the interferogram. For a given number of data points which can be sampled and transformed, aliasing permits spectral lines of widely different wavelength to be simultaneously measured with significantly better resolution than if aliasing were avoided.

A modification of an interferometrically-based system, which was first described by Dohi and Suzuki (24), is known as a selectively-modulated interferometric dispersive spectrometer. This system is a hybrid in that a rotating grating (a dispersive element) is used to limit the number of wavelengths which can interfere at any one time in a modified Michelson interferometer. The system consists of a Michelson interferometer in which the stationary reflecting mirror has been replaced with a rotatable diffraction grating, thereby eliminating the multiplex nature of the interferometer owing to the fact that interference occurs only for the Littrow wavelength of the grating. Oscillation of the remaining mirror causes interference modulation of the particular spectral component passed by the grating, and selective amplification of the ac signal component allows it to be distinguished from the remaining dc background. Because no interferogram is produced, no Fourier transform is required. One potential advantage of this system compared with a conventional dispersive system is the large Jacquinot advantage (a factor of 10^2 to 10^3) expected with the Michelson interferometer. Chester, *et al.* (25) and Fitzgerald, *et al.* (26) have studied the application of these systems to SMA and have concluded that the improved luminosity cannot lead to an improved S/N ratio in any measurement which is not limited by detector noise. Because no realistic analytical situation exists in the UV/VIS region which is detector-noise limited, this system is predicted to be of little utility in SMA. Detection limits obtained with the selectively-modulated interferometric dispersive spectrometer are much inferior to those obtained by conventional systems (25).

Time-Division Multiplexing. Time-division multiplexing has been extensively employed in communications networks to transmit data from several sources on the same line. Two nondispersive systems which have been described and are based on time-division multiplexing are the rotating filter wheel, described by Mitchell and Johansson (27) and the nondispersive atomic fluorescence system described by Palermo, *et al.* (11). In the latter system, computer-controlled hollow cathode lamps and a computer-controlled synchronous integrator are employed. Time-division multiplexing is achieved by pulsing several hollow cathode lamps out of phase in a low duty cycle mode. The fluorescence radiation from each element is transmitted through the same optical path, but is separated in time. The fluorescence radiation is transduced by a solar-blind photomultiplier. Demultiplexing is accomplished by the computer. These workers obtained good detection limits for Cd, Hg, Zn, and Pb in an argon-sheathed air/H_2 flame. Sheathing was necessary to reduce background. This system has yet to be evaluated on an actual analytical problem involving real samples, and it seems likely that it will be restricted to easily volatilizable elements because an observation height of between 5-10 cm above the burner is required. Futhermore, the use of the relatively cool air/H_2 flame will undoubtedly result in numerous volatilization interferences with real samples. Because this system is useful for transient signals, it may find application in conjunction with nonflame devices.

In a theoretical study of the advantages to be gained from nondispersive systems, Chester and Winefordner (28) have studied frequency-modulated sources in nondispersive atomic fluorescence, and have demonstrated a multiplex disadvantage for nondispersive atomic fluorescence systems. These studies have indicated that the limiting noise is flame background noise.

Finally, two time-division multiplexed spectrometers based on a dispersive system have been described. The first system, described by Lundberg and Johansson (29), consists of a 0.35-m Czerny-Turner monochromator with three exit slits arranged at the focal plane. A rotating chopper with three concentric slits is arranged so that light from only one fixed exit slit at a time reaches the single photomultiplier tube. By properly arranging the positions of the three fixed slits to pass desired resonance radiation from a hollow cathode, simultaneous determinations by atomic absorption are possible. Because of the optical arrangement employed, it is not possible to select resonance lines with a wavelength separation of less than 2 nm. It can be anticipated that this approach will probably be confined to specialized routine determinations because: (1) five elements is the expected practical upper limit for the number of elements which can be simultaneously determined; and (2) the flexibility (i.e., the ability to conveniently monitor various combinations of elements) is somewhat limited.

The second system, described by Johansson and Nilsson (30), employs a composite grating built up from several smaller gratings with different ruling characteristics, such that each covers a different spectral range. Grating characteristics are selected so that the characteristic emission lines of the elements of interest are focused by a cylindrical mirror whose axis of rotation is perpendicular to the grating's plane of diffraction. By this means, the lines of interest are focused onto a group of slits, closely spaced in a horizontal direction, but separated vertically. Radiation passing through the slits is transmitted by fiber optics whose termini form the periphery of a circle. A rotating disc with holes is used to transmit one bundle of radiation at a time to a single photomultiplier tube. Although the design shows fundamental similarities with an echelle spectrograph, it presents less stringent demands on its mechanical construction. The instrument has been designed for the routine determination of Na, K, Ca, and Mg in serum, using Li as an internal standard. Because gratings with a high groove density are required, conventionally-ruled gratings are not applicable, and holographic gratings must be employed. The use of specially-designed-and-manufactured holographic gratings currently represents the most serious obstacle to the widespread application of this system.

Dispersive Techniques

Temporal Devices. A temporal dispersive device uses a single channel which is scanned as a function of time to yield information on the intensities present in various resolution elements. Two basic approaches are possible: (1) the detector may be scanned across a fixed spectrum; or (2) the spectrum may be scanned across a fixed detector. In addition, these systems may be further differentiated on the basis of the manner in which the spectrum is scanned. Thus, linear-scan systems scan the spectrum at a constant, fixed rate. In contrast, programmed-scan systems have the capability of momentarily stopping at wavelengths of analytical interest, while spectral regions of little interest are rapidly scanned. For a complete review of the area of rapid-scanning spectrometry up to 1968, the interested reader should consult Volume 7 of Applied Optics which was entirely devoted to this subject.

Although a large number of reports on the application of linear-scan systems to SMA may be found in the literature (31-38), such systems have several drawbacks. The primary criticism of linear-scan systems is that they are basically inefficient. Large fractions of the scan time are spent scanning spectral regions of little interest (38). In contrast, resolution elements of actual analytical interest are sampled only for a short time, degrading the precision of the measurement. The range of analytically-useful scan speeds is bounded by excessive sample consumption on the low end and the response time of the electronics on the upper end. Repetitive scanning in combination with signal-averaging techniques can be used to improve the S/N ratio obtained with these systems (37).

In contrast to linear-scan systems, programmed-scan systems offer some important analytical advantages for SMA. These systems are inherently more efficient for SMA than linear-scan systems because wavelength regions of little interest are scanned rapidly while resolution elements of analytical interest are monitored for longer periods of time. Because the measurements are made in a sequential manner, the time spent in going between resolution elements of interest can be effectively used in optimization of various instrumental parameters such as atomization source conditions, observation height, slit width, and photomultiplier voltage. The possibility of individual optimization for different elements present in a sample relieves some of the problems associated with the simultaneous determination of major-, minor-, and trace elements in a sample. The use of conventional photomultiplier detectors with their large dynamic range facilitates the measurement of intensities of different magnitude. Finally, such systems are inherently flexible because it is a simple matter to program the monochromator to stop at any desired combination of analytical wavelengths. Cordos and Malmstadt (33) have described a system which can recycle through a sequence of 8-12 preset analytical wavelengths. The system, which was used for multielement atomic fluorescence measurements, has a slew rate of 20 nm/sec and a wavelength accuracy of 0.02 nm.

One critical requirement of these systems is wavelength accuracy and precision. Thus, it is essential that the system reproducibly stop at the correct measurement wavelength. Spillman and Malmstadt (36) have recently described an improved programmed-scan monochromator which ensures wavelength accuracy. The improved system uses wavelength modulation (39, 40, 41) to achieve wavelength accuracy and background correction. This system has a wavelength accuracy of 0.017 nm and can monitor any number of analytical wavelengths between 213-1000 nm. Programmable slits have been incorporated into the design to facilitate atomic emission and atomic fluorescence measurements. Square-wave modulation of the refractor plate allows time-averaging of the data. To date, the system has been used for the simultaneous determination of Na, K, Mg, Ca, and Li in blood serum.

In another reported application of an alternative computer-controlled programmed-scan system, Johnson, et al. (38) have studied the application of a 500-W Eimac lamp and a separated flame for the atomic fluoresence determination of Fe, Mg, Cu, Ag, and Cr in jet engine lubricating oils.

Another temporal device whose role in multielement analysis has been investigated is the scanning photomultiplier originally described by P. T. Farnsworth (42) in 1934. Figure 2 shows a schematic diagram of this device, which is sometimes referred to an an image-dissector photomultiplier. The image dissector consists of a photocathode separated from a conventional dynode chain electron multiplier by a plate with a slit aperture. The electron imaging section forms an electron image on the aperture plate corresponding to the light image incident on the photocathode. Electronic scanning is accomplished by electromagnetic sweep coils surrounding the tube, which sweep the electron image across the face of the plate. Only the portion of the electron image which passes through the slit in the aperture plate can reach the first dynode and be amplified by the dynode chain. As with other scanning systems, signal-averaging techniques can profitably be employed with image-dissector systems.

These tubes have been employed with both one- and two-dimensional dispersive systems. For example, Harber and Sonnek (43) described an electronic scanning spectrometer based on an image-dissector photomultiplier in conjunction with a one-dimensional dispersive system. Their system used a 12.7 cm Czerny-Turner mount with a reciprocal linear dispersion of

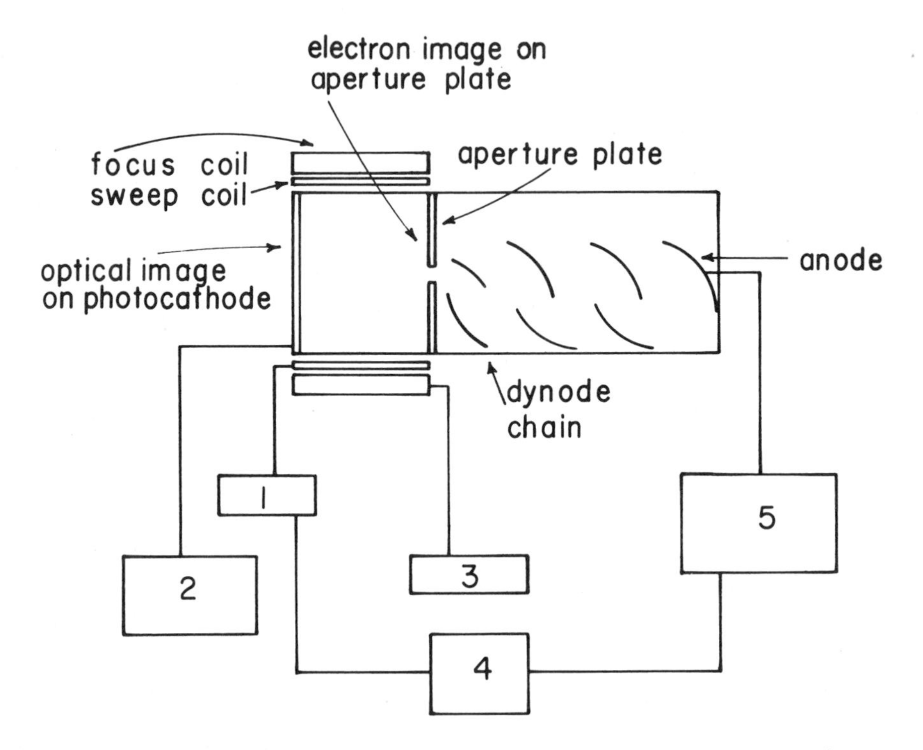

Analytical Chemistry

Figure 2. Image-dissector photomultiplier. (1) Sweep-coil electronics; (2) Photomultiplier power supply; (3) Focus-coil electronics; (4) Display; (5) Signal amplifier. (69).

13 nm/mm, and covered a spectral range of 250 nm at a scan rate of 100 or 1000 scans/sec. The one-dimensional dispersive configuration of this system requires a compromise between wavelength coverage and resolution, and represents a severe limitation in the application of this system to SMA.

Because the electronically-scanned region is spatially limited by the dimensions of the tube, the image dissector used in a one-dimensional dispersive configuration simultaneously monitors a spectral window. To increase the wavelength coverage included in the spectral window, the dispersion of the optical system must be reduced, resulting in a decrease in the resolution of the system. Ideally, a system designed for simultaneous multielement determinations by atomic spectroscopy should cover as wide a wavelength region as possible at the highest possible resolution so that analytically-useful lines of as many elements as possible may be monitored under conditions where spectral interference has been minimized. Because these two goals are clearly antithetical with this system, a compromise is required.

This compromise can be avoided by employing a two-dimensional dispersive system. These systems are all based on the echelle principle [the interested reader should consult Keliher and Wohlers (10) for a review of this subject] originally described by R. W. Wood (44) and later developed by Harrison and coworkers (45) at MIT. With this system, a special grating designed to operate in high spectral orders is employed. The optical configuration of the grating is arranged so that a large number of spectral orders overlap. A prism, arranged so that its dispersion is orthogonal to that of the grating, is used to separate the direct spectral overlap of the various orders. This results in the spectral information being dispersed in a two-dimensional array. The geometry of this format is especially convenient for various image devices. Several workers have described image dissector/echelle systems (46,47,48,49).

Danielsson and Lindblom (47,48) and Danielsson, *et al.* (49) have designed an image dissector/echelle system and have described its application to SMA. This system provides wide wavelength coverage at high resolution. For example, the system covers the whole spectral range from 200 to 800 nm with a resolution on the order of 0.001 nm. To be effective, accurate and precise control of the scanning electron beam (usually by computer) is of the utmost importance for accurate reproducible wavelength registration. Indeed, a large portion of the development work involved in designing this system has been in the area of the software development for wavelength calibration. This is not a trivial matter, when one recalls that spectral information obtained with an echelle system occurs as spectral "points" rather than spectral "lines." Thus, small errors in beam alignment can result in serious analytical errors. Because image dissector tubes have no innate storage capability, these systems present data in real time, and computer capability is required for data storage and integration. The dynamic range and sensitivity of the image dissector can probably be expected to be comparable to a conventional photomultiplier with a similar photocathode, aperture, and dynode chain [see the chapter by Felkel and Pardue, this monograph].

Spatial Devices. Spatial devices use detection elements which are separated from each other in space. Although the photographic plate may be considered the original spatial detector, this discussion will be limited to electronically-based detection systems. Such systems include the direct-reading spectrometer and various solid-state array detector spectrometers.

Multiple slit-multiple detector systems such as the direct-reading spectrometer have been known for quite some time. In this system, spectral lines are isolated from the dispersed radiation by exit slits positioned along the focal plane of the spectrometer, and detected by photomultipliers positioned behind each slit. These systems are generally large in size owing to the long focal length required to obtain the necessary high dispersion to permit detector placement. Proper positioning and alignment of the exit slits in the focal plane of the spectrometer is critical, and environmental factors such as changes in the temperature of the spectrometer and the refractive index of the air are apt to result in misalignment. Flexibility to monitor different combinations of elements is somewhat hampered by the problems associated with changing the slit placement and alignment. Additional drawbacks to direct-reading spectrometers which are often cited include: (1) only a limited number of wavelengths can be simultaneously monitored; (2) measuring closely-spaced analytical lines requires additional optical components to permit detector placement; and (3) background correction, while possible, is not conveniently accomplished.

In spite of these limitations, the direct-reading spectrometer fills many important analytical applications where the routine determination of sixteen or more elements is required. Such systems, once set up to monitor the desired elements, yield good analytical results when used with well-characterized analytical methods. In fact, in contrast with many alternative multielement detection systems, direct-reading spectrometers have two definite analytical advantages: (1) photomultiplier tubes, with their high sensitivity and wide linear dynamic range, are used, resulting in low detection limits; and (2) individual optimization of each channel is possible because each detector is independent of the others, allowing tube voltages and slit dimensions to be adjusted independently to accomodate differing light intensities.

Image Devices. Although he never assembled an actual TV-spectrometer, Margoshes was the first to recognize the potential of TV-type detectors in analytical atomic spectroscopy. In a series of reports (50,51,52) he speculated on the advantages of using an SEC tube [vide infra] to detect radiation dispersed by an echelle spectrograph. These reports and the recent availability of various solid-state array detectors have prompted numerous investigators to explore the potential applicability of these devices to SMA. Talmi (53,54) has critically reviewed the various electronic multichannel devices currently available, and has commented on their potential as spectroscopic detectors. While a variety of image devices are currently available, this discussion will be limited to those devices whose application to SMA has actually been studied--i.e., vidicons, SIT vidicons, secondary-electron conduction (SEC) tubes, and linear photodiode arrays. These devices all operate on the same general principle. First, the optical image is transduced into a charge pattern which can be stored and integrated. Then the charge pattern corresponding to the optical image is read electronically. The various types of image devices differ basically in the manner in which the charge pattern is produced and read.

Before beginning a discussion of the role of image devices in SMA, it would be helpful at this point to define some terminology used to describe various characteristics of these devices: (1) Each individual sensing element of an image detector is known as a *pixel*. (2) Cross-talk between channels caused by charge spreading to adjacent pixels is referred to as *blooming*. (3) The fraction of charge retained on the sensing element after a single readout results in a memory effect in succeeding frames, and is known as *lag*. (4) Pixel-to-pixel variations in response and dark current produce a coherent, nonrandom noise known as *fixed-pattern noise*.

Linear Photodiode Arrays. In terms of cost, the linear photodiode array is perhaps the least expensive of the currently-available image devices. For a complete review of linear photodiode arrays up to 1968, the interested reader should consult *IEEE Trans. Electron Devices*, *ED-15* (4), 1968, which was entirely devoted to this subject. Horlick and coworkers (55-62) and others (63,64,65,66) have studied the analytical utility of these devices. A complete assessment of the spectroscopic applications of linear photodiode arrays has been presented by Horlick (67).

These devices, which are available in lengths up to 26 mm, consist of a linear array of up to 1872 photodiodes. Each photodiode is connected to the output by an FET switch. The FET switches are controlled by a single bit, which is cycled through a shift register by a clock. When the FET switch to a particular diode is enabled, a reverse-bias potential is applied. This reverse bias charge, which is stored on the equivalent capacitance of the pn-junction, may be discharged by the production of electron-hole pairs in the semiconductor material. Electron-hole pair production arises from thermal- as well as photon population of the conduction band. On a subsequent scan of the array, the magnitude of the signal necessary to re-establish the original reverse-bias condition of that diode is a measure of the light intensity and dark current integrated over the period between scans.

Because dark current limits the integration times obtainable at room temperature, Peltier cooling (to -15°C) is used to reduce thermal population of the conduction band. In contrast to the silicon vidicon and the SIT [vide infra], where the presence of intense radiation may bloom out the entire sensor, blooming is greatly reduced with photodiode arrays even when intense lines saturate individual diodes.

Vidicon. Although there are several types of vidicon tubes presently available, the most promising of these for spectroscopic work is the silicon vidicon, first conceived at Bell Labs (68). Figure 3 shows a diagram of a silicon vidicon. In contrast to a photomultiplier, which is based on a photoemissive principle, the vidicon television camera tube is based on a conductivity principle, a circumstance which explains its name.

The tube target consists of an array of p-type semiconductor islands which have been grown on a wafer of n-type material, producing an array of photodiodes. An electron beam, which is focused by focusing coils surrounding the tube, is emitted by an electron gun at one end of the tube and focused on the tube target. Deflection coils surrounding the tube permit the electron beam to scan the target.

When the vidicon is in operation, the electron beam is made to scan the target, charging the p-type islands to the potential of the electron gun. Because the n-type wafer is maintained at ground potential, the photodiodes are reverse-biased, causing the depletion zone formed at the pn-junction to increase in size. Each reverse-biased diode is able to function as a storage capacitor, because the negatively-charged p-type material is separated from the n-type material at ground potential by an insulating depletion zone. These tiny charged storage capacitors may be discharged by electron-hole pair production in the n-type wafer. Electron-hole pairs can be produced by two basic mechanisms, thermal population of the conduction band and photon absorption.

In the case of photon absorption, as the n-type target material absorbs photons, electron-hole pairs are formed. Although the electrons produced by photon absorption are rapidly drained to ground, the holes diffuse across the depletion zone into the p-type islands where they combine with the excess electrons deposited there by the electron gun and are annihilated, thereby reducing the deposited charge at locations where the target is exposed to light. Thermally-generated electron-hole pairs behave in a similar fashion, producing "dark current."

When the electron beam scans the target again, electrons are redeposited on the p-type islands. This redeposition of electrons produces a charging current which is amplified as the video signal. In those regions which have been exposed to intense light, it may take several scans of the electron beam to redeposit enough electrons to recharge that region back to the potential of the electron gun. This incomplete erasure of the information on the target is the origin of lag.

In contrast to the image dissector, which measures the photon flux, the vidicon is an integrating device, where the target serves as a memory buffer, storing information until the scanning electron beam reads and erases it.

SIT Vidicon. The SIT vidicon, or silicon-intensified target tube, shown in Figure 4, is essentially the same as the silicon vidicon with the addition of an intensifier stage. The intensifier stage consists of a fiber-optic faceplate which is optically coupled to a photoemissive surface, or photocathode. An optical image focused on the fiber-optic faceplate causes photoelectrons to be emitted from the photocathode surface. These photoelectrons are focused by the curved photocathode surface and internal focusing electrodes to produce an electron image on the silicon target which corresponds as closely as possible to the optical image focused on the faceplate of the tube. Because the photocathode is maintained at a potential between 3-9 kV below the silicon target (which is at ground potential), the emitted photoelectrons strike the target with energies on the order of 3-9 keV, producing electron-hole pairs in the same manner (only more efficiently) as when a photon is absorbed directly by the silicon target.

SEC Tube. The secondary-electron conduction (SEC) tube employs a target fabricated from low-density KCl. Primary photoelectrons, emitted when light impinges on a photocathode surface, are focused, producing an electron image on the KCl target which corresponds to the optical image focused on the faceplate of the tube. These bombarding photoelectrons strike the target with high energy, producing secondary electrons. Conduction of these secondary electrons through the vacuum interstices of the KCl target under the influence of an electric field within the target, results in a positive charge pattern being produced. This charge pattern is then read in the direct beam mode by the scanning electron beam in an analogous fashion to the silicon vidicon.

In contrast to tubes with silicon targets, where thermal energy produces an appreciable dark current, the SEC exhibits a very low dark current, owing to the low rate of thermal ionization of the KCl target. As a result of the low dark current, SEC tubes can integrate signals for long periods of time at room temperature.

Analytical Considerations with Image Devices. In considering the role of image devices in SMA, one should not lose sight of the analytical constraints involved. For example, typical analytical samples contain elements present at major-, minor-, and trace levels. In most cases it will not be possible to dilute the sample extensively and still determine the trace elements. As a result, the analytical lines employed in the determination should be selected with the expected concentrations of the elements in mind. Thus less sensitive analytical lines (such as nonresonance lines if the sample is analyzed by atomic emission) should be chosen for the determination of major- or minor elements, whereas the most sensitive resonance lines will need to be used for the determination of trace elements. Even though the same set of

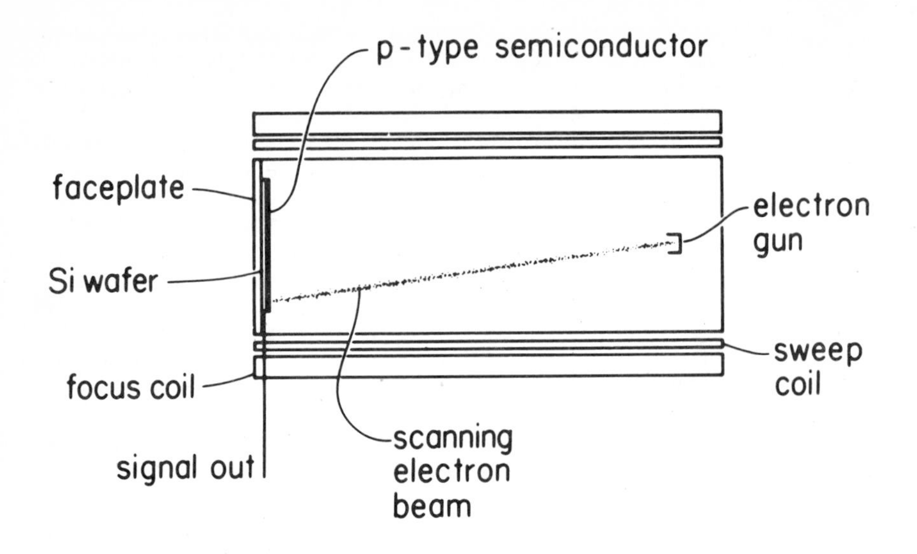

Figure 3. *Silicon vidicon* (69).

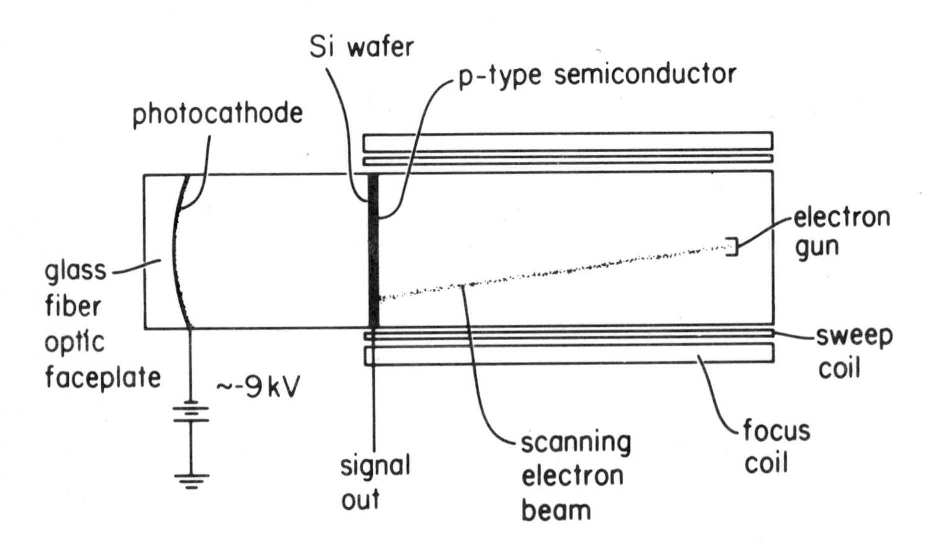

Figure 4. *SIT vidicon* (82).

elements may be determined in each case, different sets of analytical lines may be required for different sample types, owing to differences in elemental abundances between different sample types. Thus the optical system used in conjunction with the image device must provide enough wavelength coverage to permit the analyst to select the most appropriate lines for a given sample type on the basis of spectrochemical considerations without regard for limitations imposed by restricted wavelength coverage.

Consideration must also be given for the dynamic range of the image device. Thus, the presence of intense radiation striking the target of a silicon vidicon or an SIT, for example, will result in extensive blooming, incapacitating large portions of the target. For samples determined by flame techniques, intense flame background may present serious problems due to blooming. In "real" samples where matrix interferences are prevalent, high-temperature (and consequently, high background) flames such as the N_2O/C_2H_2 flame are desired. Even where low background atom reservoirs are available, blooming may still occur as a result of intense analyte emission from major elements (i.e., sodium).

Because different elements have different spectrochemical properties, optimum analytical conditions may vary from element to element (69,70). Since all elements are determined simultaneously with an image detector spectrometer, compromise analytical conditions must be employed. Brost, *et al.* (71) have described a response parameter which can be used to determine the optimum compromise analytical conditions. Because the optimum compromise analytical conditions for a given determination depend on the expected analytical concentrations of the elements present in the sample, meaningful multielement detection limits cannot be reported without reference to a particular sample type. The many reported multielement detection limits which appear in the literature simply indicate the detection limits obtained under a particular arbitrary set of conditions, and do not necessarily represent the detection limits obtainable under optimum analytical conditions for a particular sample type. Thus the detection limits achieved in an actual multielement determination are more often likely to be compromise-limited rather than instrument-limited.

The Question of Analytical Utility. In considering the analytical utility of image devices, it should be remembered that these devices were not developed or designed with spectroscopic applications in mind. Because a number of reports have appeared in the literature (72-77) which conclude that image devices are inadequate for SMA, it is worthwhile to discuss some of the approaches taken in evaluating the analytical utility of these devices.

The first approach can be characterized as the figure-of-merit approach. In an effort to place comparisons of different systems on a quantitative basis, many workers have characterized different systems on the basis of S/N considerations. Although such studies can frequently be used to point out ways of improving a measurement system, the use of this approach to predict analytical utility is open to question for several reasons.

First, the validity of the conclusions depends heavily on how closely the actual system approaches the assumptions made in the derivation of the S/N expressions. More importantly, however, conclusions regarding analytical utility based solely on S/N considerations (or any other single criterion) tend to oversimplify the analytical criteria upon which multielement systems should be evaluated. For example, no one would consider the complete evaluation of automotive systems solely on the basis of a single figure-of-merit, such as fuel economy or acceleration. The evaluation of automotive designs is based on a variety of criteria, many of which are highly subjective, and not subject to quantitation. The "best" automobile for a particular individual depends on the relative importance placed on the various criteria. Thus, S/N considerations represent but a single criterion for evaluation of new instrumentation. Only if S/N performance is so inadequate that analytical application becomes impossible will these considerations become overriding.

A further problem with these studies involves the inevitable comparison of image devices with the multiplier phototube. These comparisons are inevitably strained, owing to the fundamental differences between these detectors. Multiplier phototubes are basically rate devices whereas solid-state array detectors are integrating detectors. As a result of these differences, these evaluations tend to suffer from the dilemma of what represents a "fair" comparison. In one study, the fundamental differences between the way the SIT and photomultiplier acquire, process, and read out data is recognized, and the two detectors are compared by converting the photomultiplier rate data to an equivalent integrated signal (78). This study points out that vidicons are not suited for atomic fluorescence measurements because of the low signal intensities and UV wavelengths involved; however, these devices will achieve comparable detection powers for situations limited by spectral background noise (i.e., atomic emission with N_2O/C_2H_2 flames). Table II shows comparative detection limit data for flame emission with the nitrous oxide/acetylene flame.

Quite a number of these figure-of-merit type reports which have appeared in the literature conclude, on the basis of signal-to-noise considerations, that various image devices are inadequate for SMA. One of the most striking aspects of many of these studies reported to date in the literature on the analytical utility of image devices is the almost evangelical urgency with which the conclusions, which are often italicized in the literature for emphasis, are presented. These conclusions, which are often quite sweeping, seem to be based on somewhat limited data, and essential operating parameters are frequently not reported (i.e., the accelerating potential applied to the intensifier stage of an SIT is frequently not reported along with detection limit data).

Table II. Flame Emission Detection Limits

Element	Line, nm	PMT[a]	UV vid.[a]	SIT vid.[a]	SIT with scint.[a]	Int. pot.,kV[d]
Ag	328.1	0.002	0.3		0.1	9.0
Al	396.1	0.003	0.05	0.01	0.008	4.5
Ba	553.5	0.001	0.02	0.001	0.001	9.0
Bi	306.8	20.0	5.0		1.0	7.0
Ca	422.7	0.0001	0.001	0.0001	0.0002	5.0
Co	345.4	0.03	0.6		0.5	9.0
Cr	425.4[b]	0.002	0.01	0.002	0.002	7.9
Cu	324.7	0.01	0.07		0.07	9.0
Fe	372.0	0.005	0.2	0.01	0.04	7.5
In	451.1	0.0004	0.02	0.006	0.003	7.5
K	766.5	0.00005	0.03	0.06	0.03	9.0
Li	670.8	0.00002	0.00002	0.00001	0.00001	9.0
Mg	285.2	0.005	0.2		0.07	9.0
Mn	403.1	0.001	0.02	0.003	0.002	9.0
Mo	390.2	0.1	0.1	0.07	0.04	4.8
Na	589.0	0.0005	0.0005	0.0002	0.00007	5.6
Ni	352.5	0.02	0.1		0.2	9.0
Pb	405.8	0.1	0.8	0.2	0.1	8.0
Rb	780.0	0.008	0.1	0.1	0.08	9.0
Sr	460.7	0.0002	0.002	0.0002	0.0001	7.3
Ti	399.8[c]	0.03	0.2	0.06	0.06	5.0
V	437.9	0.007	0.5	0.02	0.02	5.5
W	400.9	0.7	3.0	1.0	0.9	4.7

[a] Values are μg/ml. [b] PMT value obtained at 359.4 nm. [c] PMT value obtained at 365.4 nm. [d] SIT Vidicon Intensifier Potential.

Reprinted from Ref. 78 with permission.

Although these studies indicate certain limitations that must be taken into account in using these devices in SMA, they cannot prove the conclusion that image devices are inadequate for SMA, for the same reason that it is impossible through the inductive process of observation to conclusively prove a universal statement. To say that all swans are white, simply because, to date, no black swans have been observed does not prove the proposition. Karl Popper, in his book, "Logik der Forschung," published in 1934, correctly points out the logical asymmetry between verification and falsification. Although universal statements cannot be verified (proved), they can be disproved. No number of observations of white swans can ever prove the proposition "All swans are white," but it is disproved by a single observation of a black swan. Thus it is more expedient to search for the black swan, because any search for conclusive verification is irrational in that it is a search for something that cannot be found. In the same fashion, it is much harder to experimentally demonstrate the analytical nonutility of a device than it is to demonstrate its utility. So, regardless of the number of studies which indicate the nonutility of image devices, the fact remains that these do not prove the proposition.

In contrast to the figure-of-merit approach, the other approach which has been taken to evaluate the analytical utility of solid-state array detectors, which is logically more expedient, is to attempt to demonstrate that these devices can actually solve real analytical problems (79-93). Although a large number of instrumental systems employing image devices have been described in the literature (55-67, 94-99) little work has been done in actually applying these systems to real multielement analytical problems. It should be remembered, however, that the inductive process of science is inherently slow, and the analytical nonutility of image devices can only be proved, if, over a significantly long period of time, no viable multielement applications for these devices can be found. In view of the fact that a limited number of analytical applications have already been reported, it is probably safe to say that many ingenious applications will be developed as more investigators obtain access to image devices.

One-Dimensional versus Two-Dimensional. It is not possible to review in detail all the studies which have been conducted to date on the application of solid-state array detectors to SMA. As in the case of temporal systems, development of image detector spectrometers has proceeded along two basic lines of development, based on the mode of dispersion.

In one-dimensional configurations, the spectral information is dispersed across the tube target with a conventional spectrographic system. In these systems, the target is generally scanned in a raster pattern of vertical sweeps. One-dimensional systems are based on a window concept (81), resulting in a compromise between resolution and wavelength coverage. Because the actively scanned portion of the target is only about 13 mm wide [this is a typical value for a vidicon], the extent of the wavelength range which can be simultaneously monitored with adequate resolution for SMA is limited. Under certain favorable circumstances (82,84,85), widely spaced spectral lines may sometimes be monitored simultaneously without unduly increasing the size of the wavelength window (and thereby suffering a loss in resolution) by monitoring spectral lines in overlapping orders. Unfortunately, the use of overlapping orders is not successful in every case, and the limited wavelength window obtained by mounting a solid-state array detector at the focal plane of a conventional spectrograph remains the most serious problem associated with the use of these devices in SMA.

To avoid the limited wavelength coverage associated with one-dimensional systems, several groups have assembled and demonstrated the feasibility of echelle systems employing either a vidicon (99) or an SEC tube (95). To overcome the somewhat limited linear dynamic range characteristics of vidicons, these systems employ random accessing.

Random accessing (100,101) improves the apparent dynamic range of these detectors by scanning target regions of high illumination more frequently than weakly illuminated regions in an effort to allow the charge pattern to develop more fully in the weakly illuminated regions, while avoiding saturation in the highly illuminated regions by frequent erasing. Nieman and Enke (97) point out, however, that random accessing is not without certain problems, among which are: (1) increased complexity of the required software, (2) the entire target must be scanned at intervals appropriate to the signal level to prevent saturation and blooming, and (3) it is necessary to measure and correct for the unequal integration times of the accessed areas. In addition, Felkel and Pardue (99) point out that the random access mode of data acquisition results in a trade-off, owing to the fact that the entire target must be primed (during which no information is accumulated) in order to interrogate less than the maximum number of resolution elements. Another problem which these authors point out concerns the smaller number of diodes per resolution element that result because the echelle system focuses spectral lines over a smaller area than conventional one-dimensional spectrographs. Although not specifically discussed by these authors, it would be anticipated that the smaller number of diodes per resolution element might result in several deleterious effects, such as poorer sensitivity and increased susceptibility to blooming and saturation. In addition, blooming is likely to be a serious problem with vidicon/echelle systems employing high-background atom reservoirs such as the N_2O/C_2H_2 flame, owing to the fact that the entire spectrum is focused on the tube target.

Switch-Board Optics. The preceding discussion has summarized the various approaches which have been taken to achieve a practical spectrometer for SMA. The direct reader, the vidicon detector, and the development of image device/echelle systems

Figure 5. Fiber-optic vidicon spectrometer. (1) Nitrous oxide/acetylene flame; (2) SIT vidicon detector; (3) Fiber-optic input lenses; (4) Fiber-optic entrance slit system; (5) 0.5-m Czerny-Turner monochromator; (6) Optical multichannel analyzer; (7) Oscilloscope display.

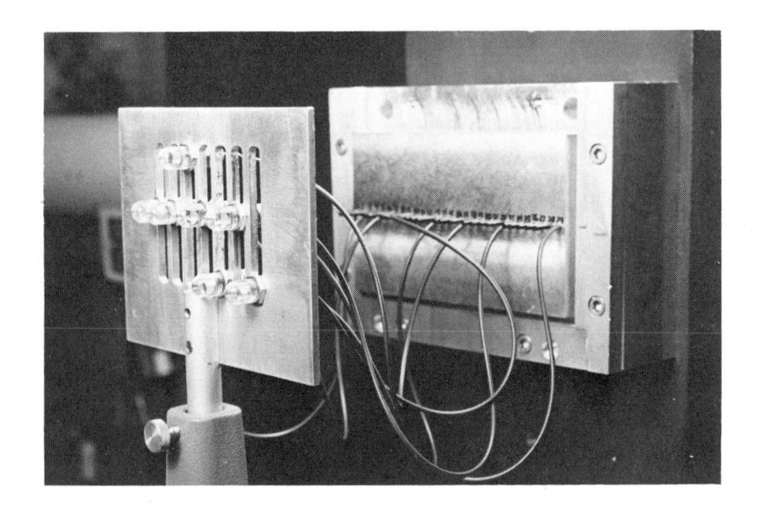

Figure 6. Fiber-optic system showing input lenses and switch-board entrance slit system

each present certain advantages for multielement analysis. If a single system could combine the individual channel control of the direct reader, the wavelength coverage of the echelle system, and the background correction capability of the vidicon into one instrument, it would present a very versatile and useful system. The construction of such an instrument would remove the wavelength window limitation characteristic of one-dimensional systems, and would permit any combination of elements within the spectral range of the detector to be determined simultaneously. Such an instrument would provide maximum flexibility in terms of the combinations of elements determined simultaneously as well as the range of analyte concentrations which could be simultaneously tolerated.

Malloy and Busch (102) have developed an instrument based on the principle of reverse optics which fulfills the above criteria. The instrument, known as a fiber-optic vidicon spectrometer and shown in Figure 5, is no larger in size than a conventional atomic absorption spectrometer, and offers the advantages of wide wavelength coverage, flexibility, and background correction. In this configuration, an ordinary one-dimensional dispersive system is employed with a series of regularly spaced entrance slits arranged in the focal plane of the entrance port, while the vidicon is mounted in the focal plane of the exit port. Each entrance slit focuses a particular 40-nm spectral region on the SIT vidicon target. Fiber-optic light guides, shown in Figure 6, are used to convey the radiation from the flame to the individual slits. These fiber optics can be "plugged in" [like a telephone switchboard] in front of any entrance slit desired, while those slits not in use can be blocked with a small opaque plug. Individual input lenses at the end of each fiber-optic strand are used to collect radiation from the flame. Each individual input lens may be positioned to observe the optimum region of the flame for the element(s) monitored by that fiber-optic strand. With an optical system having a dispersion of 3.2 nm/mm, any radiation within the total range of 384 nm may be focused on the tube target. The dual memory capability of the optical multichannel analyzer (81) used in conjunction with the SIT vidicon permits the subtraction of flame bands from the final spectrum.

Figure 7 illustrates the usefulness of this optical arrangement. Radiation from a multielement hollow cathode lamp containing Mn and Cr was allowed to fall on one fiber-optic strand. Radiation from a second hollow cathode lamp containing Li was incident on a second fiber optic strand. Individual and composite spectra are shown in the figure. With this optical system, lithium can be determined simultaneously with Cr and Mn by atomic emission, or lithium could be used as an internal standard for the analysis. To do this with a conventional one-dimensional dispersive system would require a wavelength window from 403 nm to 671 nm, resulting in poor resolution.

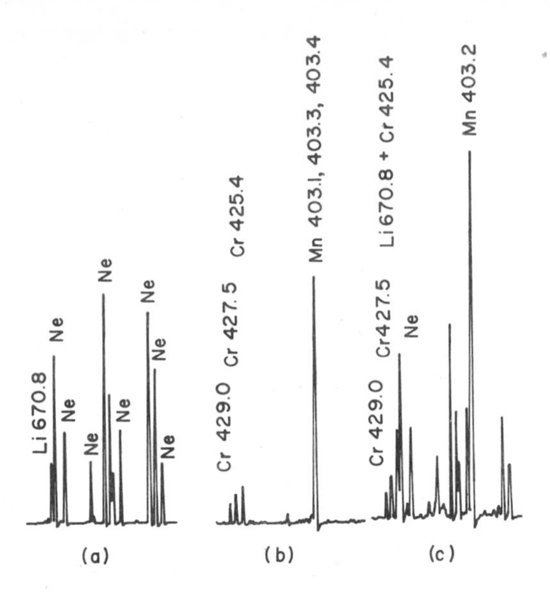

Figure 7. (a) Emission spectrum from Li hollow cathode lamp [entrance slit 29]; (b) Emission spectrum from multielement hollow cathode lamp containing Cr and Mn [entrance slit 10]; (c) Composite spectrum obtained by plugging fiber-optic strands into entrance slits 10 and 29 simultaneously.

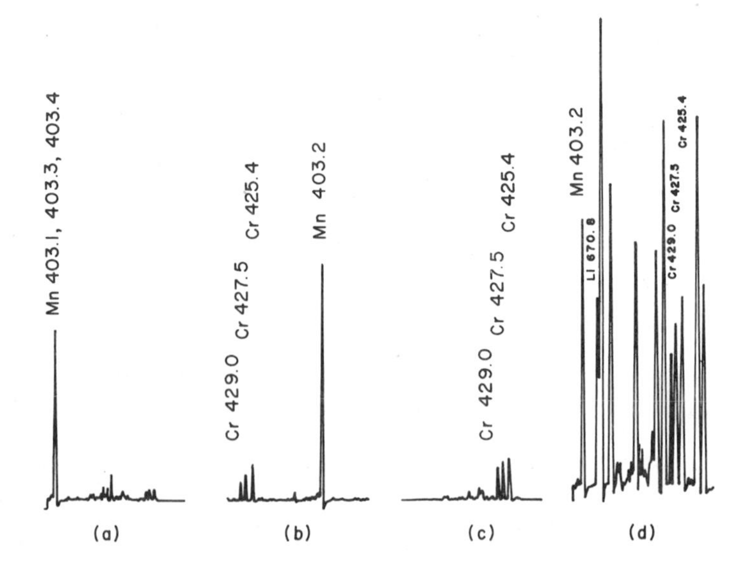

Figure 8. (a) Emission spectrum from multielement lamp [entrance slit 8]; (b) Emission spectrum from multielement lamp [entrance slit 10]; (c) Emission spectrum from multielement lamp [entrance slit 12]; (d) Composite spectrum from Li lamp and multielement lamp [entrance slits 8, 12, and 29].

Figure 8 shows a further advantage of the switch-board system. By plugging the fiber optics into different positions, individual resonance lines can be moved about over the screen to various positions in order to exclude flame bands which may be present in certain spectral regions, or to avoid accidental coincidence of lines [as in Figure 7 (c) for Cr and Li] due to the superposition of several spectra.

The switch-board system gives good resolution, while expanding the wavelength range available, all at a fraction of the cost of an echelle system. Other advantages include: (1) Simplicity--common optical components are used and simple raster scanning can be employed. (2) Flexibility--any spectral line within a 384 nm region can be accessed. (3) Individual optimization is possible--intensities from different fiber optics may be adjusted by the use of filters or by changing the particular slit dimension. This permits attenuation of the high intensity signals without decreasing the intensity of other signals; at the same time, individual observation height optimization may be carried out. (4) Blooming may be avoided by not imaging spectral regions of high intensity on the target. (5) Increased sensitivity compared with echelle systems--more pixels per spectral line. (6) Background subtraction removes everything but the spectral lines emitted by the sample. (7) The system is compact. (8) The optical arrangement may be used with other image devices and is not limited to vidicons.

The analytical applications of this system are currently being investigated in this laboratory and preliminary results by atomic emission with the N_2O/C_2H_2 flame are encouraging.

Future Prospects

All the systems discussed in this report are in the prototype stage with little information available to date on actual simultaneous multielement applications. To accurately answer the question regarding the role of image devices in SMA, more work will be required.

The introduction of image devices in analytical chemistry is hampered by economic as well as scientific considerations. Many investigators cannot justify the purchase of relatively expensive apparatus for which no viable analytical application has been demonstrated. And yet, viable analytical applications will only be developed as these devices sift down from analytical research labs into analytical applications labs. When (and if) enough potential applications have been demonstrated, it may become economically feasible for manufacturers to fabricate and manufacture image devices specifically designed for spectroscopic work.

Abstract

With the realization of the need for analytical systems capable of providing quantitative information on many elements in a sample simultaneously, analytical spectroscopists have been actively engaged in investigating the multielement capabilities of a variety of novel and ingenious systems. This paper traces the evolutionary development of multielement detection systems, and discusses the advantages and disadvantages of the various configurations which have been proposed. With this information as a background, the role of image devices in simultaneous multielement analysis is described.

A new instrument known as a fiber-optic vidicon spectrometer is described for the first time, and the potential advantages of this configuration for simultaneous multielement determinations are discussed. Using fiber-optic light guides in conjunction with an optical system having a dispersion of 3.2 nm/mm, any radiation within a total range of 384 nm may be focused on the target of the SIT vidicon with good resolution.

Literature Cited

1. Fassel, V. A., and Kniseley, R. N., Anal. Chem. (1974) 46, 1110A.
2. Fassel, V. A., and Kniseley, R. N., Anal. Chem. (1974) 46, 1155A.
3. Greenfield, S., Jones, I. L., McGeachin, H. M., and Smith, P. B., Anal. Chim. Acta (1975) 74, 225.
4. Boumans, P. W. J. M., and deBoer, F. J., Proc. Anal. Div. Chem. Soc. (1975) 12, 140.
5. Boumans, P. W. J. M. and deBoer, F. J., Spectrochim. Acta, Part B (1975) 30, 309.
6. Boumans, P. W. J. M., and deBoer, F. J., Spectrochim. Acta, Part B (1976) 31, 355.
7. Fassel, V. A., Peterson, C. A., Abercrombie, F. N., and Kniseley, R. N., Anal. Chem. (1976) 48, 517.
8. Winge, R. K., Fassel, V. A., Kniseley, R. N., DeKalb, E., and Haas, Jr., W. J., Spectrochim. Acta, Part B (1977) 32, 327.
9. Olson, K. W., Haas, Jr., W. J., and Fassel, V. A., Anal. Chem. (1977) 49, 632.
10. Keliher, P. N., and Wohlers, C. C., Anal. Chem. (1976) 48, 333A.
11. Palermo, E. F., Montaser, A., and Crouch, S. R., Anal. Chem. (1974) 46, 2155.
12. Horwit, M., Appl. Opt. (1973) 12, 285.
13. Horwit, M., Appl. Opt. (1971) 10, 1415.
14. Decker, J. A., Anal. Chem. (1972) 44, 127A.
15. Larson, N. M., Crosmun, R., and Talmi, Y., Appl. Opt. (1974) 13, 2662.
16. Plankey, F. W., Glenn, T. H., Hart, L. P., and Winefordner, J. D., Anal. Chem. (1974) 46, 1000.
17. Keir, M. J., Dawson, J. B., and Ellis, D. J., Spectrochim. Acta, Part B (1977) 32, 59.
18. Yuen, W. K., and Horlick, G., Anal. Chem. (1977) 49, 1446.
19. Chester, T. L., Fitzgerald, J. J., and Winefordner, J. D., Anal. Chem. (1976) 48, 779.
20. Horlick, G., and Yuen, W. K., Anal. Chem. (1975) 47, 775.
21. Horlick, G., and Yuen, W. K., Appl. Spectrosc. (1978) 32, 38.
22. Pruiksma, R., Ziemer, J., and Young, E. S., Anal. Chem. (1976) 48, 667.
23. Fellgett, P., Ph.D. Thesis, Cambridge University, Cambridge, 1951.
24. Dohi, T., and Suzuki, T., Appl. Opt. (1971) 10, 1359.
25. Chester, T. L., and Winefordner, J. D., Anal. Chem. (1977) 49, 113.
26. Fitzgerald, J. J., Chester, T. L., and Winefordner, J. D., Anal. Chem. (1975) 47, 2331.
27. Mitchell, D. G., and Johansson, A., Spectrochim. Acta, Part B (1970) 25, 175.

28. Chester, T. L., and Winefordner, J. D., Spectrochim. Acta, Part B (1976) 31, 21.
29. Lundberg, E., and G. Johansson, Anal. Chem. (1976) 48, 1922.
30. Johansson, A., and Nilsson, L. E., Spectrochim. Acta, Part B (1976) 31, 419.
31. Dawson, J. B., Ellis, D. J., and Milner, R., Spectrochim. Acta, Part B (1968) 23, 695.
32. Strojek, J. W., Gruver, G. A., and T. Kuwana, Anal. Chem. (1969) 41, 481.
33. Cordos, E., and Malmstadt, H. V., Anal. Chem. (1973), 45, 425.
34. Santini, R. E., Milano, Michael J., and Pardue, H. L., Anal. Chem. (1973) 45, 915A.
35. Skene, J. F., Stuart, D. C., Fritze, K., and Kennett, T. J., Spectrochim. Acta, Part B (1974) 29, 339.
36. Spillman, R. W., and Malmstadt, H. V., Anal. Chem. (1976) 48, 303.
37. Rose, Jr., O., Mincey, D. W., Yacynych, A. M., Heineman, W. R., and Caruso, J. A., Analyst (1976) 101, 753.
38. Johnson, D. J., Plankey, F. W., and Winefordner, J. D., Anal. Chem. (1975) 47, 1739.
39. Svoboda, V., Anal. Chem. (1968) 40, 1385.
40. Snelleman, W., Rains, T. C., Yee, K. W., Cooke, H. E., and Menis, O., Anal. Chem. (1970) 42, 394.
41. Snelleman, W., Spectrochim. Acta, Part B (1968) 23, 403.
42. Farnsworth, P. T., J. Franklin Inst. (1934) 218, 411.
43. Harber, R. A., and Sonnek, G. E., Appl. Opt. (1966) 5, 1039.
44. Wood, R. W., J. Opt. Soc. Am. (1947) 37, 733.
45. Harrison, G. R., J. Opt. Soc. Am. (1949) 39, 522.
46. Felkel, Jr., H. L., and Pardue, H. L., Anal. Chem. (1978) 50, 602.
47. Danielsson, A., and Lindblom, P., Phys. Scripta (1972) 5, 227.
48. Danielsson, A., and Lindblom, P., Appl. Spectrosc. (1976) 30, 151.
49. Danielsson, A., Lindblom, P., and Söderman, E., Chem. Scripta (1974) 6, 5.
50. Margoshes, M., Pittsburgh Conf. on Analytical Chemistry and Applied Spectroscopy, Cleveland, Ohio, Paper # 99, March 1970.
51. Margoshes, M., Opt. Spectra (1970) 4, 26.
52. Margoshes, M., Spectrochim. Acta, Part B (1970) 25, 113.
53. Talmi, Y., Anal. Chem. (1975) 47, 658A.
54. Talmi, Y., Anal. Chem. (1975) 47, 697A.
55. Horlick, G., and Codding, E. G., Anal. Chem. (1973) 45, 1490.
56. Horlick, G., and Codding, E. G., Anal. Chem. (1973) 45, 1749.
57. Codding, E. G., and Horlick, G., Appl. Spectrosc. (1973) 27, 366.

58. Horlick, G., and Codding, E. G., Anal. Chem. (1974) 46, 133.
59. Codding, E. G., and Horlick, G., Spectrosc. Letters (1974) 7, 33.
60. Horlick, G., and Codding, E. G., Appl. Spectrosc. (1975) 29, 167.
61. Horlick, G., Codding, E. G., and Leung, S. T., Appl. Spectrosc. (1975) 29, 48.
62. Betty, K. R., and Horlick, G., Appl. Spectrosc. (1978) 32, 31.
63. Boumans, P. W. J. M., Rumphorst, R. F., Willemsen, L., and deBoer, F. J., Spectrochim. Acta, Part B (1973) 28, 227.
64. Yates, D. A., and Kuwana, T., Anal. Chem. (1976) 48, 510.
65. Milano, M. J., and Kim, K., Anal. Chem. (1977) 49, 555.
66. Chuang, F. S., Natusch, D. F. S., and O'Keefe, K. R., Anal. Chem. (1978) 50, 525.
67. Horlick, G., Appl. Spectrosc. (1976) 30, 113.
68. Crowell, M. H., Buck, T. M., Labunda, E. E., Dalton, J. V., and Walsh, E. J., Bell Sys. Tech. J. (1967) 46(2), 491.
69. Busch, K. W., and Morrison, G. H., Anal. Chem. (1973) 45, 712A.
70. Boumans, P. W. J. M., and deBoer, F. J., Spectrochim. Acta, Part B (1972) 27, 391.
71. Brost, D. F., Malloy, B., and Busch, K. W., Anal. Chem. (1977) 49, 2280.
72. Winefordner, J. D., Fitzgerald, J. J., and Omenetto, N., Appl. Spectrosc. (1975) 29, 369.
73. Chester, T. L., Haraguchi, H., Knapp, D. O., Messman, J. D., and Winefordner, J. D., Appl. Spectrosc. (1976) 30, 410.
74. Winefordner, J. D., Avni, R., Chester, T. L., Fitzgerald, J. J., Hart, L. P., Johnson, D. J., and Plankey, F. W., Spectrochim. Acta, Part B (1976) 31, 1.
75. Cooney, R. P., Vo-Dinh, T., Walden, G., and Winefordner, J. D., Anal. Chem. (1977) 49, 939.
76. Cooney, R. P., Boutillier, G. D., and Winefordner, J. D., Anal. Chem. (1977) 49, 1048
77. Knapp, D. O., Omenetto, N., Hart, L. P., Plankey, F. W., and Winefordner, J. D., Anal. Chim. Acta (1974) 69, 455.
78. Howell, N. G., and Morrison, G. H., Anal. Chem. (1977) 49, 106.
79. Mitchell, D. G., Jackson, K. W., and Aldous, K. M., Anal. Chem. (1973) 45, 1215A.
80. Jackson, K. W., Aldous, K. M., and Mitchell, D. G., Spectrosc. Letters (1973) 6, 315.
81. Busch, K. W., Howell, N. G., and Morrison, G. H., Anal. Chem. (1974) 46, 575.
82. Busch, K. W., Howell, N. G., and Morrison, G. H., Anal. Chem. (1974) 46, 1231.
83. Busch, K. W., Howell, N. G., and Morrison, G. H., Anal. Chem. (1974) 46, 2074.

84. Howell, N. G., Ganjei, J. D., and Morrison, G. H., Anal. Chem. (1976) 48, 319.
85. Ganjei, J. D., Howell, N. G., Roth, J. R., and Morrison, G. H., Anal. Chem. (1976) 48, 505.
86. McDowell, A, and Pardue, H. L., Anal. Chem. (1976) 48, 1815.
87. McDowell, A. E., and Pardue, H. L., Anal. Chem. (1977) 49, 1171.
88. Jadamec, J. R., Saner, W. A., and Talmi, Y., Anal. Chem. (1977) 49, 1316.
89. Cook, T. E., Milano, M. J., and Pardue, H. L., Clin. Chem. (1974) 20, 1422.
90. Fricke, F. L., Rose, Jr., O., and Caruso, J. A., Anal. Chem. (1975) 47, 2018.
91. Aldous, K. M., Mitchell, D. G., and Jackson, K. W., Anal. Chem. (1975) 47, 1035.
92. Jackson, K. W., Aldous, K. M., and Mitchell, D. G., Appl. Spectrosc. (1974) 28, 569.
93. Milano, M. J., and Pardue, H. L., Anal. Chem. (1975), 47, 25.
94. Milano, M. J., Pardue, H. L., Cook, T. E., Santini, R. E., Magerum, D. W., and Raycheba, J. M. T., Anal. Chem. (1974) 46, 374.
95. Wood, D. L., Dargis, A. B., and Nash, D. L., Appl. Spectrosc. (1975) 29, 310.
96. Cook, T. E., Pardue, H. L., and Santini, R. E., Anal. Chem. (1976) 48, 451.
97. Nieman, T. A., and Enke, C. G., Anal. Chem. (1976) 48, 619.
98. Cook, T. E., Santini, R. E., and Pardue, H. L., Anal. Chem. (1977) 49, 871.
99. Felkel, Jr., H. L., and Pardue, H. L., Anal. Chem. (1977) 49, 1112.
100. Hirschfeld, T., U. S. Patent 3,728,029, April 17, 1973.
101. Vogelthaler, R., and Margoshes, M., U.S. Patent 3,728,576.
102. Malloy, B., and Busch, K. W., unpublished results.

RECEIVED February 13, 1979.

3

Simultaneous Multielement Determinations by Atomic Absorption and Atomic Emission with a Computerized Echelle Spectrometer/Imaging Detector System

HUGO L. FELKEL, JR.[1] and HARRY L. PARDUE

Department of Chemistry, Purdue University, W. Lafayette, IN 47907

Basic and applied studies in many areas including clinical and forensic chemistry, biomedical and nutritional research, environmental pollution, fuel composition, and fuel combustion studies often require the determination of multiple elements in the same sample. A recent issue of CLINICAL CHEMISTRY (April, 1975) was devoted to the subject of trace elements in clinical chemistry, and a recent publication of the proceedings of a symposium on clinical chemistry and chemical toxicology of metals (1) includes discussions of the fundamental aspects of the toxicology of metals. Papers in these and other publications emphasize the interrelationships that exist among multiple elements and the resulting fact that it is often important to determine multiple elements before meaningful conclusions can be drawn. Most instruments used for elemental determinations are designed to determine just one or, at most, two elements at a time. This is an inefficient approach if there is a real need for more than just one or two elements. Because it is often necessary to work with large numbers of small samples, there is strong motivation to measure multiple elements simultaneously whenever possible.

Recent work in this and other laboratories has demonstrated the feasibility of using imaging detectors, such as solid state diode arrays, vidicons, and image dissector tubes as multiwavelength detectors for the simultaneous determination of multiple elements (2-20). Most of these reports have described systems in which the imaging detector is adapted to conventional optics for either atomic absorption or atomic emission spectrometry (5-17). Although these papers have demonstrated the feasibility of using imaging detectors for simultaneous multielement determinations, they have also emphasized a severe limitation of systems involving conventional optics. Because the conventional optics disperse optical spectra in only one dimension, and because the imaging detectors have finite lengths, the analyst must exercise a rather severe trade-off between spectral range and spectral resolution.

[1]Current address: Drawer M, Elloree, SC 29407

0-8412-0504-3/79/47-102-059$10.50/0

Because most of the imaging detectors have only 100 to 500 independent resolution elements along one axis, if one is to achieve 1 Å resolution, then the total spectral range that can be covered with a single experiment is 100 to 500 Å.

This range vs. resolution problem can be solved by taking advantage of the two-dimensional character of some imaging detectors so that electronic resolution elements along both dimensions of the tube are used to resolve different regions of the optical spectrum. One approach to accomplish this, first suggested by Margoshes (21), is to employ an echelle grating spectrometer to disperse the optical spectrum into a two-dimensional pattern (22, 23, 24) and to use a two-dimensional imaging detector scanning mode to interrogate detector elements corresponding to different spectral lines. Some recent reports have demonstrated the feasibility of using echelle grating spectrometers to take advantage of the two-dimensional character of some imaging detectors to obtain good resolution over spectral ranges of several hundred nanometers. Wood and coworkers (18) employed a commercially available computer controlled camera system utilizing an SEC vidicon for arc source emission analyses. Danielson et al. (19, 20) have described a computer controlled echelle spectrometer for emission analysis based on an image dissector, in which the detector is used in a photon counting mode. Although high sensitivities are attainable, long times must be used to have acceptable counting statistics.

Because of the superfluous nature of much of the information available with atomic spectroscopy, a computer controlled random access mode of interrogation has been used with the imaging detector/echelle spectrometer systems. By using the random access mode of interrogation in which only the line intensities of interest are measured, a reduction in computer time and space required, as well as greatly simplified data reduction, is realized for high resolution, wide spectral coverage measurements. The versatility of a computer controlled instrument lies in the ability to easily change scanning formats by software changes rather than by hardware modifications. Many experiments not readily accomplished by hardware sequencers can easily be carried out under computer control. In addition to control functions, the computer may be used to implement a variety of data processing options for enhancing signal to noise ratios (S/N).

One objective of this paper is to present the fundamental concepts and design considerations for coupling a silicon target vidicon and an image dissector to an echelle grating spectrometer to accomplish simultaneous multielement determinations. The optical modifications necessary to adapt the imaging detectors to a commercially available echelle grating spectrometer are discussed in addition to presenting a description of both the hardware and software necessary to implement computer controlled random access interrogation of selected elemental analysis lines.

Another goal of this work is to evaluate the performance characteristics of the imaging detector/echelle spectrometer systems for simultaneous multielement determinations by atomic absorption and atomic emission spectroscopy. The first part of this study identifies important characteristics and necessary operating procedures inherent in the utilization of a vidicon detector for random access interrogation as well as presenting a comparison of the spectral resolution, wavelength addressing accuracy, and luminous sensitivity of the detectors. The fundamental noise characteristics of both detectors are also identified and used to suggest interrogation schemes for the detectors that optimize the signal-to-noise ratio for the measurement of any spectral line. The second part of this study compares the capabilities of the imaging detectors for simultaneous multielement determinations by atomic absorption spectrometry. A comparison of the photometric reliability of the detectors is also presented and conditions are established for the simultaneous determination of Cu, Cr, Mn, Fe, Co, and Ni. The last part of this work describes and compares results obtained with a direct current plasma source for atomic emission spectroscopy.

General Considerations

Because some of the components used in this work are rather unique, the concepts and characteristics of some of the devices will be discussed.

Echelle grating spectrometer. The concept of the echelle grating was developed in the late 1940's by Harrison and coworkers (22, 23) to circumvent some of the difficulties associated with high dispersion and resolution in conventional spectrometers. In conventional spectrometers, high dispersion is obtained with very long focal lengths and high resolution is realized with finely ruled gratings. However, long focal length spectrometers suffer from low throughput and finely ruled gratings generally have low efficiencies. Instead of using a small groove spacing, d, to achieve high resolution as for conventional gratings, the echelle grating is a coarsely ruled grating. The grating used in this work has 79 grooves/mm. However, the echelle grating also increases the blaze angle, β, and therefore, the order, m, to produce very high resolution as illustrated by the basic formula

$$\frac{\lambda}{\Delta\lambda} = \frac{2Nd \sin \beta}{\lambda} = mN \qquad (1)$$

where λ is the wavelength, Δλ is the smallest wavelength interval that can be resolved, and N is the number of grooves illuminated on the grating. Because high orders (113 at 2000 Å to 32 at 7000 Å) are used to obtain high resolution with the echelle grating spectrometer, the grating spectrum alone consists of numerous superimposed orders with the wavelengths in each order dispersed along only one dimension. For example, the 2250 Å line in the 100th order will be located at the same position as the 4500 Å line in the 50th order. Because of this superimposition of orders, the unmodified spectrum is not particularly useful for spectrochemical measurements. However, if a prism is placed such that its dispersion is at right angles to the dispersion of the echelle grating, then the prism will effectively separate the superimposed orders. The net result of the combined functions of the echelle grating and prism, operating at right angles to one another, is to produce a two-dimensional pattern where vertical position corresponds to the grating order, and horizontal position corresponds to wavelength within each order. Thus, the spectra obtained with the echelle grating spectrometer have a two-dimensional format that is continuous in wavelength. The continuity in wavelength allows measurements to start in a higher order (eg. m = 53) at the exact wavelength in the spectrum at which measurements were terminated in the previous order (eg. m = 52). The free spectral range, which is the wavelength range best covered in one order, varies from about 18 Å at 2000 Å to about 219 Å at 7000 Å. The reciprocal linear dispersion varies from 0.57 Å/mm at 2000 Å to about 1.9 Å/mm at 7000 Å. Thus, the resolution of the echelle grating spectrometer is highest in the ultraviolet region of the spectrum, where the most sensitive absorption and emission lines occur for numerous elements.

The result of the concepts discussed here are represented diagramatically in Figure 1. In the figure, the symbol for each element is located at a point relative to the other elements at which a principal absorption line would occur in the two-dimensional spectrum from the echelle grating spectrometer. Some lines included in the figure (left to right and top to bottom) are Mg(2852Å), Mn(2795Å), Fe(2483Å), Co(2407Å), Pd(2448Å), Ni(2320Å) and Ir(2089Å). In this figure, the different wavelengths within an order are on the horizontal axis, and the different orders are arranged along the vertical axis. It is noted that Mn is listed twice; both listings correspond to the same line that would occur near the end of one order and the beginning of the next order. This figure represents only a fraction of the total spectrum and is intended for illustrative purposes only. The echelle spectrometer used in this work covers the range from below 2000 Å to above 7000 Å so that a representation of the complete spectrum analogous to the segment represented in Figure 1 would have the Hg(1849.50Å) line near the bottom and the K(7698.98Å) line near the top.

In the work reported here, the two-dimensional spectrum from the echelle spectrometer is displayed onto the active surface of a two-dimensional imaging detector that can monitor the different lines independently so that emission or absorption lines for multiple elements can be monitored simultaneously.

Silicon target vidicon tube. The photosensitive surface of a silicon target vidicon consists of a two-dimensional array of several thousand discrete photodiodes. The silicon vidicon used in this work has the photodiodes spaced on 15 μm centers (25). Initially, the target, or array of photodiodes, is charged by a scanning electron beam, causing any given diode to be reverse biased and to have a depletion region corresponding to a net charge stored in the diode. Absorbed photons generate electron-hole pairs which diffuse through the depletion region and reduce the charge stored in the diode. The amount of charge which is neutralized is proportional to the number of photons absorbed since the last scanning cycle. When an electron beam is focused on the diode surface, it restores the charge neutralized by the absorbed photons and the charging current can be measured and related to the integrated intensity. The resolution capabilities of the vidicon are determined primarily by the effective size of the electron scan beam. The target position interrogated by the electron beam is controlled by two orthogonal deflection fields. Thus, if the two-dimensional spectrum from the echelle spectrometer is focused onto the target, then the integrated intensity of different spectral lines can be determined by changing the deflection fields.

One of the most attractive features of the vidicon is the ability to develop a charge proportional to the integrated intensity between sampling cycles. This integrating capability improves the random component of the signal to noise ratio of any resolution element by a factor of $\sqrt{N}$ as compared to the sequential monitoring of N resolution elements by a non-integrating sensor for the same total time. Two of the more serious technical problems with the vidicon are the lag and blooming characteristics. Lag is manifested as the incomplete erasure of images on the first few readout cycles after storage. This phenomenon is caused by target capacitance and reduced beam acceptance at low discharge levels. This characteristic is more of a problem for low level signals. For example, consider target signals of 100% and 10% of the maximum signal. After the first readout, the 100% signal will be reduced to about 5-10%, while the original 10% signal is reduced to only 4-8%. Blooming, or signal spreading, is caused by the lateral diffusion of charge from a region of high spectral intensity to a region of low spectral intensity. The migration of charge is caused by the potential gradient existing between the two regions and is a result of finite target conductivity. Blooming increases with increasing signal levels and causes a loss of resolution. Blooming may also prohibit the acquisition of information from a low intensity line in close proximity to a strong line.

Image dissector tube. Figure 2 shows a schematic representation of an image dissector tube. The active surface of the image dissector tube is an S-20 photocathode (26) similar to that

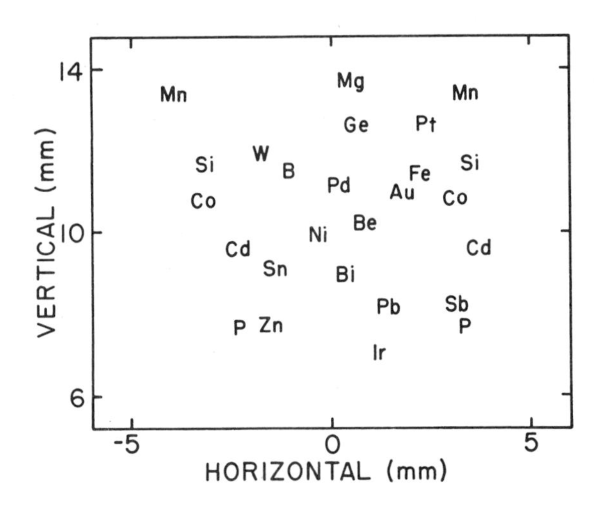

Clinical Chemistry

Figure 1. Relative locations of the most sensitive absorption lines for selected elements in the two-dimensional echelle spectrometer display (30).

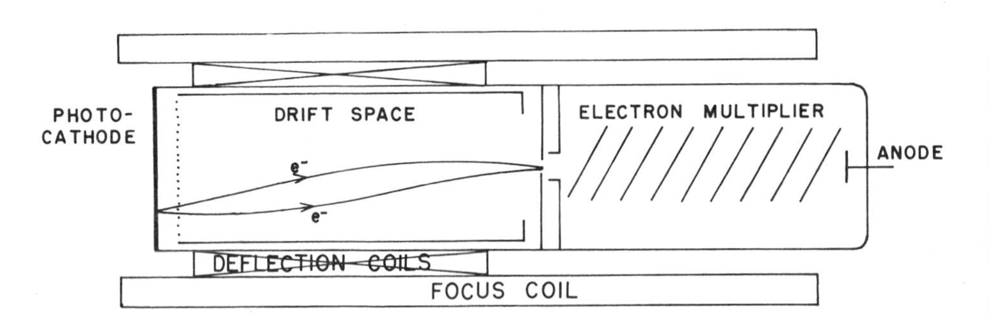

Figure 2. Schematic representation of an image dissector tube

used in ordinary phototubes and photomultipliers. Unlike an ordinary photomultiplier however, the image dissector tube includes magnetic focussing and deflecting circuitry. An electron lens accelerates and focuses all electrons emitted from each point on the photocathode to a corresponding single point (or small area) in the plane of the dissecting aperture. The resulting electron image can be electronically deflected across the aperture. Thus, the aperture samples the photoelectrons from a small, well-defined area of the input optical image incident on the photocathode. Within limits, the resolution capability of an image dissector is determined entirely by the size and shape of the aperture. Following the aperture, the sampled photoelectrons are multiplied in an electron multiplier by about 10^6 and produce a current at the anode that is linearly related to the input photon flux. Thus, if the two-dimensional spectrum from the echelle spectrometer is displayed onto the photocathode, then photoelectrons from different spectral lines can be selected by changing the deflecting magnetic field, and intensities can be determined for several lines.

Some of the major advantages of an image dissector are the excellent resolution, the large dynamic range (typically 10^5-10^6), and the virtual absence of lag and blooming effects. Unlike a vidicon, the image dissector can be operated at stationary deflection, which greatly simplifies software control and permits more rapid acquisition of spectral information. Although blooming does not occur with the image dissector, an analogous phenomenon may reduce the available linear dynamic range. If bright images are incident on the photocathode when a measurement of illumination at a low level is being made, the back scattered flux from internal tube parts may limit the available dynamic range to only 2 or 3 orders of magnitude, depending on the area, brightness, and location of the disturbing flux. Another limitation of the device is that it is not an integrating sensor, such as the vidicon. This means the device cannot accumulate and store information from one part of an image while another region is being interrogated. Thus, if one is scanning N resolution elements in a given time, then the random component of the signal to noise ratio for each element would be degraded by a factor of $\sqrt{N}$ as compared to the continuous monitoring of a single resolution element for the same time period.

Combined Characteristics. Figure 3 shows pseudo three-dimensional representations of the echelle spectra from a mercury pen lamp recorded with an image dissector and a silicon target vidicon. In this figure the intensity signals are displayed along the Z axis for different wavelengths along the horizontal, X, axis and for different orders along the vertical, Y, axis. The vertical scale in each spectrum has been expanded for clarity, and one division along the vertical axis corresponds to one division on the horizontal axis. The data displayed here covers the spectral

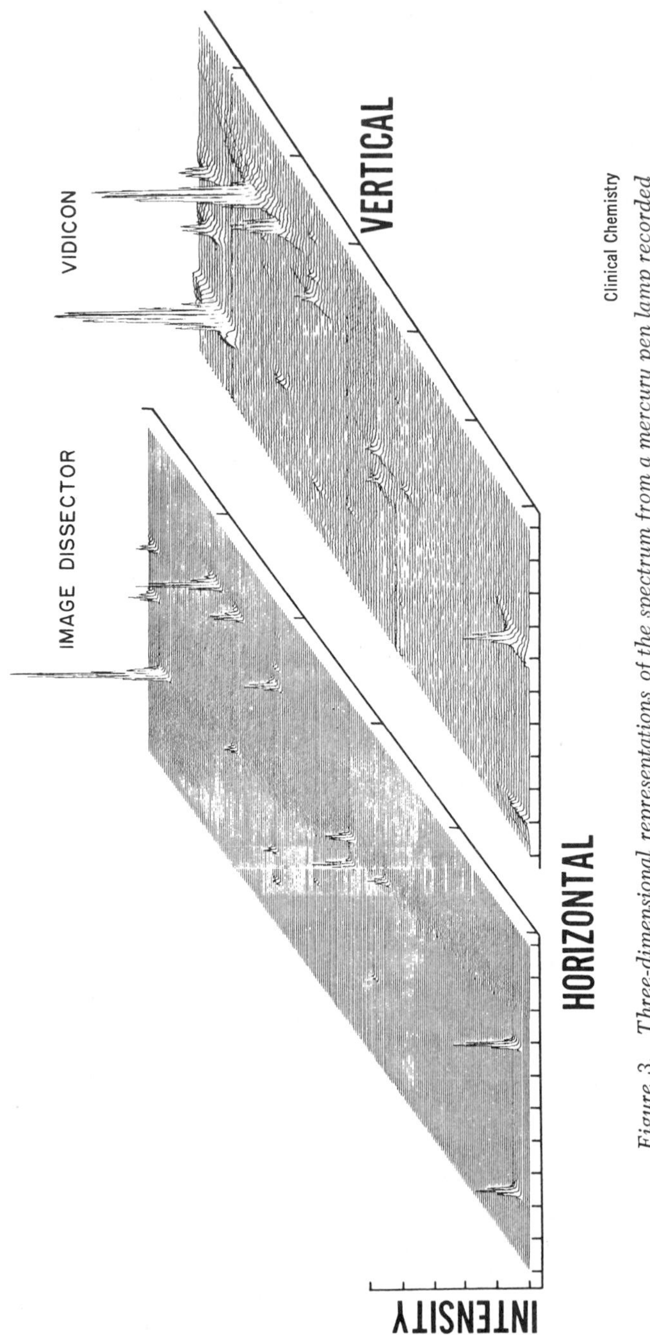

Clinical Chemistry

Figure 3. Three-dimensional representations of the spectrum from a mercury pen lamp recorded with an image dissector and a silicon target vidicon (30)

region from approximately 2500 Å to about 5800 Å. The two peaks at the lower end of each spectrum are for the 2536.55 Å line that appears in two adjacent orders monitored by the imaging detectors. These data were acquired and displayed with a small computer that operates on-line with the echelle spectrometer/imaging detector systems.

The most apparent difference in these two spectra is that the spectral resolution for the image dissector system is better than for the vidicon system. This difference is largely due to the smaller effective size of the aperture of the image dissector relative to the size of the electron scan beam of the vidicon. Charge blooming on the target of the vidicon is also a factor in the resolution difference observed here. This effect is especially apparent along the vertical axis, and causes the relatively large tails on the peaks scanned with the vidicon.

Instrumentation and Procedures.

The general layout of the random access vidicon detector and echelle grating spectrometer when used for atomic absorption measurements is shown schematically in the block diagram of Figure 4. The same general configuration is used with the image dissector, except the image dissector camera system replaces the vidicon detector. The fundamental units composing the system are: 1) the optical system and dispersion devices, 2) the imaging detector, 3) the control logic and signal processing module, and 4) the computer system and its associated peripherals. The system is also used for plasma emission spectroscopy by replacing the flame cell and hollow cathode lamp with a plasma source.

Optical system. The spectrometer is a modified version of a prototype 0.75 meter Spectraspan echelle grating spectrometer (Spectrametrics, Inc., Andover, MA 01810) with a 79 grooves/mm echelle grating having a blaze angle of 63°26' and a 30° quartz prism. The approach used to obtain an image suitable for interrogation by the imaging detectors is to introduce auxiliary optics (M3 - M5) which reduce the size of the focal plane from approximately 50-mm by 75-mm to 9-mm by 12-mm for the vidicon, or 13-mm by 20-mm for the image dissector while maintaining adequate spatial resolution and a flat focal plane over the spectral region from 2000 to 8000 Å. The auxiliary folding mirror, which is located a few inches behind the normal focal plane, generates a "white light" (i.e., all wavelengths present) image of the echelle grating just before the cassigrainian mirror system, composed of M4 and M5. This mirror system produces a second focal plane on the imaging detector surface, which is a reduced image of the first spectral focal plane. This approach to image reduction circumvents the difficulties associated with short focal length optics which suffer from severe vignetting,

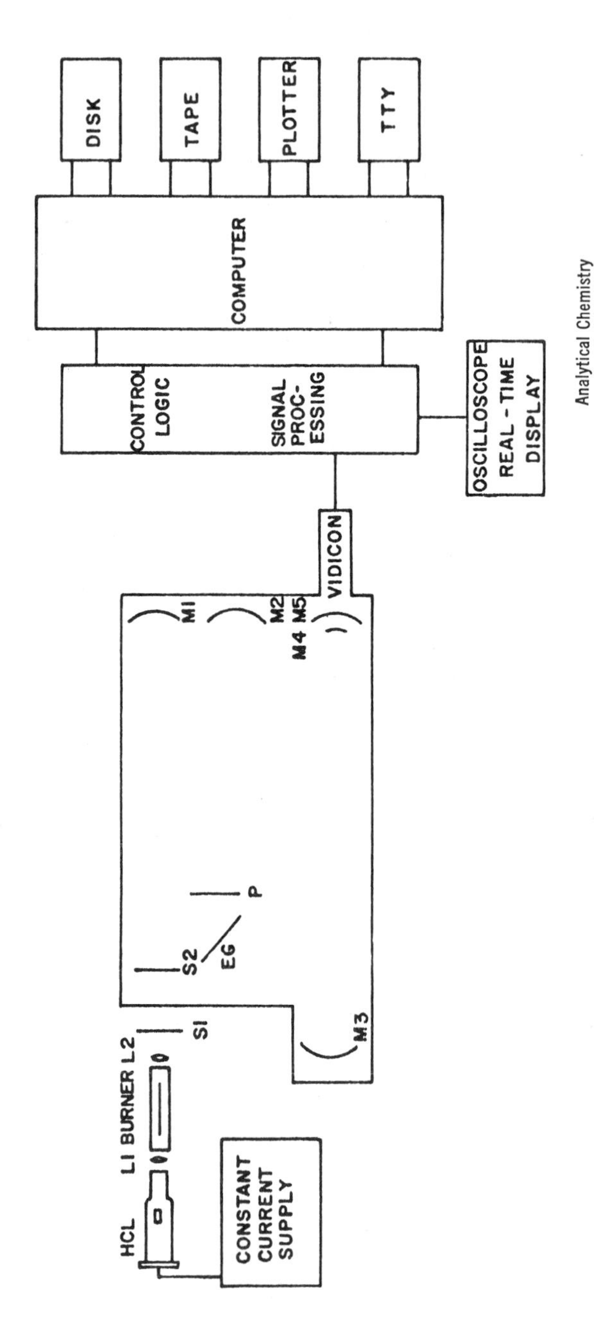

Figure 4. Block diagram of computer controlled random access spectrometer (2)

aberations, or limited spectral range. The auxiliary folding mirror has a focal length of 78-cm and a diameter of 10.7-cm. The focal length of the cassigrainian mirror system (Nye Optical Co., Spring Valley, CA 92077) used with the vidicon is 13.5-cm at f/1.6. The only change required to adapt the system to the image dissector tube is to replace the 13.5-cm focal length f/1.6 mirror system with a 20.0-cm focal length f/2.8 mirror system (Nye Optical Co.). This mirror system produces an image reduction of 3.9 for the image dissector compared to 5.8 for the silicon vidicon. Image reduction increases the effective f/number experienced by the imaging detectors from f/10 to approximately f/1.6 for the vidicon, or f/2.8 for the image dissector. This increases the flux per unit area by a factor of $10^2/1.6^2$ or about 40 for the vidicon, or about $10^2/2.8^2$ or 13 for the image dissector as compared to the unmodified spectrometer.

A low speed shutter (S2) is used for making computer controlled dark current measurements. A high speed electromagnetic shutter (S1, 22-8411, Ealing Corp., South Natick, MA 01760) is used for controlling the time interval that the vidicon is illuminated. Exposure times are entered into the shutter control module from a multiplier and a decade switch register providing shutter times of from 30 ms to 10 s.

Hollow cathode lamps and flame atomizer. Energy from a hollow cathode lamp is imaged by lens-1 over the center of the 10-cm slot high solids burner for air-acetylene (No. 02-1000036-00, Varian, Louisville, KY 40207) and lens-2 then refocuses the radiation onto the entrance slit of the echelle spectrometer. Unless otherwise specified, an entrance slit width of 200 μm and height of 500 μm was used throughout these experiments. Lens-1 is a 6-cm focal length quartz lens with a 4-cm diameter that is stopped down to 1.6-cm by an iris diaphragm. Lens-2 is a 1.5-cm diameter quartz lens with a 5-cm focal length. Various lamps were used in this work and include a multielement hollow cathode lamp containing Co, Cr, Cu, Fe, Mn and Ni (No. JA45599, Jarrell-Ash, Waltham, MA 02154) as well as single element hollow cathode lamps for Cr (Varian No. 2T300), Cu (Varian No. 5D874), Fe (WL22810, Westinghouse Electric Corp., Elmira, NY 14902), and Mn (Westinghouse No. WL22936). The lamps are powered by a constant current supply removed from a prototype atomic absorption spectrometer (No. 5960A, Hewlett-Packard, Avondale, PA 19311).

A 10-cm slot type burner (No. 02-1000036-00, Varian) with an air-acetylene flame was used as the atomizer source. The flow rates were 4.2 ℓ/min for air and 1.8 ℓ/min for acetylene. The observation height was 5 mm as measured from the top of the burner to the center of the hollow cathode lamp.

Plasma source. The excitation source used in this work is an argon supported, dc plasma source (Spectrametrics, Inc., Model 53000, Spectra Jet II). The argon flow rate to the cathode and anode electrodes (thoriated tungsten) was 1.6 ℓ/min and the flow rate through the ceramic nebulizer was 3.1 ℓ/min. The plasma is sustained by passing 7.5 A at 40 V dc between the two electrodes. The sample uptake rate for this plasma is about 2 ml/min with a nebulizer efficiency approaching 10%. The characterization of this plasma by Skogerboe and coworkers (27) suggests that the analyte experiences effective source temperatures of 6000-7000°K in the excitation region. The small volume of the excitation region of this plasma is particularly well suited for use with the echelle spectrometer because a rather short entrance slit height is used, providing for optimum signal-to-background ratios.

Vidicon circuitry. Commercial power supplies were used to power the vidicon and the associated electronics. The sweep/addressing circuitry and signal processing amplifiers necessary for random access interrogation were designed and constructed in this laboratory. The voltages applied to the silicon target vidicon tube (No. C23246, Radio Corp. of America, Harrison, NJ 07029) are derived from an adjustable general purpose power supply (No. 240A, Keithley Instruments, Inc., Cleveland, OH 44139). The decelerating grid (grid 4), the accelerating grid (grid 2), and the beam focus electrode (grid 3) are operated at 340, 300, and 290 V respectively. The beam current control grid (grid 1) is nominally held at a potential of -30V derived from a 90 V dry cell battery. The magnetic focus coil is driven by an adjustable power supply (IP-18, Heath Company, Benton Harbor, MI 49022).

Image dissector system. A commercially available image dissector camera system (Model 658A, EMR Photoelectric, Princeton, NJ 08540) with an EMR 575E image dissector tube was used in this work. The camera system interface for the computer used in this work (PDP-8/M, Digital Equipment Corporation, Maynard, MA 01754) was custom designed using the M1709 Omnibus Interface Foundation Module (DEC). Scan controller and signal amplifier/ADC modules that link the camera system with the computer were also developed.

The image dissector tube has a sapphire window and an S-20 photocathode surface that combine to give useful spectral response from about 1800 Å to about 7500 Å. The photocathode is circular with a diameter of about 43 mm. In this sensor, the photoelectrons generated by the optical image on the photocathode are magnetically focused onto a plate which has a 38 μm circular aperture. The photoelectrons passing through this aperture are then multiplied by the 13-stage, Cu-Be, venetian blind electron multiplier, producing a current at the anode that is linearly related to the input photon flux. The voltage applied to the electron multiplier is approximately 2.4 kV, providing a current gain of about 6 x 10^5. The gain of the electron multiplier of the image dissector was maintained constant throughout these experiments. The dimensions of the aperture were chosen to provide the best intensity-resolution tradeoff for this particular application. The 38 μm diameter aperture should permit the 43 mm photocathode to be resolved into about $(43 \times 10^3\ \mu m)^2/(38\ \mu m)^2$ or about 1.3×10^6 electronic resolution elements. Because there are problems with any of these imaging detectors when one attempts to use areas of the responsive surface near the edge, a 22.4 mm square area of the photocathode was used, so that the 38 μm aperture would correspond to about $(22.4 \times 10^3\ \mu m)^2/(38/2)^2\ \pi$ or about 4.4×10^5 electronic resolution elements.

The entire electron image of the photocathode is deflected by two digitally-controlled magnetic fields, allowing any region of the photocathode to be addressed. The addressing accuracy of this system is rated by the manufacturer to be 3% of field with a repeatability of 0.1%; however, wavelength prediction accuracy data show that these are rather conservative specifications. The image deflection fields are produced by coil drivers that function as voltage-to-current converters. The voltage supplied to the coil drivers is controlled by 12-bit horizontal (X) and vertical (Y) position DAC's. Thus, position input to the sensor consists of 12-bit parallel binary X or Y position information, load X, and load Y command lines.

There are also two additional lines which are decoded to select one of four possible bandwidths in the video processor. The standard bandwidths available vary from 0.1 to 100 kHz in decade steps; however, the system was modified to provide a bandwidth range of 10 Hz to 10 kHz. The minimum time interrogating a given resolution element, called the dwell time, Δt, is determined by the bandwidth of the video processor, Δf, as given by the following expression.

$$\Delta t = \frac{1}{2\Delta f_M} \quad (2)$$

After the appropriate dwell time has elapsed, the sample command is issued and initiates ADC conversion of the elemental intensity. The basic camera system is supplied with an 8-bit ADC, however, to take full advantage of the dynamic range available with the image dissector, an auxiliary signal amplifier/12-bit ADC module was incorporated into the system.

A scan controller provides several functions under computer control, namely detector coordinate redefinition, position and command display, ADC selection, and diagnostic analysis of interface subassemblies. Coordinate redefinition was necessary because the format of the 12-bit word presented to the X or Y DAC is straight binary, whereas the 12-bit computer employs offset binary (two's complement arithmetic). Thus, the word outputted to the X or Y DAC from the computer is converted from offset binary to straight binary. The scan coordinate specified by the computer is displayed in a 12-bit LED register. The load X, load

Y, and sample commands are also indicated by a 3-bit LED display register.

The hardware design of the scan controller also allows diagnostic analysis of interface subassemblies. The software tests that can be performed check the device flag, the integrity of input and output transfers, the bandwidth and shutter control register, the sync generator, and the 12-bit ADC. If a malfunction occurs in the scan controller or interface module, error messages produced by the supporting software enable the source of the problem to be readily identified.

More complete details of the hardware/software systems have been published (28).

Interrogation modes. For the silicon vidicon, the target was primed between 200 ms exposures by 20 erase cycles of 10 ms duration each. Twenty-five points were acquired at each wavelength and corrected for background. The approach used for this correction was to subtract from the peak height or area measurement a weighted average of the background signal either side of the peak. Of the 20 to 25 points taken at each wavelength, about two-thirds contain information about the line intensity and the rest are background data. Since the variation in sensitivity and dark current over small regions of the target is very low, this approach provides an excellent means of correcting line source data. Initial attempts to correct the data by acquiring dark current spectra and subtracting these from line spectra yielded data that contained relatively high levels of background, resulting in calibration plots with significant curvature. The background is probably due to blooming and/or inadequate priming of the target prior to random access interrogation.

For the image dissector, the bandwidth of the video processor was reduced to 10 Hz and multiple measurements were averaged at each peak maximum and corrected for background by subtracting the average of measurements made on both sides of each spectral line. The data reported for the image dissector are based on the average of 2048 measurements each at the peak maximum and two background positions during a 1 s interval at each wavelength.

Considerations involved in the selection of these interrogation modes have been discussed elsewhere (2, 29, 30).

Reagents and solutions. The Ca and Li analyte solutions were prepared by dissolving reagent grade $CaCO_3$ and Li_2CO_3 in dilute HCl. Solutions containing Ba, Na, and K were prepared from the reagent grade chloride salts. The other analyte solutions were certified atomic absorption standards (Fisher Scientific Co., Fair Lawn, NJ 07410) prepared from the metal (Mg, Ni, Mn, Mo, Co), the oxide (Cu, Cr), the chloride (Fe), or the carbonate (Sr) and contain dilute HCl, HNO_3, or aqua regia as the solvent. For the emission studies, all solutions were prepared to contain 1000 mg/ℓ rubidium to reduce interelement effects observed for alkali and alkaline earth metals (29).

Performance Characteristics.

Response characteristics of the silicon vidicon and image dissector for a variety of scan formats were evaluated and have been presented elsewhere (2, 29, 30). Only those data most pertinent to analytical applications with the selected operating conditions are included here.

Resolution. Because one of the main objectives of this work is to provide high resolution with wide spectral coverage, an investigation of the resolution capabilities of each detector/ spectrometer system was undertaken. The method used for determining the experimental resolution was to measure the full width at half maximum (FWHM) of several atomic lines from various hollow cathode lamps and a mercury pen lamp. The resolution is then determined by multiplying the FWHM by the reciprocal linear dispersion (RLD). The experimental RLD was evaluated by determining the number of DAC steps between the peak maxima of two wavelengths in the same grating order and dividing this into the separation (in Angstroms) of the two lines. The theoretical resolution was calculated in a similar manner, except that the FWHM is replaced by the effective slit width, where the effective slit dimensions for the spectrometer are the entrance slit dimensions divided by the image reduction factor, 5.8 for the vidicon and 3.9 for the image dissector, and the RLD is determined by calculating the separations in millimeters of the wavelengths of interest. Table I shows a comparison of the resolution capabilities for each detector system. For these data, the slit height was 500 µm and the width was 200 µm, except for the silicon vidicon data at 3737.13 Å where 500 µm slit width was used.

These data show that for the image dissector there is excellent agreement between experimental and theoretical resolution and that the resolution of the image dissector system is about twice as good as that of the vidicon system. The deviation of the resolution of the image dissector from theoretical at 7024.05 Å may be attributed to curvature of field in the reduced image of the spectral focal plane because the line is near the edge of the photocathode.

It should be noted that the 200 µm slit width used here does not represent the smallest practical slit width that can be used with the image dissector. The photoelectrons from the photocathode of the image dissector are focused so that they produce a 1:1 image of the photocathode surface on a 38 µm diameter circular aperture. Only those electrons that are focused onto the aperture are passed to the dynode chain where they are amplified. However, the 200 µm slit width used here produces a slit image width of 51 µm on the photocathode, and thus, the ultimate resolution should be about 25% better than that shown in Table I,

Table I
Comparison of spectral resolution with silicon target vidicon and image dissector tubes

Order[a]	Wavelength (Å)	Resolution, Å Expected	Vidicon	Image dissector
72 (Hg)	3125.66 3131.55	0.18 (0.33)[c]	0.40	0.20
62 (Hg)	3650.15 3654.84	0.20	----	0.26
60 (Fe)	3737.13 3745.56	0.23 (0.56)[b]	0.60	0.25
56 (Mn)	4033.07 4034.49	0.23 (0.41)[c]	0.53	----
39 (Hg)	5769.59 5790.65	0.33 (0.60)[c]	0.76	0.47
32 (Ne)	7024.05 7032.41	0.42 (0.75)[c]	0.89	0.74

[a]Mercury lines from mercury pen lamp, Mn lines from Mn hollow cathode lamp, Fe and Ne lines from Fe hollow cathode lamp. [b]The value in parentheses is for the silicon vidicon with a slit width of 500 μm. [c]Resolution imposed by width of electron beam in the vidicon.

if a 150 μm slit width were used. Because a 22.4 mm square area of the photocathode was used for this work, the 51 μm effective slit width produces about 440 horizontal resolution elements or about 1.9×10^5 two-dimensional resolution elements.

The vidicon data show good agreement between experimental and theoretical resolution at a 500 μm slit width. However, the experimental resolution is poorer than the expected resolution for a 200 μm slit width. The large discrepancies observed at narrow slit widths are primarily due to the size of the electron scan beam. This assertion was proven by making measurements of the beam diameter using an approach similar to that of Enke and Nieman (31). The method employed was to scan through a wavelength using different sizes of DAC steps between interrogation points. When the step size is smaller than the beam diameter, the beam overlaps a portion of the next adjacent position so that when this position is sampled a smaller signal is observed than for no overlap. The results of this experiment showed a maximum signal for a step size of about five DAC bits. From system calibration data for the vidicon, it is known that one DAC increment corresponds to 0.0125 mm, yielding a beam diameter of 0.0623 mm. If this beam diameter is used as the effective slit width, the theoretical resolutions shown in parentheses are calculated, which are in better agreement with the experimentally observed resolutions. It should be noted that the difference between the experimental resolutions and the beam diameter limited resolution corresponds to an uncertainty of one DAC increment in determining the FWHM of the atomic line. This value for beam diameter leads to the conclusion that there are approximately 200 horizontal resolution elements on the vidicon target which corresponds to approximately 4 x 4 diodes covered at any one position.

Wavelength accuracy. In order to evaluate the ability of each system to locate spectral lines, a preliminary wavelength calibration was carred out with the emission spectrum of a mercury pen lamp and then the peak maxima of several atomic lines from an iron hollow cathode lamp were located. The root mean square (RMS) prediction error, which is the difference between the predicted and the observed location of a line, for the vidicon detector system was 1.4 DAC steps. Because it is known from system calibration data that one DAC increment corresponds to 0.0125 mm, the absolute error in position prediction is 0.018 mm. For the image dissector, the RMS prediction error was 7.6 DAC steps, and because one DAC step for this system corresponds to 0.0055 mm, the absolute error in the predicted coordinate is 0.042 mm. The data in Table II represent a comparison of the wavelength position prediction errors for the two detectors. These values were calculated by multiplying the absolute errors of the predicted positions by the RLD at each wavelength. These data show that wavelength positions can be predicted somewhat more accurately with the vidicon than with the image dissector.

Table II
Comparison of errors in predicting locations of spectral lines

	RMS Wavelength Error, Å	
Wavelength, Å	Vidicon[a]	Image dissector[b]
2000	0.03	0.05
3000	0.05	0.07
4000	0.06	0.10
5000	0.08	0.12
6000	0.10	0.16
7000	0.11	0.18

[a] One DAC step is equivalent to 0.0125 mm which corresponds to an RMS error of 0.018 mm. [b] One DAC step is equivalent to 0.00548 mm which corresponds to an RMS error of 0.042 mm.

The wavelength location prediction accuracy of the program used to calculate the locations of specified wavelengths in the normal focal plane of the echelle spectrometer is rated by the supplier (Spectrametrics, Inc., Andover, MA 01810) to be 0.050 mm. The modified routine is expected to have a wavelength position uncertainty of approximately 0.009 mm in the vidicon focal plane or about 0.013 mm in the focal plane of the image dissector. The differences between the observed and the expected errors in wavelength position uncertainty may be attributed to distortion in either the reduced image, or the deflection assemblies of the detectors. A comparison of the expected errors with the observed errors reveals that the distortion is about 1.6 times greater for the image dissector than for the silicon vidicon. Because shorter focal length optics are used with the vidicon, optical distortion is expected to be larger for the vidicon than for the image dissector, and it is concluded that the deflection assemblies of the detectors probably contribute more to distortion than the image reduction optics. It is probable that the distortion could be compensated for by using more than the twelve calibration wavelengths used in this work, and including higher order terms (X^2 or X^3) in the models used to transform the predicted positions of wavelengths to DAC coordinates. However, the uncertainties reported in Table II are already well within the FWHM of a spectral line, and it is simpler and more reliable to use an optimization routine for locating peak maxima after the approximate location of a line has been identified.

Another source of error in the predicted location of a line is influenced by the number of significant figures included in the wavelength specification. Six digits of wavelength information are necessary to achieve a round-off error of less than one DAC step in the predicted coordinate of a wavelength less than 8000 Å when observed with the image dissector. For the vidicon, only five digits of wavelength information are needed above approximately 4500 Å. Therefore, to minimize this contribution to the wavelength location prediction error, six digits of wavelength information were specified in all experiments.

Sensitivity. Data related to detector sensitivities are included in Table III. The two data columns for each detector give the 100%T current and the standard deviation for each spectral line.

For those lines for which useful responses were obtained with both detectors, the ratios of 100%T currents for the image dissector to the vidicon range from a low of 100:1 for the Cu(3274Å) line to a high of 290:1 for the Mn(4031Å) line with most ratios being in the range of 130:1 to 190:1. For the limited number of lines below 3000 Å examined (Co(2407Å), Fe(2483Å), Mn(2795Å), and Ni(2320Å)) using the multielement hollow cathode lamp (MEHCL), the signals from the vidicon at these wavelengths were only marginally measurable above background whereas the image dissector gave useful responses. This was surprising because Mitchell et al. (12) obtained adequate signals for numerous elements with lines below 3000 Å using single element hollow cathode lamps (SEHCL) with a silicon target vidicon system. Whether this apparent discrepancy results from lower line intensities in the MEHCL compared to the SEHCL's, differences in

Table III
Comparison of the luminous sensitivities of the image dissector and the silicon target vidicon

	Image Dissector		Silicon Target Vidicon		
	100%T current (nA)	Std. Dev.[a] (nA@100%T)	100%T current (nA)	Std. Dev.[b] (nA@100%T)	100%T current ratio (ID/STU)[c]
Cr(4254.33)	1393.0	1.20	10.5	0.038	130
Cr(3578.69)	784.2	0.64	4.5	0.036	170
Cu(3247.54)	879.8	1.23	4.7	0.033	190
Cu(3273.96)	217.9	0.46	2.1	0.027	100
Fe(3719.94)	505.3	0.63	3.5	0.025	140
Fe(3020.64)	95.4	0.25	0.65	0.042	150
Mn(4030.76)	4369.9	3.65	15.1	0.042	290
Mn(2794.82)	228.9	0.46	d	---	---
Ni(3414.77)	571.1	0.98	4.1	0.029	140
Ni(2320.03)	4.3	0.08	d	---	---
Co(3453.51)	466.3	0.98	4.3	0.045	110
Co(2407.25)	4.1	0.07	d	---	---

[a]Based on ten replicate measurements. [b]Based on seven replicate measurements. [c]Ratio of the 100%T current for the image dissector divided by the 100%T current for the silicon target vidicon.
[d]Line intensity too weak to give meaningful measurements.

responses of the vidicon detectors, differences in efficiencies of the dispersion optics, the smaller number of diodes included in each resolution element, differences in integration times (not specified in ref. 12), or a combination of these and other factors is not known at this time. However, signals from the image dissector at the shortest wavelengths are about 100 times smaller (4 nA at 2400 Å) than signals at longer wavelengths (500 nA at 3400 Å) whereas the difference in quantum efficiency for an S-20 photocathode at these wavelengths is only 2% (17% at 2400 Å versus 19% at 3400 Å). Thus, the most logical reason for the decrease in sensitivity of both detectors at short wavelengths is a loss in dispersion efficiency for the echelle grating spectrometer.

Noise characteristics. For repeated measurements of currents between 2 and 15 nA with the silicon vidicon, standard deviations ranged from 0.025 to 0.045 nA with an average value of 0.035 nA. To a first approximation, the noise level for the silicon vidicon is independent of the signal level. For repeated measurements of currents between 4 and 4,400 nA with the image dissector, a log-log plot of imprecision vs. signal is linear with a slope of 0.51 ± 0.07 (30) confirming the expected shot-noise behavior.

Atomic Absorption

The systems described above have been evaluated for the simultaneous determination of chromium, copper, cobalt, nickel, iron, and manganese in mixtures by atomic absorption. The experimental conditions described earlier were selected to give reasonable responses for all elements and involved compromises for some selected elements as discussed previously (30).

Linearity. Figure 5 represents linearity plots of data from the vidicon for solutions containing Cr, Cu, Co, Ni, Fe and Mn. The solid lines represent the unweighted least-squares fits to the data sets. Each data point shown is the average of 4 replicate determinations. Although at least two analysis lines were observed for most of the elements, only one line per element is shown here for clarity. Statistical information for the data is given in Tables IV and V. The expected linear relationship between elemental concentration and absorbance was also confirmed with the image dissector. The sensitivity data included in Table IV represent slopes of calibration plots for three standards over a four fold concentration range for each element. Intercepts for these data were all statistically zero at the 95% confidence level. Standard errors of estimate for the image dissector ranged from 0.00095 to 0.0087 for Cr(4254Å) and Co(2407Å), respectively.

There are some important features of these data that should be noted. In all cases, sensitivities for the silicon vidicon and image dissector are not statistically different at the 95% confidence level. However, in all cases but one (Co(3453Å)), the uncertainties in the slopes are lower for the image dissector than for the silicon vidicon. Average values of coefficients of variation are 4.8% for the silicon vidicon and 2.5% for the image dissector and the image dissector data include wavelengths that are not accessible with the silicon vidicon. Plotted data (A vs C) would be similar to those reported above except that plots for the image dissector would include data for shorter wavelengths (Mn(2795Å), Ni(2320Å), and Co(2407Å)) and the data would exhibit less scatter by a factor of two or more.

Detection limits. The 100%T peak currents (i_o), the standard deviations of the peak current measurements (SD), and the sensitivity figures (S) in Tables IV and V combine to determine the detection limits of the elements. The detection limit for any element is given by

$$DL = \varepsilon_{A_o}/S = [-\log(1 - \frac{\varepsilon_{i_o}}{i_o})]/S \qquad (3a)$$

where ε_{A_o} and ε_{i_o} are the uncertainties in the absorbance and current measurements at 100%T expressed at any desired confidence

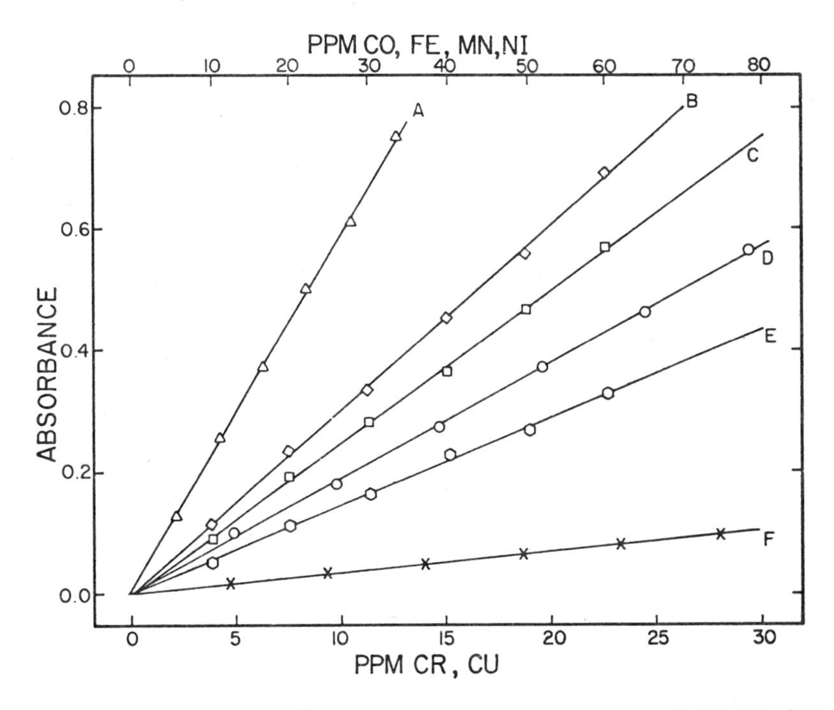

Analytical Chemistry

Figure 5. Linearity plots for simultaneous determination of copper, nickel, manganese, chromium, iron, and cobalt with the silicon target vidicon (2). (A) Cu (3247.54 Å); (B) Ni (3414.77 Å); (C) Mn (4030.76 Å); (D) Cr (4254.33 Å); (E) Fe (3719.94 Å); (F) Co (3453.51 Å).

Table IV
Performance data for the image dissector used to determine Cr, Cu, Fe, Mn, Ni, and Co in synthetic samples by atomic absorption. (With permission, Clin. Chem., 24, 602 (1978).)

	100%T current (nA)	Std. Dev.[a] (nA@100%T)	Sensitivity[b] (ΔA/mg/ℓ x 10^3)	Detection[c] Limit (mg/ℓ)
Cr(4254.33)	1393.0	1.20	18.4 ± 0.4	0.041
Cr(3578.69)	784.2	0.64	29.8 ± 1.0	0.024
Cu(3247.54)	879.8	1.23	56.3 ± 0.7	0.022
Cu(3273.96)	217.9	0.46	26.3 ± 1.1	0.070
Fe(3719.94)	505.3	0.63	6.1 ± 0.3	0.178
Fe(3020.64)	95.4	0.25	14.0 ± 0.7	0.161
Mn(4030.76)	4369.9	3.65	9.4 ± 0.3	0.077
Mn(2794.82)	228.9	0.46	92.3 ± 1.4	0.019
Ni(3414.77)	571.1	0.98	11.6 ± 0.4	0.129
Ni(2320.03)	4.3	0.08	21.7 ± 0.8	0.778
Co(3453.51)	466.3	0.98	1.6 ± 0.3	1.147
Co(2407.25)	4.1	0.07	31.8 ± 1.1	0.516

[a]Based on ten replicate measurements. [b]Slope of calibration plot times 10^3 based on three replicate measurements at each concentration. [c]Concentration producing a decrease in 100%T equal to twice the standard deviation in 100%T.

level. Using a series expansion of the log term ($\ln(1 + x) \simeq (x - 1) - 1/2(x-1)^2 + \ldots$ for $-1 < x < 1$) and ignoring the higher order terms, it follows that the detection limit for an element is approximated by

$$DL \simeq \varepsilon_{i_o}/2.3\ i_o S \qquad (3b)$$

The standard deviations of 100%T currents measured with the vidicon vary over a rather narrow range (0.025 to 0.045 nA) and we have observed similar values at shorter and longer wavelengths. The average standard deviation of the 100%T current is about 0.035 nA, which would correspond to a value of $\varepsilon_{i_{o,STV}} \simeq 0.07$ nA at the 95% confidence level. Thus, a reasonable representation of the 95% confidence level detection limits for the vidicon system is

$$DL_{STV} = 0.030/i_{o,STV}S \qquad (3c)$$

For the image dissector, a log-log plot of standard deviation vs. current has a zero intercept of -1.48 ± 0.18, suggesting a standard deviation of about $0.033\sqrt{i_{o,ID}}$. This corresponds to a

95% confidence level of $\varepsilon_{i_{o,ID}} \simeq 0.066\sqrt{i_{o,ID}}$ for the image dissector system. Substituting into eq 3b, this yields

$$DL_{ID} \simeq 0.029/\sqrt{i_{o,ID}S} \qquad (3d)$$

for the image dissector at the 95% confidence level. Therefore, the expected detection limit ratios for the two systems would be given by dividing eq 3c by eq 3d.

$$\frac{DL_{STV}}{DL_{ID}} = \frac{0.030/i_{o,STV}S}{0.029/\sqrt{i_{o,ID}S}} = 1.03\ \frac{\sqrt{i_{o,ID}}}{i_{o,STV}} \qquad (3e)$$

This shows that the detection limit ratios should equal the square root of the image dissector current divided by the silicon vidicon current, assuming the equal elemental sensitivities observed experimentally. Equation 3e, current and sensitivity data in Tables IV and V are used to compute detection limit ratios included in the last column of Table V. These detection limit ratios show that the image dissector has an advantage by a factor of 4 to 27 over the vidicon for every element and every wavelength examined. While detection limits are useful, it is desirable to compare the performance of the detectors at other concentration levels.

Relative photometric errors. The fixed current error for the vidicon and the variable error for the image dissector have been discussed under the headings of independent and square-root errors (32). Using eq 8c from the photometric errors paper (32), and noting that the relative absorbance error, RS_A, is equal to the relative concentration error, RS_C, it can be shown that the relative concentration errors for the vidicon, $RS_{C,STV}$, and the image dissector, $RS_{C,ID}$, are given by

$$RS_{C,STV} = S^o_{T,0}/T \ln T \qquad (4a)$$

$$RS_{C,ID} = S^o_{T,1/2}/\sqrt{T} \ln T \qquad (4b)$$

where T is the transmittance and $S^o_{T,0}$ and $S^o_{T,1/2}$ are the standard deviations of the 100%T current measurements (see Table V). These equations are used to compute the photometric error curves shown in Figure 6 for two elements (Cu(3274Å) and Cr(4254Å)) that represent the range of differences between the vidicon and image dissector. The upper two curves, A and B, represent the relative absorbance errors predicted for Cu and Cr respectively when measurements are made with the silicon target vidicon. The lower two curves, C and D, also show the photometric errors for Cu and Cr respectively, but when the image dissector is

Table V
Performance data for silicon vidicon used to determine Cr, Cu, Fe, Mn, Ni and Co in synthetic samples by atomic absorption. (With permission, Clin. Chem., 24, 602 (1978).)

	100%T current (nA)	Std. Dev.[a] (nA@100%T)	Sensitivity[b] (ΔA/mg/ℓ x 10^3)	Detection[c] Limit (mg/ℓ)	Detection[d] Limit Ratio ($\frac{STV}{ID}$)
Cr(4254.33)	10.5	0.038	19.0 ± 0.9	0.17	4.1
Cr(3578.69)	4.5	0.036	30.8 ± 1.1	0.23	9.6
Cu(3247.54)	4.7	0.033	58.4 ± 2.2	0.11	5.0
Cu(3273.96)	2.1	0.027	27.6 ± 1.3	0.41	5.9
Fe(3719.94)	3.5	0.025	5.4 ± 0.4	1.15	6.5
Fe(3020.64)	0.65	0.042	13.8 ± 0.8	4.35	27.0
Mn(4030.76)	15.1	0.042	9.6 ± 0.6	0.25	3.2
Mn(2794.82)	f	---	---	---	---
Ni(3414.77)	4.1	0.029	11.4 ± 0.6	0.55	4.3
Ni(2320.03)	f	---	---	---	---
Co(3453.51)	4.3	0.045	1.3 ± 0.03	7.2	6.3
Co(2407.25)	f	---	---	---	---

[a]Based on seven replicate measurements. [b]Slope of calibration plot times 10^3 based on four replicate measurements. [c]Ratio of the detection limits with the vidicon divided by the detection limits with the image dissector. [d]Line intensity too weak to give meaningful measurements.

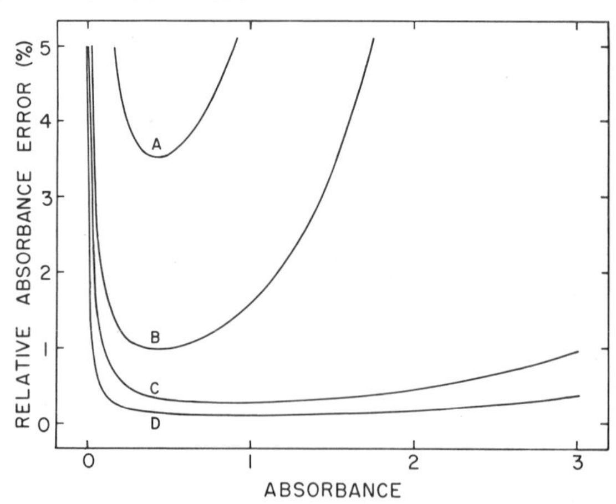

Clinical Chemistry

Figure 6. Relative absorbance errors for the vidicon and the image dissector (30). Silicon target vidicon: (A) Cu (3273.96 Å), $S^0_{T,0}$ = 1.29%; (B) Cr (4254.33 Å), $S^0_{T,0}$ = 0.36%. Image dissector: (C) Cu (3273.96 Å), $S^0_{T,½}$ = 0.21%; (D) Cr (4254.33 Å), $^0_{T,½}$ = 0.086%.

used for quantification. The abscissae can be converted to concentration units by multiplying the sensitivity values in Table V for different elements.

Differences in shapes between the vidicon and image dissector curves reflect the nature of the photometric errors that predominate for each detector. The relative amplitudes of the errors are determined by both the nature of the noise and the amplitude of the 100%T signal relative to the noise level. For the vidicon, the Cu(3274Å) line has a 100%T current of only 2.1 nA compared to 10.5 nA for the Cr(4254Å) line and this difference is reflected in the error curves. For the image dissector, the Cu line has a 100%T current of 218 nA compared to 1393 nA for the Cr line, but because the image dissector is shot noise limited, a difference of a factor of only 2.5 is observed in the minimum errors. These curves also reveal that the absorbance range over which the image dissector gives near optimum performance is much broader than for the silicon vidicon. For all the lines investigated in the study, the errors were smaller for the image dissector than for the vidicon. Thus, the image dissector exhibits significant advantages over the silicon target vidicon for multielement determinations by atomic absorption.

Comparisons with other systems. Data presented in Table VI provide a comparison of results obtained with the image dissector with results reported by others with other systems. Results in the second column represent multielement detection limits observed in this work. Results in the third and fourth columns represent detection limits reported for single element determinations with conventional optics and a silicon vidicon (12) and a commercial atomic absorption instrument (33).

The multielement detection limits with the echelle/image dissector are comparable to, or better than, single element detection limits reported for a silicon vidicon and conventional optics. Detection limits for Cr, Cu, and Mn with the echelle/image dissector compare favorably with single element data reported for a conventional atomic absorption instrument with a photomultiplier detector, but detection limits obtained here for Ni and Co are higher by factors of 10 or more than for the conventional instrument. The echelle/image dissector system should be adaptable to a so-called 'flameless' atomizer and be subject to the same improvements in sensitivities and detection limits as conventional detector systems.

Atomic Emission

The observation region in the plasma was selected to provide the best compromise in the signal-to-background ratio observed for the largest possible number of wavelengths. The effect of this compromise on sensitivity has been discussed as have the interelement effects among alkali and alkaline earth elements,

Table VI
Comparison of detection limits for different atomic absorption instruments.[a]

Element	ID[b]	STV, others[c]	Conventional AA[d]
Cr	0.024	0.1	0.02
Cu	0.022	0.07	0.01
Fe	0.161	0.3	0.07
Mn	0.019	0.09	0.01
Ni	0.129	0.3	0.05
Co	0.516	0.3	0.03

[a]The detection limits are expressed as mg/ℓ. [b]Image dissector, this work. [c]Silicon target vidicon, other investigators (12). [d]Techtron AA-120 (33).

and the inclusion of rubidium to overcome these effects (29).

After the preliminary characterization of the dc plasma source was completed, an investigation comparing the utility of the silicon vidicon and image dissector systems for atomic emission determinations was carred out. The vidicon data were obtained using a tube with a glass faceplace (No. 4532A, RCA) which dictated that the comparison be made with the alkali and alkaline earth metals, because the strongest emission lines for these elements are in the visible region of the spectrum. This comparison of detectors is valid because the wavelength range was confined to a region in which the response of the vidicon with the glass faceplate is similar to that of the tube with a fused silica faceplate (2).

Linearity and detection limits. Figure 7 represents plots of data from the image dissector for solutions containing Li, Na, K, Mg, Ca, Sr, and Ba. The solid lines represent unweighted least-squares fits to the data sets. Each data point shown is the average of three replicate determinations. Although multiple wavelengths were observed for most of the elements, only the most intense line is shown here to avoid congestion. The slopes of the log-log plots range from 0.983 ± 0.027 for Ba to 1.022 ± 0.036 for Mg with standard errors of estimate of 0.014 and 0.018 respectively. Additionally, a linear analysis of the data showed that intercepts are not statistically different from zero. Standard errors of estimate ranged from 1.04 to 16.8 for K and Ca, respectively. The average coefficient of variation for the data obtained with both detectors is about 3.0%, as estimated from the slopes and confidence intervals listed in Tables VII and VIII, which is indicative of the precision of measurements obtainable with this plasma source.

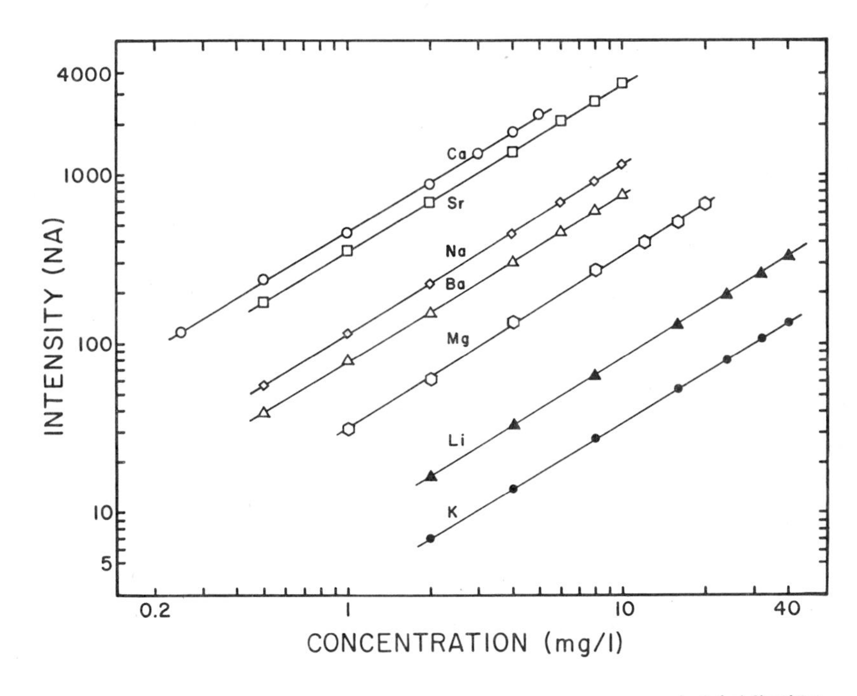

Analytical Chemistry

Figure 7. Linearity plots for the simultaneous determination of lithium, sodium, potassium, magnesium, calcium, strontium, and barium by atomic emission spectrometry (29). Ca (3933.67 Å); Sr (4077.1 Å); Na (5889.95 Å); Ba (4554.04 Å); Mg (2795.53 Å); Li (6103.64 Å); K (7698.98 Å).

Table VII
Performance data for the silicon vidicon used for the simultaneous determination of Li, Na, K, Mg, Ca, Sr, and Ba with a dc plasma. (With permission, Anal. Chem., 50, 602 (1978).)

Element (λ)	Background[a] std. dev. (nA)	Sensitivity[b] (nA/mg/ℓ)	Detection[c] Limit (mg/ℓ)
Li(6103.64)	0.043	0.317 ± 0.003	0.271
Na(5889.95)	0.051	3.75 ± 0.19	0.027
Na(5895.92)	0.058	1.90 ± 0.06	0.061
K(7698.98)	0.052	0.701 ± 0.007	0.148
Mg(5183.62)	0.056	0.042 ± 0.002	2.667
Ca(3933.67)	0.047	4.13 ± 0.16	0.023
Ca(4226.73)	0.055	1.98 ± 0.02	0.056
Sr(4077.71)	0.052	2.64 ± 0.05	0.039
Sr(4215.52)	0.043	1.72 ± 0.04	0.050
Sr(4607.33)	0.057	0.91 ± 0.02	0.125
Ba(4554.04)	0.056	1.48 ± 0.06	0.076

[a]Based on six replicate measurements of the Rb blank. [b]Slope of the calibration plot based on three measurements at each concentration used. [c]Concentration producing a signal equal to twice the background standard deviation.

Table VIII
Performance data for the image dissector used for the simultaneous determination of Li, Na, K, Mg, Ca, Sr, and Ba with a dc plasma. (With permission, Anal. Chem., 50, 602 (1978).)

Element (λ)	Background[a] std. dev. (nA)	Sensitivity[b] (nA/mg/ℓ)	Detection[c] Limit (mg/ℓ)	Detection Limit Ratio (STV/ID)
Li(6103.64)	0.081	8.2 ± 0.4	0.020	14
Na(5889.95)	0.089	115 ± 3	0.0015	18
Na(5895.92)	0.093	69 ± 2	0.0027	23
K(7698.98)	0.064	3.28 ± 0.09	0.039	4
Mg(5183.62)	0.105	1.08 ± 0.06	0.194	14
Mg(2795.53)	0.063	33.5 ± 0.9	0.0038	--
Ca(3933.67)	0.161	449 ± 11	0.00072	32
Ca(4226.73)	0.098	122 ± 3	0.0016	35
Sr(4077.71)	0.171	346 ± 5	0.00099	39
Sr(4215.52)	0.161	127 ± 4	0.0025	20
Sr(4607.33)	0.128	36.9 ± 0.9	0.0069	18
Ba(4554.04)	0.112	75.1 ± 2.8	0.0030	25

[a]Based on six replicate measurements of the Rb blank. [b]Slope of the calibration plot based on three measurements at each

concentration used. [c]Concentration producing a signal equal to twice the background standard deviation.

The data in Tables VII and VIII suggest that for emission measurements, the detection limits for the image dissector are lower than those for the silicon vidicon by a factor of about 24. The decrease in the detection limit ratio at longer wavelengths (> ∿5000A) results from a decrease in the luminous sensitivity of the image dissector relative to the silicon vidicon. The effect is quite apparent in the case of potassium.

Because the image dissector exhibits a significant sensitivity advantage in relation to the silicon vidicon, the remainder of this study was devoted to the image dissector. Solutions containing varying amounts of Cu, Cr, Mo, Mn, Co, Ni, Fe, and V were measured with the image dissector, and results are summarized in Figure 8 and Table IX. Slopes of plots in Figure 8 do not deviate significantly from unity at the 95% confidence level. These data, like those in Figure 7, demonstrate good linearity over two orders of magnitude or more for all elements examined. Also, intercepts did not differ significantly from zero at the 95% confidence level. Sensitivities and detection limits are summarized in Table IX.

Comparisons of results. Experiments were carried out to evaluate effects of compromise conditions on sensitivities of the elements in the two groups discussed earlier. Near optimum conditions were established for each element determined individually, and the sensitivity of that element under the optimum conditions is compared with the sensitivity obtained with compromise conditions used for multielement determinations. Results are presented in Table X for these comparisons.

The data show that single element sensitivities for the alkali and alkaline earth elements are about 30% higher than the multielement sensitivities. On the other hand, for the transition elements, there is little difference between single- and multielement sensitivities. The differences result because the alkali metals tend to emit most strongly in cooler regions of the plasma while the alkaline earth elements tend to emit most strongly in somewhat hotter regions of the plasma. In the case of the transition elements, optimum emission regions are in close proximity so that all elements are determined at near optimum conditions.

Data presented in Table XI provide a comparison of results obtained with the present instrument with results reported by others with other systems. Results in the second column represent detection limits observed in this work. Results in the third and fourth columns represent detection limits reported for single element determinations with conventional optics and photomultiplier detectors. The results in the third column were obtained with similar dc plasmas (27, 34, 35, 36) and the results

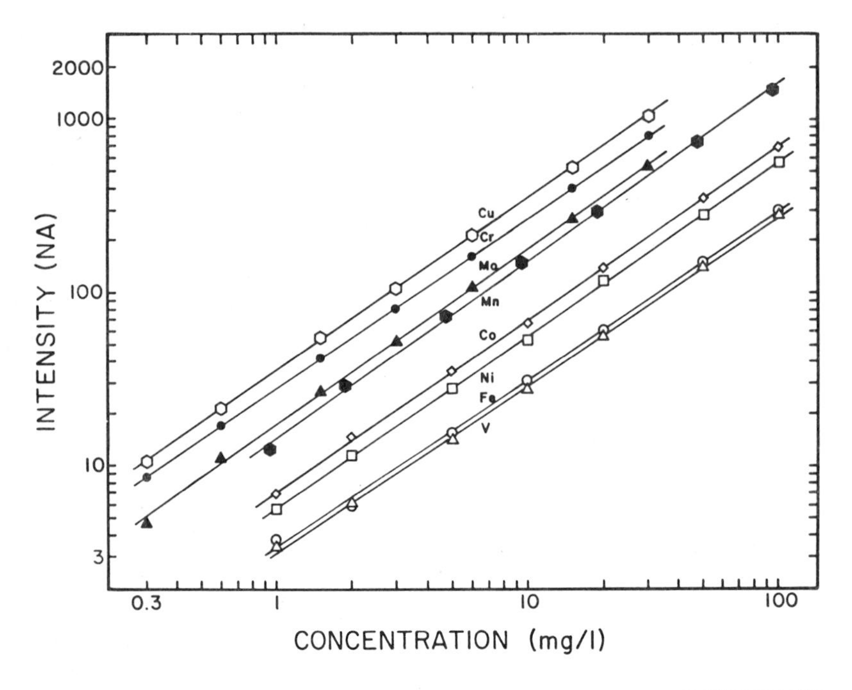

Analytical Chemistry

Figure 8. Linearity plots for the simultaneous determinations of copper, chromium, molybdenum, manganese, cobalt, nickel, iron, and vanadium by atomic emission spectrometry (29). Cu (3247.54 Å); Cr (4254.35 Å); Mo (3798.25 Å); Mn (4030.76 Å); Co (3453.51 Å) Ni (3619.32 Å); Fe (3737.13 Å); V (4379.24 Å).

Table IX
Statistical data for simultaneous determination of Cu, Cr, Mo, Mn, Co, Ni, Fe, and V with an image dissector and dc plasma. (With permission, Anal. Chem., 50, 602 (1978).)

Element	Background[a] std. dev. (nA)	Sensitivity[b] (nA/mg/ℓ)	Detection[c] Limit (mg/ℓ)	Intercept (nA)	Log-Log Slope
Cu(3247.54)	0.086	35.0 ± 0.3	0.004	0.46 ± 2.5	0.995 ± 0.010
Cr(4254.35)	0.071	26.4 ± 0.2	0.005	0.92 ± 3.4	0.979 ± 0.024
Mo(3798.25)	0.090	17.8 ± 0.5	0.010	-4.3 ± 5.6	1.013 ± 0.035
Mn(4030.76)	0.095	15.6 ± 0.4	0.012	3.4 ± 3.8	1.023 ± 0.033
Co(3453.51)	0.093	6.93 ± 0.08	0.027	0.07 ± 2.9	0.996 ± 0.019
Ni(3619.32)	0.122	5.63 ± 0.08	0.043	1.8 ± 3.8	0.999 ± 0.021
Fe(3737.13)	0.107	2.94 ± 0.07	0.073	0.79 ± 2.9	0.966 ± 0.043
V(4379.24)	0.047	2.80 ± 0.07	0.034	-3.2 ± 3.3	0.976 ± 0.032

[a]Based on six replicate measurements of the Rb blank. [b]Slope of calibration plot based on three replicate measurements at each concentration used. [c]Concentration producing a signal equal to twice the background standard deviation.

Table X
Comparison of single element and multielement sensitivities. (With permission, Anal. Chem., 50, 602 (1978).)

Element	Single Element[a] Sensitivity (nA/mg/ℓ)	Multielement[b] Sensitivity (nA/mg/ℓ)	Sensitivity[c] Ratio (SE/ME)
Li(6103.64)	9.6 ± 0.3	8.3 ± 0.4	1.17 ± 0.09
Na(5889.95)	166 ± 8	115 ± 3	1.44 ± 0.11
Na(5895.92)	92 ± 3	69 ±	1.34 ± 0.08
K(7698.98)	4.68 ± 0.21	3.28 ± 0.09	1.43 ± 0.10
Mg(2795.53)	41.4 ± 1.5	33.5 ± 0.9	1.24 ± 0.08
Mg(5183.62)	2.02 ± 0.09	1.08 ± 0.06	1.87 ± 0.19
Ca(3933.67)	493 ± 20	449 ± 8	1.10 ± 0.06
Ca(4226.73)	161 ± 5	122 ± 3	1.32 ± 0.07
Sr(4077.71)	360 ± 8	346 ± 5	1.04 ± 0.04
Sr(4215.52)	144 ± 5	127 ± 4	1.13 ± 0.07
Sr(4607.33)	46 ± 1	36.9 ± 0.9	1.25 ± 0.06
Ba(4554.04)	80 ± 2	75.1 ± 2.8	1.07 ± 0.07
Cu(3247.54)	41.2 ± 0.6	35.0 ± 0.3	1.17 ± 0.03
Cr(4354.35)	28.2 ± 0.4	26.4 ± 0.2	1.07 ± 0.02
Mn(4030.76)	16.3 ± 0.1	15.6 ± 0.4	1.04 ± 0.03
Mo(3798.25)	18.3 ± 0.1	17.8 ± 0.5	1.03 ± 0.03
Co(3453.51)	7.23 ± 0.09	6.93 ± 0.08	1.04 ± 0.02
V(4379.24)	3.44 ± 0.09	2.80 ± 0.07	1.23 ± 0.08
Ni(3619.32)	5.50 ± 0.04	5.63 ± 0.08	0.98 ± 0.02
Fe(3737.13)	3.20 ± 0.05	2.94 ± 0.07	1.09 ± 0.04

[a]Slope of calibration plot based on two replicate measurements at each concentration. [b]Slope of calibration plot based on three replicate measurements at each concentration. [c]Single element sensitivity divided by the multielement sensitivity.

Table XI
Comparison of detection limits for different plasma sources.[a]
(With permission, Anal. Chem., 50, 602 (1978).)

Element	ID-DCP[b]	PMT-DCP[c]	ICP[d]
Li	0.029	0.001	---
Na	0.0015	0.02	0.0002
K	0.039	---	---
Mg	0.0038	0.002	0.0007
Ca	0.00072	0.002	0.00007
Sr	0.00099	0.01	0.00002
Ba	0.003	0.2	0.0001
Cu	0.004	0.02	0.001
Cr	0.005	0.009	0.001
Mn	0.012	0.02	0.0007
Mo	0.010	0.1	0.005
Co	0.027	0.8	0.003
V	0.034	0.01	0.006
Ni	0.043	0.01	0.006
Fe	0.073	0.02	0.005

[a]The detection limits are expressed as mg/ℓ (1 mg/ℓ = 1 ppm). [b]Image dissector-dc plasma. [c]dc plasma, other investigators (27, 34, 35, 36). [d]Inductively coupled plasma (37).

in the fourth column were evaluated with an inductively coupled plasma (37).

Detection limits obtained in this work compare favorably with other results reported with the dc plasma, but are significantly higher than those reported with an inductively coupled plasma. Some of the differences between results obtained here and with the inductively coupled plasma (ICP) could result from different observation times. Although the observation time was not specified for the ICP data in Table XI (37), earlier work had involved 20 s integrations (38). If a 20 s observation time were used (37), and if S/N in each case were shot noise limited, then the detection limits ratios (dc plasma: ICP) would be about $\sqrt{20\ s/1\ s}$:1 or 4.5:1 with all other factors being equal. Probably the most significant conclusion to be drawn from this comparison is that the echelle spectrometer/image dissector data compare very favorably with the conventional optics/photomultiplier data obtained with the same excitation source. Any advantages relative to the dc plasma offered by another excitation source such as the inductively coupled plasma with conventional optics/detectors should also be realizable with the echelle/image dissector system.

Summary

The data presented here show that the imaging detector/echelle grating spectrometer concept yields both the resolution and spectral range required for practical simultaneous multielement determinations, and that it is possible to realize the numerous advantages associated with electronic selection of the wavelengths of interest without significant compromises in performance characteristics. The data also suggest that the image dissector is a more viable detector for atomic emission and absorption spectroscopy than the silicon target vidicon because of the greater spectral sensitivity and resolution, wavelength range, and photometric reliability. Dynamic range considerations also show the superiority of the image dissector, which has a linear dynamic range of about 10^5 as indicated by the emission measurements, as compared to the vidicon, which has a useful dynamic range of about 2×10^3.

All comparisons made between the silicon vidicon and image dissector systems apply for spectrometer configurations in which approximately the same spectral range was displayed on both detectors. Because of the different sizes of the active surfaces of the detectors, the output focal lengths and linear dispersions were different with the values for the image dissector being 20.0/13.5 or 1.48 times larger than corresponding values for the silicon vidicon.

If the silicon vidicon were used with the same optical configuration as the image dissector, then the spectral resolution reported here for the vidicon should be improved by the factor of 1.5 and would approach more closely the values observed with the image dissector. However, this improved resolution with the vidicon would be achieved at the expense of some other characteristics. One of the most obvious tradeoffs would be spectral range; and this loss could be more serious than just a reduction of the number of orders that could be accommodated along the vertical axis. The increased dispersion would force regions at the ends of orders onto the edges of the active surface of the vidicon where performance is degraded. Thus, not only would the spectral range be reduced, but some segments of the range would be lost. Another less obvious tradeoff would involve sensitivity and detection limits. The increased dispersion would concentrate less of the available energy on individual electronic resolution elements, resulting in lower signals for the same total flux. Because the background imprecision of the vidicon camera system is fixed at about 40 pA, this would mean an increase in detection limits by a factor of about 1.5^2 or 2.3 over those reported here for the vidicon.

One important difference between these detectors that has not been represented by any data presented here involves interactions among different electronic resolution elements. The vidicon and other integrating types of detectors are subject to charge migration or 'blooming' effects. Preliminary data obtained for the optical configurations used here indicate that charge migration on the vidicon target can cause significant signals in two to three orders on either side of the order for a moderately intense line. Similar data for the image dissector suggest interactions across no more than one order on either side of the order in which a line is observed, and this interaction could probably be reduced by working with a smaller slit height at the expense of some sensitivity. Although the 'blooming' effect is absent for the image dissector, an analogous phenomenon may reduce the available linear dynamic range. If bright images are incident on the photocathode when a measurement of illumination at a low level is being made, the back-scattered flux from internal tube parts may limit the dynamic range to only 2 or 3 orders of magnitude, depending on the area, brightness, and location of the disturbing flux. However, because no quantitative data have been acquired to elucidate the extent and magnitude of this phenomenon, the full ramifications of this effect on practical simultaneous multielement determinations should be addressed in fugure investigations.

One of the most attractive features of integrating sensors, such as the silicon target vidicon, is the capability to enhance the S/N of weak lines by allowing the signal to accumulate between interrogations. However, at the same time, this integrating capability is the major drawback in utilizing the device for random access interrogation of selected analysis lines. Because the vidicon detector is an integrating sensor, attempts to interrogate only a few isolated regions of the target will prove futile. The target areas that are not scanned will discharge and blooming will occur destroying the charge placed on the random accessed diodes so that a saturation signal will be observed that is independent of intensity. Therefore, to avoid this difficulty, the target must be scanned or erased prior to random access interrogation. Since a vidicon detector is capable of having approximately 10^4 to 10^5 resolution elements, we are forced to trade off the time required to prime the target during which no information is accumulated in order to interrogate less than the maximum number of possible resolution elements during random access data acquisition. Unlike storage camera tubes, the output signal from an image dissector is completely independent of scan rates or scan history, and therefore, there is no need to erase or prime the target between random access scans. This simplifies software control and permits more rapid acquisition of spectral information.

While these data show that the image dissector is superior to the silicon target vidicon in several respects for atomic spectroscopy, the silicon vidicon and other integrating detectors retain significant advantages for molecular absorption (39) and fluorescence spectroscopy (40) where resolution requirements are not so demanding, available radiant fluxes are higher, and a relatively large number of data points are required per scan.

Acknowledgments

This work was supproted by Research Grant No. CHE 75-13404 from the National Science Foundation and Research Grant No. GM 13326 from the NIGMS, NIH, USPHS. H.L.F. expresses appreciation for an ACS Analytical Division Fellowship sponsored by Procter and Gamble Co.

Literature Cited

1. Brown, S.S., ed., "Clinical Chemistry and Chemical Toxicology of Metals," Elsevier North-Holland, Inc., New York, N. Y. 10017, 1977.
2. Felkel, H. L., Jr., and Pardue, H. L., Anal. Chem., (1977), 49, 1112.
3. Talmi, Y., Anal. Chem., (1975), 47, 658A.
4. Talmi, Y., Anal. Chem., (1975), 47, 697A.
5. Cook, T. E., Milano, M. J., and Pardue, H. L., Clin. Chem., (1974), 20, 1422.
6. Milano, M. J., Pardue, H. L., Cook, T. E., Santini, R. E., Margerum, D. W., and Raycheba, J. M. T., Anal. Chem., (1974), 46, 374.
7. Milano, M. J. and Pardue, H. L., Anal. Chem., (1975), 47, 25.
8. Milano, M. J. and Pardue, H. L., Clin. Chem., (1975), 21, 211.
9. Horlick, G., Codding, E. G., and Leung, S. T., Appl. Spectrosc., (1975), 29, 48.
10. Horlick, G. and Codding, E. G., Anal. Chem., (1973), 45, 1490.
11. Aldous, K. M., Mitchell, D. G., and Jackson, K. W., Anal. Chem., (1975), 47, 1034.
12. Mitchell, D. G., Jackson, K. W., and Aldous, K. M., Anal. Chem., (1973), 45, 1215A.
13. Chester, T. L., Haraguchi, H., Knapp, D. O., Messman, J. D., and Winefordner, J. D., Appl. Spectrosc., (1976), 30, 410.
14. Knapp, D. O., Omenetto, N., Hart, L. P., Plankey, F. W., and Winefordner, J. D., Anal. Chim. Acta, (1974), 69, 455.
15. Busch, K. W., Howell, N. G., and Morrison, G. H., Anal. Chem., (1974), 46, 1231.
16. Howell, N. G. and Morrison, G. H., Anal. Chem., (1977), 49, 106.
17. Howell, N. G., Ganjei, J. D., and Morrison, G. H., Anal. Chem., (1976), 48, 319.
18. Wood, D. L., Dargis, A. B., and Nash, D. L., Appl. Spectrosc. (1975), 27, 310.
19. Danielsson, A., Lindblom, P., and Söderman, E., Chem. Scr., (1974), 6, 5.
20. Danielsson, A. and Lindblom, P., Appl. Spectrosc., (1976), 30, 151.
21. Margoshes, M., Spectrochim. Acta, (1970), 25B, 113.
22. Harrison, G. R., J. Opt. Soc. Am., (1949), 39, 522.
23. Harrison, G. R., Archer, J. E., and Camus, J., J. Opt. Soc. Am., (1952), 42, 706.
24. Keliher, P. N. and Wohlers, C. C., Anal. Chem., (1976), 48, 333A.
25. Johnson, R. E., Application Note AN-4623, RCA Electronics Components, 1971.

26. "RCA Photomultiplier Manual", RCA, Harrison, N. J. 07029, 1970.
27. Skogerboe, R. K., Urasa, I. T., Coleman, G. N., Appl. Spectrosc., (1976), 30, 500.
28. Felkel, H. L., Jr., "Evaluation of imaging detector coupled to an echelle grating spectrometer for atomic spectroscopy", Ph.D. Thesis, Purdue University, 1978.
29. Felkel, H. L., Jr. and Pardue, H. L., Anal. Chem., (1978), 50, 602.
30. Felkel, H. L., Jr. and Pardue, H. L., Clin. Chem., (1978), 24, 602.
31. Nieman, T. A. and Enke, C. G., Anal. Chem., (1976), 48, 619.
32. Pardue, H. L., Hewitt, T. E., and Milano, M. J., Clin. Chem., (Winston-Salem, N.C.) (1974), 20, 1028.
33. Jackson, K. W., Aldous, K. M., and Mitchell, D. G., Spectrosc. Lett., (1973), 6, 315.
34. Valente, S. E. and Schrenk, W. G., Appl. Spectrosc., (1970) 24, 197.
35. Rippetoe, W. E., Johnson, E. R., and Vickers, T. J., Anal. Chem., (1975), 47, 436.
36. Chapman, J. F., Dale, L. S., and Whittem, R. N., Analyst (London), (1973), 98, 529.
37. Fassel, V. A. and Kniseley, R. N., Anal. Chem., (1974), 46, 1110A.
38. Larson, G. F., Fassel, V. A., Scott, R. H., and Kniseley, R. N., Anal. Chem., (1975), 47, 238.
39. McDowell, A. E. and Pardue, H. L., Anal. Chem., (1977), 49, (1977).
40. Warner, I. M., Callis, J. B., Davidson, E. R. and Christian, G. D., Clin. Chem., (Winston-Salem, N. C.), (1976) 22, 1483.

RECEIVED December 26, 1978.

Higher Order Strategies for Fluorescence Analysis Using an Imaging Detector

D. W. JOHNSON[1], J. B. CALLIS, and G. D. CHRISTIAN

Dept. of Chemistry, BG-10, University of Washington, Seattle, WA 98195

Tomas Hirshfeld, in his encyclopedic essay "Limits of Detection (1)," has provided us with a thought-provoking account of the problems and challenges which confront modern analytical chemistry. He observes that, increasingly, a given analysis requires determination of trace or ultratrace components in extremely complex matrices, and moreover, it must often be global; i.e., one must detect and measure as many sample constituents, both known and unknown, as possible. Clearly, then, a new generation of analytical strategies must be developed which provide both multicomponent quantitation and qualitation. As Hirschfeld observes, one possible route to such a development is to incorporate into modern instruments as many redundant and independent measurements of the sample's chemical characteristics as possible. Indeed, the successful application of the GC-MS to a number of contemporary analytic problems illustrates the potential of such a strategy. For the fluorescence specialist, the task then is quite clear: to preserve or even extend the sensitivity advantage of the technique while improving its capabilities for simultaneous multicomponent analysis. If such improvements cannot be made, fluorescence analysis will surely be eclipsed by other techniques.

We were among the first to exploit the capabilities of low light level imaging devices to acquire fluorescence data in multiple wavelength channels (2). Our rationale was that an image detector offered the possibility of obtaining an entire spectrum of a sample in the same time that a single wavelength pair measurement could be performed in a conventional instrument. The increased amount of data could, with appropriate data reduction strategies (3,4,5), be used to improve the specificity of an assay. A recent review by Talmi (6) provides ample evidence to show the efficacy of this rationale. In most of the work reviewed by this author, however, the imaging detector was used in

[1] Current Address: DuPont Experimental Station, Wilmington DE 19898

0-8412-0504-3/79/47-102-097$05.00/0

a one dimensional mode to acquire a single fluorescence emission spectrum at a time at a fixed wavelength of excitation. In contrast, the recently described Video Fluorometer (7), is capable of acquiring a set of up to 241 fluorescence spectra, each measured at up to 256 sequenced emission wavelengths, and each excited at a different sequenced wavelength, all in a time as short as 17 msec. Other features of note are: the wavelength range covered in each wavelength domain is 241 nm, the spectral resolution is ∿5 nm, and limits of detection for many polycyclic aromatic hydrocarbons reach into the sub PPB region with linear response observed over three decades of concentration. Even though further improvements are possible (8,9), this instrument is suitable for application to a wide variety of analytical problems. Data from the video fluorometer is output as a complete spectral profile of the sample in the form of an Emission-Excitation Matrix (EEM). We have devised a number of strategies for analysis of the EEM which allow qualitative characterization of a sample containing a number of simultaneously emitting species, even though the spectra of the individual components overlap significantly (3,4,5).

In this communication, we will illustrate the application of the Video Fluorometer to simultaneous analysis of polycyclic aromatic hydrocarbons and warfarin and its metabolite 7-OH warfarin. We hope to convince the reader of the utility of "higher-order" strategies in fluorescence analysis made practicable by imaging detector based instrumentation.

Instrumentation

The optics of the Video Fluorometer were designed so that excitation and emission spectra could be simultaneously measured by means of an imaging photometry system. The manner in which this is accomplished is shown in Figure 1. For the sake of concreteness, let us suppose that we desire to measure the fluorescence properties of a homogeneous substance whose emission and excitation spectra are as in Figure 1A. In our system, a standard fluorescence cuvet containing the sample is irradiated with a polychromatic beam of light. Figure 1B shows how this cuvet would appear if filled with the substance shown in Figure 1A. The polychromatic excitation beam is formed by focusing the radiation from a Xenon arc lamp onto the entrance slit of a monochromator which is mounted on its side, and from which the exit slit assembly has been removed. The "rainbow" of radiation emerging from the exit slit plane is then focused into the cuvet as shown in Figure 1B. At right angles to the excitation beam are the analyzing optics. The fluorescent image of the cuvet as in 1B is projected by means of a lens onto the entrance slit of a monochromator mounted in the usual upright position with the long axis of the entrance slit parallel to the long axis of the cuvet. The exit slit of the monochromator has been removed, and the spectro-

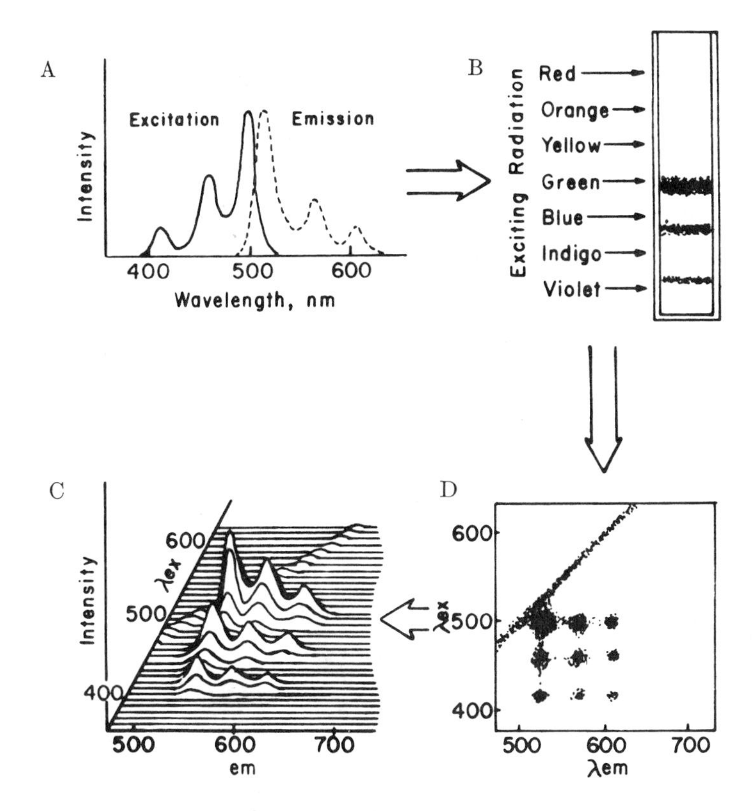

Figure 1. Production of an EEM for a hypothetical substance. (1A) Excitation and emission spectra of substance; (B) Fluorescence of cuvet filled with substance in A and illuminated with a polychromatic beam; (C) EEM image at exit slit plane of analyzing monochromator; (D) Isometric projection of EEM as may be obtained on an oscilloscope or graphics terminal.

scopic image present at the exit slit plane is focused with demagnification onto the photosensitive surface of a low light level television camera. The effect of the analyzing monochromator is to disperse horizontally that portion of the fluorescent cuvet image subtended by the entrance slit into its component wavelenghts of emission. Moreover, since spatial information along the slit height is preserved with good fidelity, the vertical dimension of the output image is proportional to the excitation wavelength. In Figure 1C, the image expected for the substance shown in 1A is illustrated. Since scattered radiation is also usually present, Figure 1C includes this as well. Figure 1D also shows how the fluorescent image will appear as an isometric projection in which the vertical axis represents the intensity of fluorescence. For clarity, all hidden lines have been removed.

The spectroscopic image produced by this optical system constitutes a unique fingerprint or EEM of the fluorescent specie's emission and excitation properties (3,4,5,10,11,12,13). A careful examination of Figure 1C and 1D show how useful such images can be in the qualitative characterization of a fluorescent material. Obviously, a scan along the horizontal axis of the image at a fixed vertical coordinate provides the fluorescence emission spectrum at a particular excitation wavelength, while a scan along the vertical direction at a fixed horizontal position yields the excitation spectrum monitored at a particular fluorescence wavelength. Once this is realized, a glance at 1C and D is sufficient to ascertain that only one emitting specie is present because all of the emission spectra are identical within a scale factor. Scattered light is quite easily distinguished because it falls on a straight line where the wavelengths of emission and excitation are coincident.

The serious student of fluorescence analysis will also recognize that the "EEMs" generated by our instrument have considerable potential value in quantitative analysis of mixtures of fluorescent species as well. Thus, we have developed a computerized imaging photometry system based upon a Silicon Intensified Target (SIT) vidicon, as shown in Figure 2. The SIT camera is scanned in a non-interlaced format at the standard rate of sixty fields/second. The video signal is digitized by a high speed sample and hold and deposited in a fast buffer memory. Through the incorporation of an arithmetic logic unit (pixel processor), incoming data may be added to or subtracted from memory, and spatial resolution traded off for intensity dynamic range. Moreover, the newly processed data can be simultaneously displayed on a television monitor while it is being stored in memory. Further details are available in another article (7).

After the image has been successfully captured, the contents of the buffer memory may be mapped onto the address space of the Unibus of a PDP11/04 minicomputer for quantitive analysis, via a group of programs (SIM-1) (7). Approaches to analysis available to us include least squares fitting (5), eigen analysis (3), and

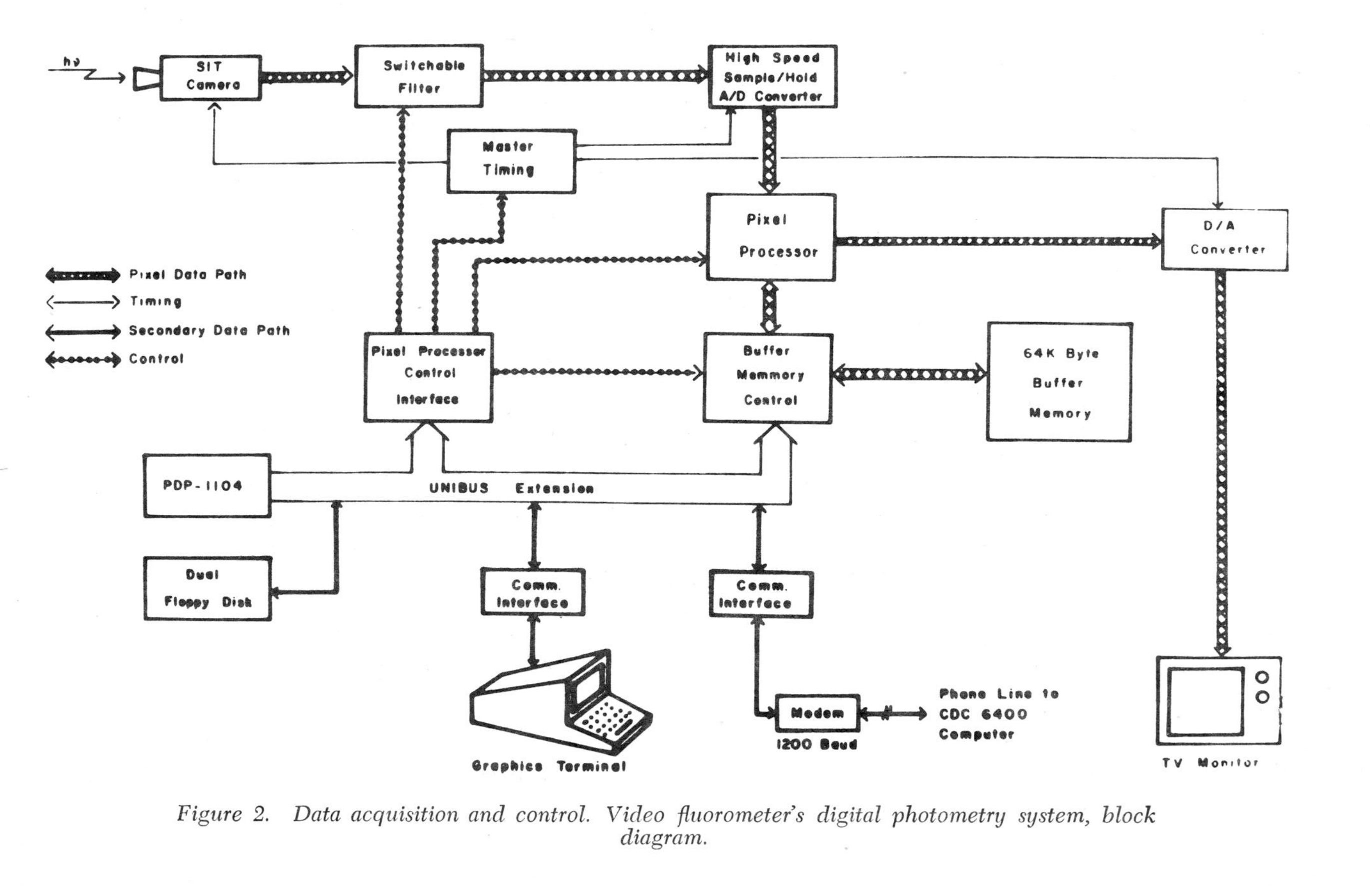

Figure 2. Data acquisition and control. Video fluorometer's digital photometry system, block diagram.

rank annihilation (4).

Experimental

Materials. The polycyclic aromatic hydrocarbons were purified by zone refining (James Hinton Co.). The samples of warfarin and 7-OH warfarin were chromatigraphically pure and were the kind gift of Dr. W. Trager. Water was double distilled. Cyclohexane was spectroquality. Neither solvent contributed any appreciable blank fluorescence.

Instrumentation. The Video Fluorometer described above was used to acquire all fluorescence data. The excitation and emission slits were selected to give a band pass of 6.6 nm. All data was acquired at a resolution of 64 X 64 pixels and is the result of summation of 512 frames to memory followed by subtraction of 512 dark frames. The data acquisition, display and analysis programs were written in PDP-11 Fortran IV under RT-11 and the listings are contained in the first author's Ph.D. dissertation (14).

Results - Polycyclic Aromatic Hydrocarbons

A Single Component. Table I and Figure 3 present the results of the dynamic range and detection limit studies of perylene. A three-order linear dynamic range was obtained. The upper limit of the dynamic range is 1 X 10^{-6}M. Above this concentration, the relationship of concentration and signal intensity became nonlinear due to the inner filter effect. This effect could be considerably decreased by working with a 1 mm X 1 mm cuvette and we believe that in this case the linear concentration range could easily be extended upwards to 10^{-5}M.

Some idea of the systems capability for S/N enhancement by summation to memory and blank subtraction may be gained by examination of Figure 4. Figure 4A shows a single frame integration of a sample of 5 X 10^{-9}M perylene in cyclohexane. Only the scattered exciting light is plainly visible. Figure 4B shows the result of summation of 512 frames to memory. Here the perylene spectrum is more apparent but is superimposed upon dome shaped dark current and obscured by imperfections in the silicon target of the vidicon. In Figure 4C, 512 dark frames have been subtracted from the image. The perylene signal is readily apparent but still obscured somewhat by the Raman line of the solvent. Finally, the clearest presentation is obtained when the solvent blank is subtracted in Figure 4D.

Two Components. Figures 5 and 6 summarize the least squares analysis of perylene and dimethylanthracene respectively in the presence of 10^{-5}M anthracene. In both cases, the variable component can be easily quantitated in the presence of a one hundred fold excess of anthracene, even when the spectral overlaps

Table I Perylene Dynamic Range Study

Reference Standard: 1.1×10^{-6}M Perylene in Cyclohexane

Trial	Expected Coefficient	Experimental Coefficient	Percent Error
1	1.00	1.00	0
2	0.50	0.55 ± 0.048	10
3	0.10	0.099 ± 0.0039	1
4	0.050	0.052 ± 0.0044	4
5	0.010	0.011 ± 0.00097	1
6	0.0050	0.0050 ± 0.00034	0
7	0.0010	0.00099 ± 0.00023	1
8	0.00050	0.00039 ± 0.000036	22

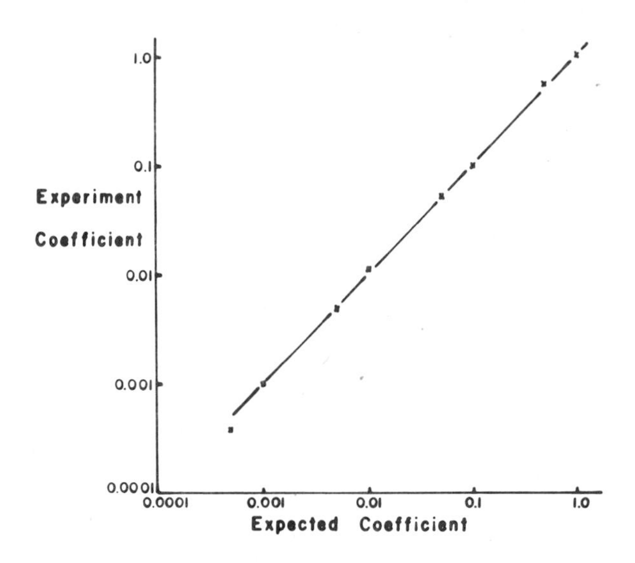

Figure 3. Perylene dynamic range. Standard: 1.1 $\times$ 10^{-6}M perylene in cyclohexane.

Review of Scientific Instruments

Figure 4. Data acquisition with the Video Fluorometer. (A) Single frame EEM for 1 $\times$ 10^{-6}M perylene using 64 $\times$ 64 format; (B) EEM for same sample after summation of 512 frames to memory; (C) As in B but with subtraction of 512 dark frames; (D) As in C but with subtraction of solvent blank.

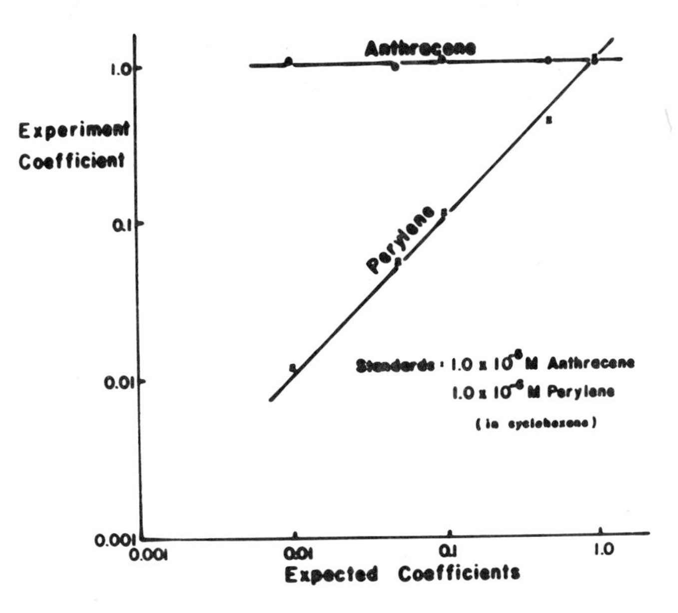

Figure 5. Analytical curves for the determination of perylene in the presence of anthracene

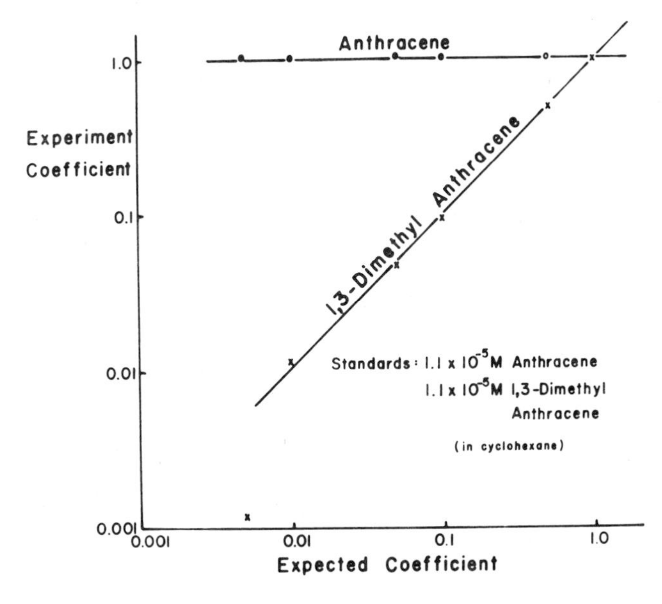

Figure 6. Analytical curves for the determination of 1,3-dimethyl anthracene in the presence of anthracene

are significant. At the spatial resolution employed here, we do not see any effects due pixel "cross talk." Apparently, stray light in the optical system and/or "veiling glare" in the fiber optic faceplate of the vidicon are negligible.

Six Components. Computer Simulations by Warner et al (15) indicated that in favorable cases at least five fluorescent aromatic hydrocarbons could be quantitated simultaneously. Figure 7 shows contour maps generated by the Video Fluorometer for six polycyclic components selected for a trial study. Figure 8A shows a contour map for a mixture of the six components, while Figure 8B shows an isometric projection drawing of the same components. We wish to emphasize that these illustrations were drawn in a few minutes by our minicomputer using simple FORTRAN IV programs and photographed directly from the Tektronix display terminal. Table II presents the results of a quantitative analysis of the data, along with the average results of six repetitions of the experiment. All of the concentration coefficients were well within ten percent of the expected values. Further studies will be aimed at defining the dynamic range of quantitation in mixtures such as these.

Analysis of Warfarin - A Higher Order Strategy

The oral anticoagulant drug, warfarin, is widely used in the treatment of various thromboembolic disorders. However, because of interindividual variations in rates of metabolism of the drug and the well-documented interactions with other drugs, maintenance of a stable anticoagulant state is notoriously difficult to maintain (16). Thus, it is imperative that the clinician receive as much information as possible about the levels of warfarin and its metabolites in the blood stream. The existing fluorescence assay (17) for warfarin has been strongly criticized for its failure to distinguish warfarin from its metabolites (18,19). The data shown below illustrates how the concept of multidimensional analysis might be used to devise a simultaneous fluorescence assay of warfarin and its major metabolite, 7-OH warfarin.

Our first attempts at a straight-forward analysis of these two compounds was frustrated by the broad, structureless and highly overlapping spectra. However, it was known from previous studies that the parent's fluorescence is quenched under acid conditions whereas that of the metabolite is relatively unaffected. This fact suggested that a higher order strategy could be devised: an EEM would be obtained under two pH conditions, acid and base. In this case, the data would be an array $\underset{\sim}{T}$ indexed by three subscripts:

$$\underset{\sim}{T} = \{\underset{\sim}{M}_{\ell}\} = \{(m_{ij})_{\ell}\} = \{t_{ij\ell}\}. \qquad 1)$$

Here, $\{t_{ij\ell}\}$ is the set of fluorescence intensities measured at

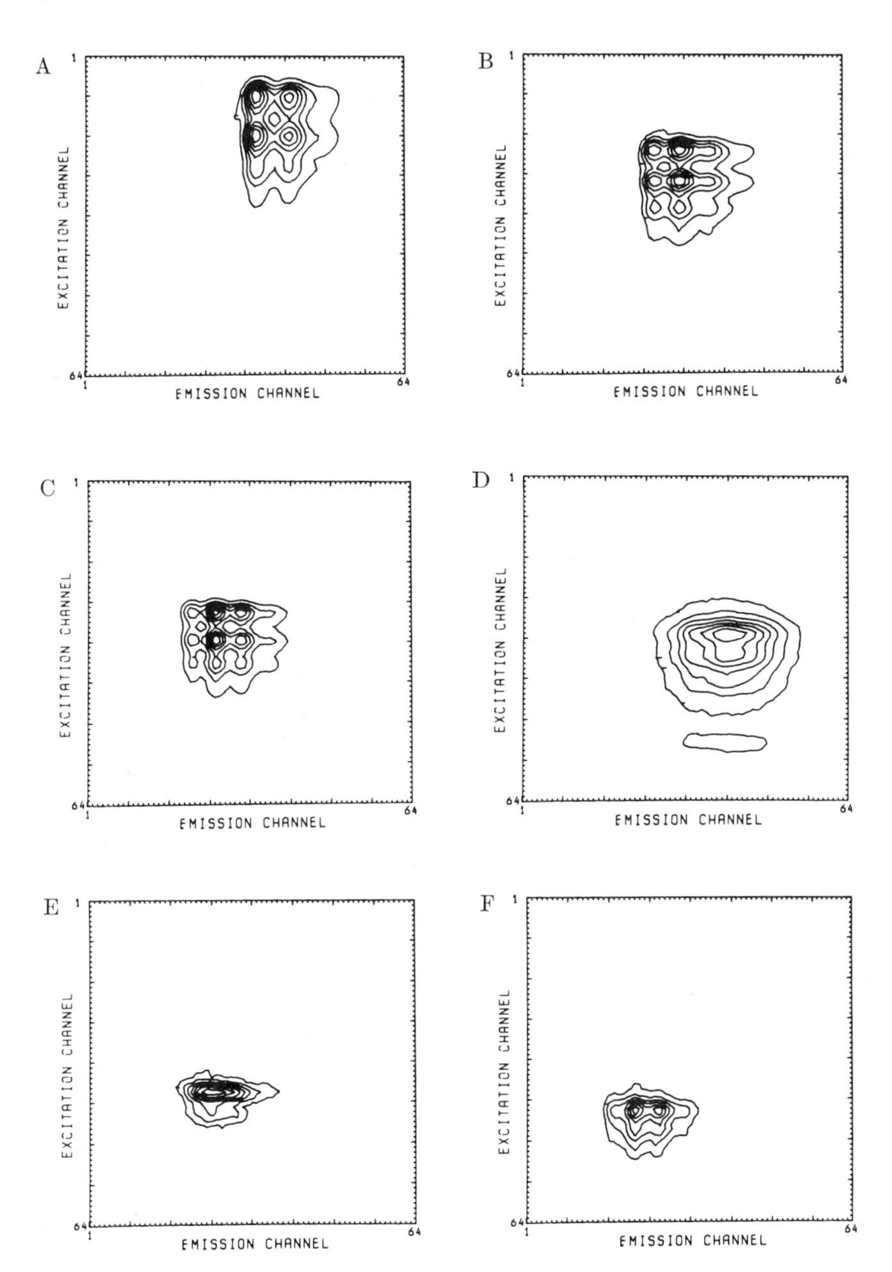

Figure 7. Contour maps of the spectral distributions of the components of the six component PAH mixture (in cyclohexane). (A) 1.2 × 10^{-7}M perylene; (B) 9.9 × 10^{-7}M 1,3-dimethyl anthracene; (C) 7.6 × 10^{-7}M anthracene; (D) 3.4 × 10^{-6}M fluoranthene; (E) 1.6 × 10^{-6}M pyrene; (F) 7.4 × 10^{-7}M chrysene.

A

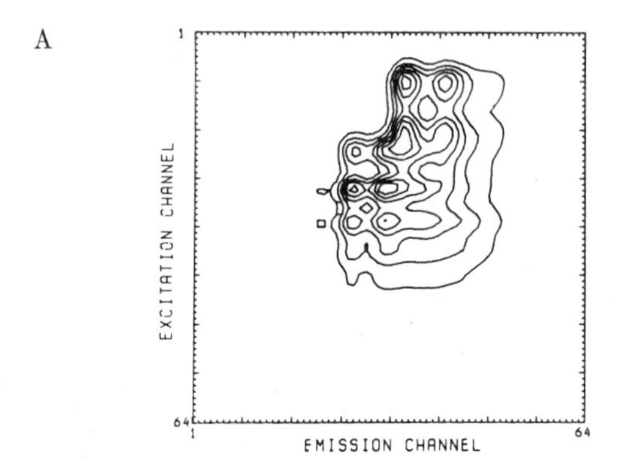

B

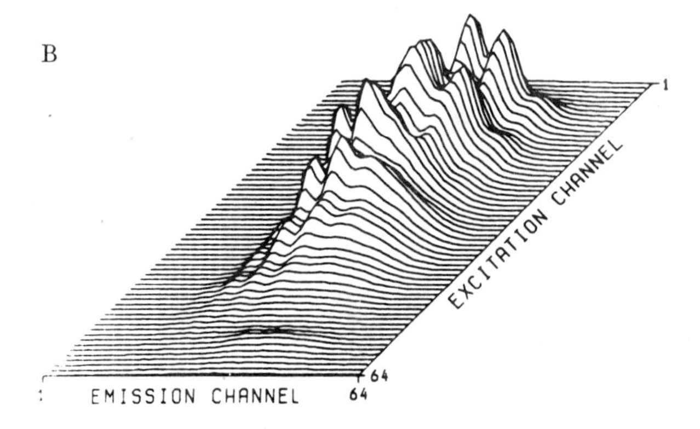

Figure 8. (A) Contour map of the six component PAH mixture EEM; (B) Isometric projection of the mixture EEM.

Table II
Least Squares Analysis of Six Component PAH Mixture

Component	Mixture 1 expected coeff.	Mixture 1 exper. coeff.	Six Replicates exper. coeff.	Six Replicates ave. rel. deviation	ave. %error
Perylene	1.00	1.01	1.02	0.01	2%
Dimethyl Anthracene	0.60	0.60	0.60	0.03	1%
Anthracene	0.60	0.57	0.56	0.01	7%
Fluoranthene	5.0	4.8	4.81	0.02	4%
Pyrene	1.0	0.94	0.95	0.03	5%
Chrysene	1.0	1.01	1.05	0.03	5%

Standards: (in cyclonexane)
1.2×10^{-7} M Perylene
9.9×10^{-7} M 1,3-Dimethyl Anthracene
7.6×10^{-7} M Anthracene
3.4×10^{-7} M Fluoranthene
1.6×10^{-6} M Pyrene
7.4×10^{-7} Chrysene

particular values of three variables: (a) the wavelength of excitation indexed by i, (b) the wavelength of emission indexed by j, and (c) the pH indexed by ℓ. Equation 1) shows also that the array can be built up from a collection of EEM's $\{M_\ell\} = \{(M_{ij})_\ell\}$, taken at various values of the pH.

In the case where the components are knowns for which standard EEM's have been collected under the same conditions of pH as the unknown one can use a straight forward least squares procedure to obtain the unknown concentrations. The array $\tilde{T}^{obs}$ may be written as:

$$\tilde{T}^{obs} = \sum_{k=1}^{r} (c^k/c_o^k)\tilde{T}^k \qquad 2)$$

where c^k is the sought for concentration and c_o^k is the concentration at which the standard array T^k for the kth specie is determined. It is then easily shown that the ratios c^k/c_o^k can be determined from the set of linear equations

$$\sum_k \{\sum_{i,j\ell} (t_{ij\ell})^p (t_{ij\ell})^k\}(c^k/c_o^k) = \sum_{i,j,\ell} (t_{ij\ell})^k (t_{ij\ell})^{obs}, \qquad 3)$$

where $(t_{ij\ell})^p$ and $(t_{ij\ell})^k$ are the elements of the standard arrays for the pth and kth components.

Using the Video Fluorometer, we obtained a series of standard intensity values for the individual standard compounds (warfarin, 7-OH warfarin) at known concentrations under acidic and basic conditions. Then a series of mixtures of known composition was made up, and intensity values were obtained for these under acidic and basic conditions. The concentrations of the individual components of the mixtures was then determined by Equation 3.

The data was analyzed three ways: first the acidic and neutral solution data was used simultaneously to arrive at the best c^k's, then the neutral data alone and finally the acidic solution data alone. As can be seen from Table III, accurate simultaneous analysis of both substances can be obtained only by including the differential variation of fluorescence with pH. The results for the simultaneous analysis in three dimensions (λem, λex, pH) are presented graphically in Figure 9. This shows that we can easily quantitate both warfarin and its 7-OH metabolite simultaneously, even in the case where the latter is 100x less concentrated than the former.

Discussion

A great deal of evidence now exists to support the notion that the SIT detector approaches the characteristics of an ideal multichannel detector (20). Sensitivity on a per/channel basis is comparable to that of the the photomultipliers, so that almost

Table III

True Concentration		Concentration Determined by Simultaneous Analysis		Concentration Determined by Analysis of Neutral Solution		Concentration Determined by Analysis of Acid Solution	
W	7-OH	W	7-OH	W	7-OH	W	7-OH
330ng/ml	150ng/ml	333ng/ml	139ng/ml	306ng/ml	153ng/ml	191.7ng/ml	156ng/ml
330	75.0	298	74.2	343	55.2	152	76.6
330	30.0	320	30.9	300	39.3	396	31.4
330	15.0	305	15.8	308	13.3	564	17.4
330	6.0	316	6.12	346	6.69	277	6.90
330	1.50	343	1.48	296	18.9	356	0.68

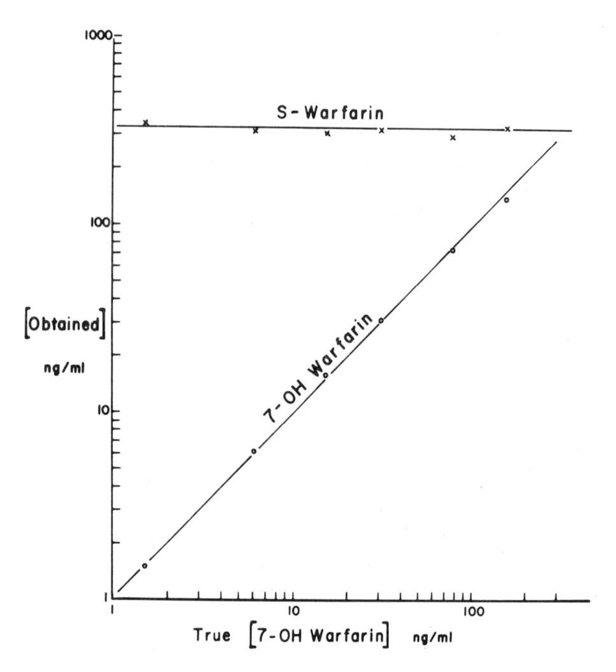

Figure 9. Simultaneous analysis of Warfarin and 7-OH Warfarin

the full multichannel (multiplex) advantage can be realized. Moreover, with a cooled detector, the Raman lines of the solvent are easily observed; indeed the capability of observing Raman lines has been suggested as a benchmark for fluorescence instruments by at least one author (21).

Our instrument is unique in that it uses the full two-dimensional capability of the SIT detector to acquire fluorescence data in two dimensions (excitation wavelength and emission wavelength) simultaneously. It is our belief that the greater the dimension of the analysis the less ambiguous it is likely to be. Faulkner and students (22,23) have shown that use of excitation wavelength information greatly increases the ability of file searching alogorithms to recognize molecules on the basis of their fluorescence. Also, the use of selective excitation can be extremely useful in simultaneous quantitation. For example, Talmi et al (6) shows a rather impressive least squares analysis of pyrene, diphenylstilbene, and anthracene. The fluorescence spectra of these substances overlap quite severely. However, the excitation spectra of these components are quite different, and it would be interesting to see whether addition of the excitation dimension to the analysis would provide an even better quantitation.

Finally, we point out the efficacy of higher order strategies in fluorescence analysis. We have shown that when the dimension of pH is added to the simultaneous analysis of warfarin and 7-OH warfarin an improvement in quantitation results. Other dimensions may be added as well, for example, a series of excitation emission matrices may be recorded as a function of chromatographic retention time, time after delta-function excitation, or as a function of concentration of an added quencher. New strategies will be required to analyze such large multidimension data sets, but the benefits will be even larger--the quantitative and qualitative analysis of ever more complex mixtures.

Acknowledgement

This research was supported by NIH grant GM22311. We gratefully acknowledge useful discussion with Professor E. R. Davidson.

Literature Cited

1. Hirschfeld, T., Anal. Chem. (1976), 48, 16A.
2. Warner, I. M., Callis, J. B., Davidson, E. R., Gouterman, M. P., and Christian, G. D., Anal. Lett. (1975), 8, 655.
3. Warner, I. M., Christian, G. D. Davidson, E. R., and Callis, J. B., Anal. Chem. (1977), 49, 564.
4. Warner, I. M., Davidson, E. R., and Christian, G. D., ibid. (1977), 49, 2155.

5. Ho, C. N., Christian, G. D., and Davidson, E. R., ibid. (1978), 50, 1108.
6. Talmi, Y., Baker, D. C., Jadamec, J. R., and Saner, W. A., ibid, (1978), 50, 936A (1978).
7. Johnson, D. W., Gladden, J. A., Callis, J. B., and Christian, G. D., Rev. Sci. Inst. (1979), 50, 118.
8. Warner, I. M., private communication.
9. Giering, L. P., private communication.
10. Johnson, D. W., Callis, J. B., and Christian, G. D., Anal. Chem. (1977), 49, 747A.
11. Rho, J. H. and Stuart, J. L., ibid. (1978) 50, 620.
12. Giering, L. P. and Hornig, A. W., Amer. Lab (1977), 9, 113.
13. Weiner, E. R., Anal. Chem. (1978), 50, 1583.
14. Johnson, D. W., Ph.D. Thesis, (1978), University of Washington, Seattle.
15. Warner, I. M., Callis, J. B., Davidson, E. R., and Christian, G. D. in Chen, Y. T., ed., "Pattern Recognition Applied to Oil Identification," pp. 129-135, IEEE Computer Society, Long Beach, CA, 1977.
16. Weser, J. K., and Sellers, E. M., New Engl. J. Med. (1971), 285, 547.
17. Corn, M. and Berberich, R., Clin. Chem. (1967), 13, 126.
18. Lewis, R. J., Ilnicki, L. P., and Carlstrom, M., Biochem. Med. (1970), 4, 376.
19. Vessell, E. S. and Shively, C. A., Science (1976), 184, 466.
20. Talmi, Y., Anal. Chem. (1975), 47, 685A, 697A.
21. White, J. U., ibid. (1976), 48, 2089.
22. Miller, T. C. and Faulkner, L. R., ibid (1976), 48, 2089.
23. Yim, K. W. K., Miller, T. C., and Faulkner, L. R., ibid. (1977), 49, 2069.

RECEIVED January 29, 1979.

5

Versatility of an Optical Multichannel Analyzer as an HPLC Detector

J. RICHARD JADAMEC, WILLIAM A. SANER, and RICHARD W. SAGER

U. S. Coast Guard Research and Development Center, Groton, CT 06340

High pressure liquid chromatography (HPLC) has been used by many investigators to concentrate and separate complex mixtures of polyaromatic hydrocarbons (PAH's) from environmental samples (1-6). The specific identification of the separated eluates (i.e, the separated HPLC fractions), until recently, has been achieved by using one or a combination of the following approaches: a) fraction collection and subsequent analysis of the collected fractions by various spectroscopic techniques; b) stop flow methods where the column flow is stopped and the UV absorption, fluorescence, or other spectroscopic data are obtained; c) relative chromatographic retention times; d) relative chromatographic retention times and absorbance ratios at two or more fixed wavelengths; e) spiking the environmental sample with known compounds of interest; f) selective fluorescence excitation and emission wavelengths. If a known PAH is being monitored, or the number of components present in the sample is relatively small, then any of the above approaches can be effectively used to identify or tentatively identify an HPLC fraction. However, as the number of PAH's increase within a given environmental sample, then each of these above approaches becomes ineffective and/or impractical.

HPLC column technology has produced highly effective and efficient analytical columns and, as has been previously stated (7), this development has led to a demand for more sensitive and versatile detectors for HPLC systems. HPLC detector development within the past several years has been aimed at increasing sensitivity, as evidenced by the development of fluorescence detectors capable of quantitating subnanogram levels of PAH's. Similarly, UV/VIS detectors have been developed which can detect nanogram levels of PAH's.

Recently, several investigators have demonstrated the utility of optoelectronic image devices as detectors for HPLC systems, allowing the analyst to obtain spectral information of the separated HPLC eluate "on-the-fly" (8-13). This capability in the past has been largely confined to gas chromatographic (GC) systems, where the mass spectra of GC fractions have been recorded "on-the-fly" and stored for subsequent retrieval and identification. Optoelectronic image devices are currently at the stage of development where they can be used to convert standard spectrometers into polychromators for use as detectors to record the UV/VIS absorption or fluorescence spectra of HPLC eluates.

This report will discuss the results of a study in which an optical multichannel analyzer (OMA) was coupled to standard spectrometers to record both the UV/VIS absorption and fluorescence emission spectra of complex mixtures of PAH's separated by HPLC techniques "on-the-fly" (i.e., one second spectral scans of the HPLC effluent stream) and stored on a floppy disc for subsequent retrieval and data analysis. The system described has the capability of storing 250 (500 point) spectra and can readily be used to increase the effectiveness of HPLC analysis by allowing both quantitative and qualitative data to be obtained.

Experimental

Liquid Chromatograph. The liquid chromatograph was comprised of a Waters 660 Solvent Programmer, two Waters 6000A pumps, a Waters U6-K Injector and a Waters 440 absorbance detector (254 nm). Whatman micro-capillary tubing (0.007" ID) was used to transfer the HPLC column effluent from the 254 nm absorption detector to the fluorescence detector.

All chromatographic separations were made using an ES Industries 0.46 x 15 cm reverse-phase column packed with E. Merck 5 µm Lichrosorb RP-18. A Whatman pre-column (0.21 x 7 cm) packed with CO:PELL ODS (Reeve-Angel) was used to protect the analytical column from both particulate matter and irreversible bonding of injected components onto the stationary phase. The pre-column is also used to dampen mobile phase pulsations from the chromatographic pumps.

Absorption and Fluorescence Instrumentation. Absorption spectra were obtained using a Princeton Applied Research Corp. (PARC) Model 1208 polychromator, a Perkin-Elmer 8 µL absorption flow-cell and a 50 watt deuterium light source. Fluorescence spectra were obtained using a Farrand Mark 1 Spectrofluorometer (previously described (13)) and either a 10 µL Farrand micro flow-cell, or a Precision Cells, Inc. (Model No. 8830) 20 µL flow-cell. A PARC Model 1254 SIT detector, having a UV scintillator, was mounted on both the absorption polychromator and fluorescence spectrofluorometer. Spectral coverage in the absorption and fluorescence modes was 60 and 115 nm, respectively. All absorption and fluorescence spectra were obtained in one second, i.e., 32 scans of the SIT target.

Optical Multichannel Analyzer System (OMA 2). The OMA 2 system consisted of a PARC Model 1215 console, two PARC Model 1254 SIT detectors, two PARC Model 1216 detector controllers, and a PARC Model 1217 flexible disc drive. The SIT detector is controlled by the 1216 detector controller, which provides both power and scanning voltages and processes the signal for transmission to the OMA 2 console. The OMA 2 console performs all necessary control functions, data acquisitions, data processing and storage of spectra. The system can store 250 (500 points) spectral curves when equipped with the Model 1217 flexible disc drive.

Reagents. Millipore Q system water and spectroquality methanol (MCBMX 475) were used as the mobile phase in the liquid chromatograph. Fluoropore filters (FGLP 04700) having a 0.22 μm pore diameter were used to filter the methanol prior to use. All aromatic standards, except benzene (MCBBX 215), were obtained from Duke Standards Co., Palo Alto, California. Solutions of the standards were prepared in spectroquality methanol. Glacial acetic acid (reagent grade) was used to acidify the spectroquality methanol to prepare the oil extracting solution (0.4% acetic acid in methanol).

Sample Preparation. Petroleum oils were extracted with acidified methanol, according to a procedure previously described (14). Samples of sea water containing soluble petroleum oil fractions were prepared by gently spreading an oil layer (1-2 mm thick) on fresh sea water contained in a 4 liter Pyrex® beaker. A glass tube extending from the bottom of the beaker to above the water surface, was used to contain a Teflon® siphon from which oil free water samples were withdrawn from the bottom at intervals over a two week period. The beaker containing the oil and water was not disturbed nor agitated during this two week period to preclude mixing or emulsification of the oil/water layers. Various sample volumes (50 or 250 ml) of sea water drawn from the bottom of the beaker were pumped through Whatman guard columns packed with 33-44 μm CO: PELL ODS at a 10 ml/min. flow rate. The Whatman guard columns were then connected ahead of the analytical column for chromatographic analysis.

Separation Procedure. Methanolic oil extracts were chromatographically separated using a linear gradient from 50/50 methanol in water to 100% methanol in 50 minutes at a flow rate of 1 ml/min. (∿ 1200 psi). The analytical column was preconditioned for 23 minutes with 50% (v/v) methanol in water at a flow rate of 1 ml/min. prior to beginning the gradient.

The loaded pre-columns were connected between the injector and the analytical column. Linear two segment gradients were used; 0% to 50% (v/v) methanol/water in 20 minutes, followed by 50% to 100% (v/v) methanol/water in 50 minutes.

Discussion

Fluorescence Measurements. A previous study (13) described the use of an OMA system to record the fluorescence emission spectra of petroleum oil aromatic hydrocarbons separated by HPLC. In this earlier study, the fluorescence spectra were recorded by either photographing a monitor scope or plotting the spectra on a continuously moving strip chart recorder at a plot rate of 16.4 s per spectrum. Both of these approaches are however, impractical, since they allowed only enough time to record chromatographic peak maxima as a result of the comparatively long recording time relative to the short observation time (1 s). The OMA 2 system used in the present study is capable of storing a spectrum within 10 seconds, allowing for a more effectual monitoring of the HPLC effluent stream. This 10 second interval can be reduced to less than 3 seconds by modifying the software (written in FORTH) used to control the OMA 2 system.

A second problem encountered in the earlier study was a loss in sensitivity and an increase in scatter associated with the use of a 10 μL cylindrical flow-cell. Figure 1 compares spectra obtained for a 2 ppm naphthalene solution in the 10 μL flow-cell and in a standard 10 x 10 mm cuvette (3.7 ml). Figure 2 compares the fluorescence response of a 1 ppm solution of chrysene obtained using a 1 x 1 x 21 mm rectangular flow-cell and a standard 10 x 10 mm cuvette. These spectra were obtained using a Farrand Mark I Spectrofluorometer. The fluorescence intensities in microamperes at several points on the two spectra indicate that a substantial increase in signal is obtained with the 1 x 1 x 21 mm flow-cell. The solvent signal blank was 0.001 microamperes for the cuvette and 0.003 microamperes for the flow-cell. The peak to peak variation in the photomultiplier detector response at a flow rate of 1 ml/minute for both the flow-cell and standard cuvette spectra were the same, indicating that a flowing (non-static) condition does not induce noise. Similar flow-cell and cuvette comparisons were made using 1 ppm solutions of pyrene, 2-methylnaphthalene, and fluorene. In each case the fluorescence signal obtained from the flow-cell was greater than that from the standard cuvette. Spectral response differences were found to vary with the aromatic standard used and are probably attributable to inner filter effects and quenching.

The 1 x 1 x 21 mm flow-cell is shown in Figure 3. A lens assembly refocuses the exit slit image of the excitation monochromator onto the flow-cell. This refocusing essentially reduces the optical window of the HPLC effluent stream being monitored by 2/3 (from 20 mm to approximately 6 mm, vertical height). This region is shown as the dashed area in Figure 3. The HPLC effluent flow through this cell is from bottom to top, and at a flow rate of 1 ml/min, then 16.7 μL of the effluent stream has passed through this region in one second. Assuming an elution volume of 500 μL (which at a 1 ml/min flow rate requires 30 s) then

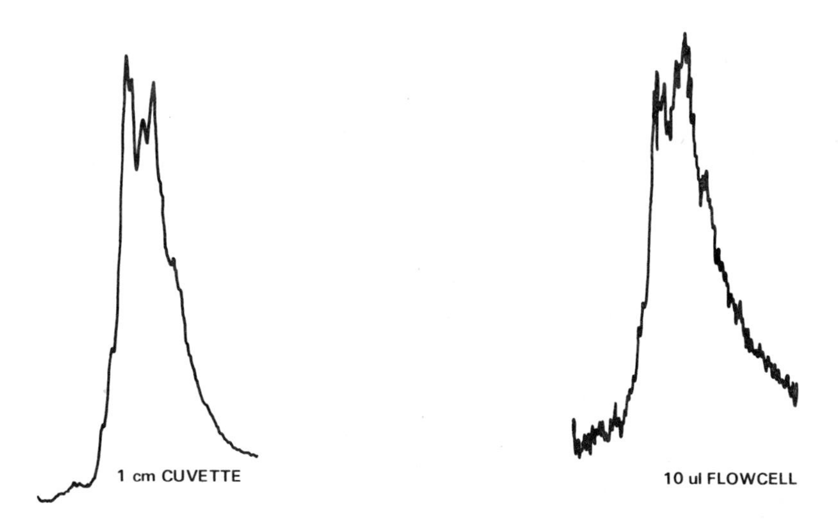

Figure 1. Comparison of fluorescence spectra from a standard cuvette and a 10 μL flow-cell of 2 ppm naphthalene in methanol: 100 (A-B) OMA accumulations, Em bandwidth 0.5 nm.

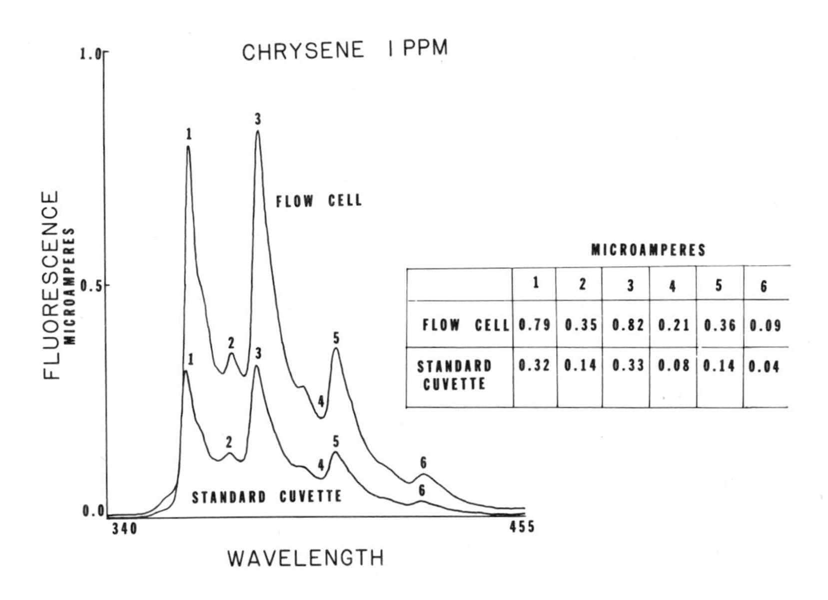

	1	2	3	4	5	6
FLOW CELL	0.79	0.35	0.82	0.21	0.36	0.09
STANDARD CUVETTE	0.32	0.14	0.33	0.08	0.14	0.04

Figure 2. Comparison of fluorescence spectra from a standard cuvette and a 20 μL flow-cell of 1 ppm chrysene in methanol using a PMT, Em bandwidth 2.0 nm.

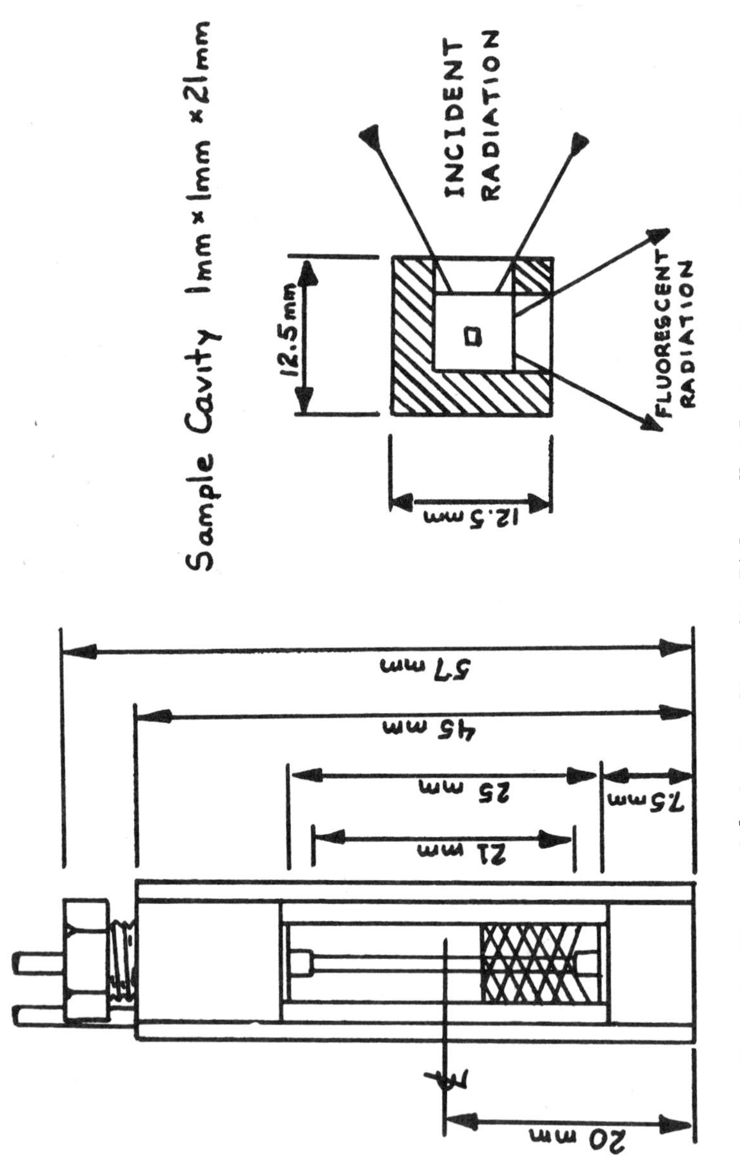

Figure 3. Diagram of the 1 × 1 × 21 mm (20 μL) flow cell. Effective volume of the HPLC effluent stream being monitored indicated by hash marks.

an "on-the-fly" observation time of 1 s is the equivalent of 1/30 th of the elution volume.

The average concentration of the solution within the mobile phase passing through the flow-cell at peak maximum is approximately twice the injected amount of material divided by the elution volume (15). Therefore, if 1 nanogram of solute were injected and on-column dilution of 500 μL occurred, then the concentration of the solute passing through the flow-cell at peak maximum would be 0.004 ng per microliter,or 4 ppb, a concentration easily detected by fluorescence spectroscopic techniques. It is obvious that as the elution volume decreases (chromatographic efficiency increases) the concentration of the solute at peak maximum within the flow cell will increase. Figure 4 (A-B) shows the fluorescence spectrum of chrysene obtained in 1 second (at the peak maximum) when 4 ng was injected at a flow rate of 1 ml/min. This spectrum was obtained using the 10 μL flow-cell and OMA system previously described (13). Apparently, improved detectability (i.e., identifiable spectrum) is attainable, even when using a small volume flow-cell, as evidenced by the spectra shown in Figures 1 and 2.

The optical lens assembly, in addition to reducing the optical window on the flow-cell, also serves as a mask to limit the slit image height at the exit plane of the emission monochromator to approximately 6 mm. This masking effect precludes the need to use the full diode array of the SIT detector and prevents vertical distortions (pincushion effects which are present in the SIT detector), from adversely affecting the spectral data.

UV Absorption Measurements. The absorbance (A) at any given wavelength, using an OMA system, is defined as:

$$A = \log_{10} \frac{(Io - x)}{(I - x)}$$

where Io is the incident radiant energy, I the radiant energy transmitted by the sample, and x the dark current of the optoelectronic image device. A previously described OMA system (13) automatically subtracts dark current in the recording of Io and I values. The OMA 2 system also has a dark current which becomes constant after the SIT detector has reached equilibrium with the ambient temperature. However, this dark current is not automatically removed. It must be recorded and subtracted from Io and I for calculating true absorbances. The OMA 2, however, can be programmed to record dark current readings throughout a chromatographic analysis.

An optoelectronic image device has been used as an HPLC detector to obtain UV absorption spectra of shale oil aromatic hydrocarbons separated isocratically (10). Since isocratic separations maintain a constant mobile phase composition, the

Io in the above equation remains constant. However, during a gradient elution, Io is continuously changing since the composition of the mobile phase varies during the chromatographic analysis. This becomes a critical consideration when using the OMA system as a detector to analyze low concentrations of aromatic hydrocarbons separated by gradient elution techniques. In this study, (Io - x) values for every 5% change in the methanol/water gradient (from 50 to 100% methanol) were stored in memory and used to determine the absorption spectra of the HPLC eluates at the appropriate gradient composition. Another approach is currently under development (16) in which two microflow-cells will be interchanged into the optical path, one containing the HPLC effluent stream (from the outlet of the analytical column) and the second containing only the changing mobile phase composition (prior to the injector and consequently devoid of sample) to allow both (Io - x) and I - x) values to be obtained for nearly identical gradient compositions. (The lag time between sample mobile phase composition and blank mobile phase composition will be minimal and should not present a problem unless very fast gradient run times over large and/or rapid mobile phase compositional changes are employed.)

Another factor which can cause spectral distortions is the fluctuation of the output energy of the radiant source. The OMA 2 system incorporates a capability to correct spectral data for variations in source output energy (17). The source compensation mode continuously monitors the output energy of the lamp and automatically corrects incoming spectral data for source intensity fluctuations prior to storing that data.

HPLC/OMA System. In this study, the HPLC effluent stream was passed through three flow-cells connected in series with different lengths of Whatman micro-capillary (0.007 " I.D.) tubing. The first flow-cell monitored the absorption at 254 nm and was used to key the recording of absorption and fluorescence spectra of the effluent stream passing through the second and third flow-cells, respectively, at peak maxima.

Figure 5 shows an HPLC absorption chromatogram of what appears to be a two component mixture of benzene and ethyl benzene separated isocratically. Figures 6 and 7 are the absorption and fluorescence spectra of the first eluting compound (benzene) obtained as the HPLC effluent stream passed through the second and third flow-cells, respectively. Each spectrum was obtained in one second, (i.e., 32 scans of the SIT detector). It can be seen in Figures 6 and 7 that the absorption and fluorescence spectra obtained using the OMA system agrees with published benzene spectra.

Figures 8 and 9 are the OMA absorption and fluorescence spectra obtained at the peak maxima of the second fraction (ethylbenzene) as the HPLC effluent stream passed through the

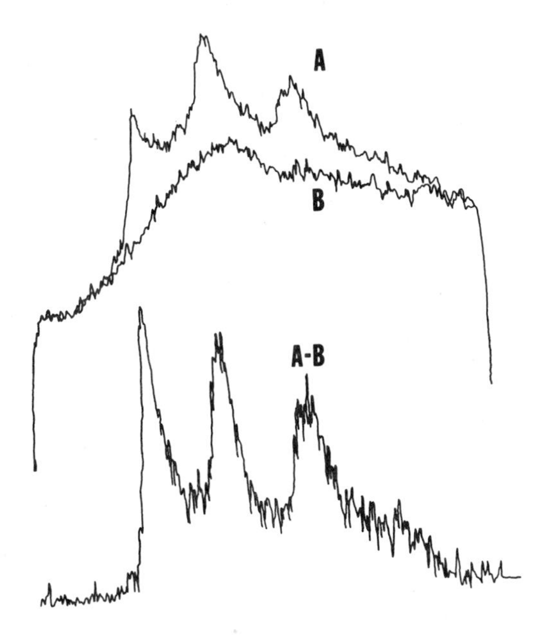

Figure 4. *Fluorescence spectra of a 4 ng injection of chrysene onto an HPLC column: 32 (A-B) OMA accumulations, Em bandwidth 2 nm.*

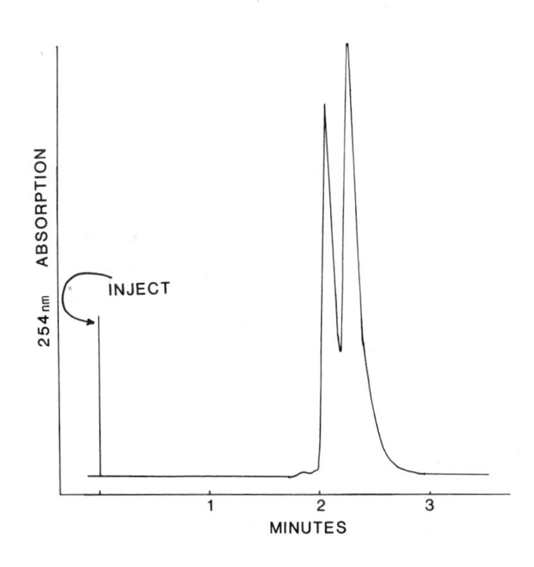

Figure 5. *HPLC absorption chromatogram (254 nm) of a contaminated two component mixture separated isocratically*

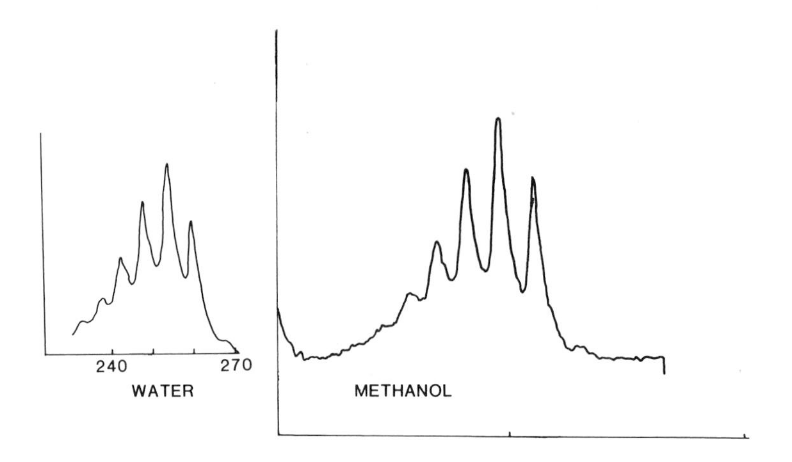

Figure 6. Comparison of benzene absorption spectrum in methanol (32 OMA accumulations) with published absorption spectrum of benzene in water

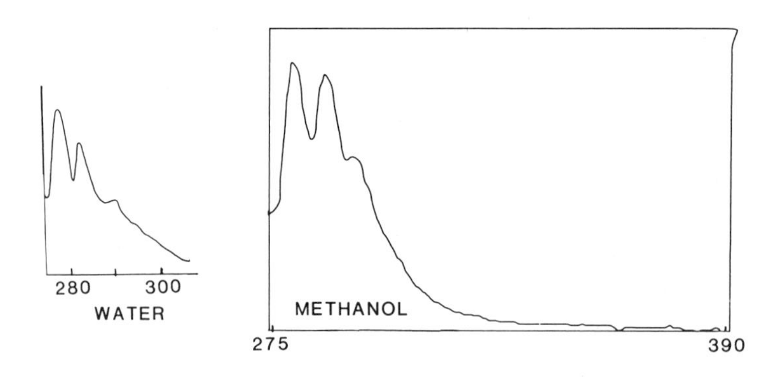

Figure 7. Comparison of fluorescence spectrum of benzene in methanol (32 OMA accumulations) with published fluorescence spectrum of benzene in water

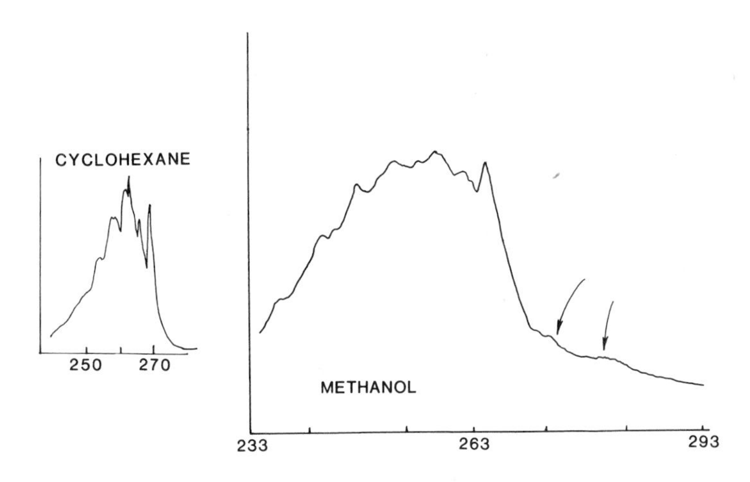

Figure 8. Comparison of ethylbenzene absorption spectrum in methanol (32 OMA accumulations) with published fluorescence spectrum in cyclohexane. Arrows indicate spectral region of difference.

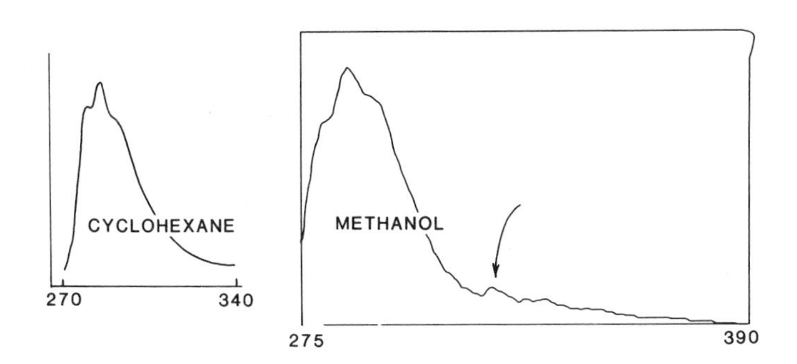

Figure 9. Comparison of ethylbenzene fluorescence spectrum in methanol (32 OMA accumulations) with published fluorescence spectrum in cyclohexane. Arrows indicate spectral region of difference.

second and third flow-cells, respectively. However, it can be seen in Figures 8 and 9, that the UV absorption and fluorescence spectra obtained for ethylbenzene did not compare exactly to the published spectra of ethylbenzene; the spectral regions where differences occur are indicated by arrows.

These differences were caused by a trace amount of naphthalene contamination. The 5 μL syringe that was used to inject the mixture (32 μg each of benzene and ethylbenzene) had purposely not been cleaned prior to the injection of this mixture. The chromatogram in Figure 5 clearly indicates a two component mixture, with no peak shoulders and good peak symmetry. No indication of the trace contaminant is present in the second eluting peak. However, peak symmetry is not a good indicator of peak purity (18). Although single wavelength monitoring of the HPLC stream by either absorption or fluorescence detectors is an effective approach to quantitating known components, it cannot solely be used to determine peak purity reliably, especially when a poorly resolved contaminant is present at trace levels. Figure 10 is an enlargement of the OMA fluorescence emission spectrum of the ethylbenzene peak clearly showing the extraneous emission due to the presence of the naphthalene contaminant.

Figure 11 shows the published UV absorption spectra for both ethylbenzene and naphthalene. The spectral band width and location of the standard fixed wavelength UV absorption HPLC detector (254 nm) are shown, in a region where both compounds absorb. However, since the chromatographic retention times of these two components are nearly identical (under the chromatographic conditions employed), the standard single wavelength absorption is actually the sum of two components absorbing in this region, and monitoring a region of spectral overlap for two poorly resolved compounds minimizes the chances of detecting the minor component. The contaminant peak could be detected using multiple fixed absorption wavelengths, particularly in non-overlapping spectral regions, but this requires multiple detectors or repeated chromatographic injections. The OMA system can be used to record multiple wavelength absorption or fluorescence chromatograms (in addition to the spectra of the eluting fractions) since these represent only slices of the spectral windows.

Stop-flow, or fraction collection, also could be used to identify the presence of naphthalene in the second eluting fraction, but only at a considerable sacrifice in time relative to the rapid scanning capability of the OMA. However, as the complexity of a chromatographic separation increases, these approaches become impractical in terms of the time required to spectrally determine the peak purity of each fraction.

Figure 12 shows the 254 nm absorption chromatogram of a complex mixutre of PAH's extracted from a marine diesel fuel and separated on a reverse-phase C-18 column using a methanol/water gradient. For this analysis the OMA 2 system was program-

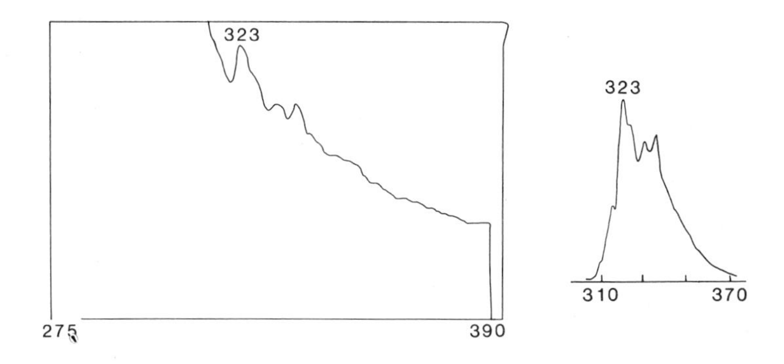

Figure 10. Enlargement of spectral region where differences exist in the fluorescence spectrum of ethylbenzene (Figure 9) indicating the presence of naphthalene

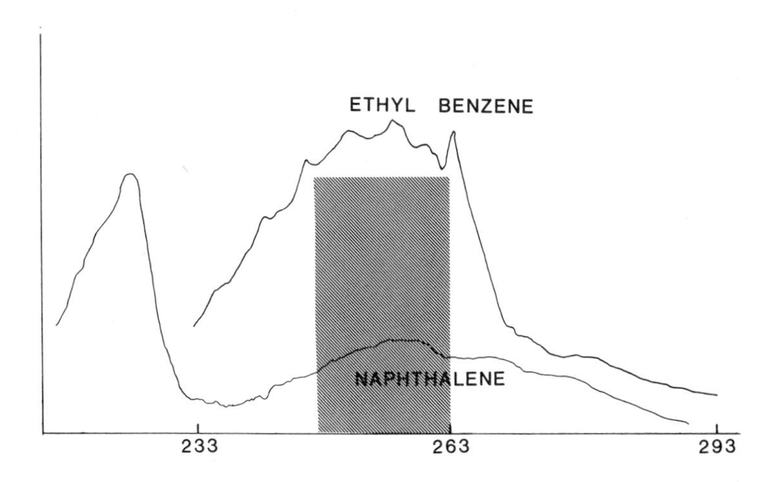

Figure 11. Absorption spectra of ethylbenzene and naphthalene indicating region of overlap at 254 nm

med to take fluorescence spectra of the effluent stream every 10 seconds throughout the chromatographic run. Figure 13 is an enlargement of the rectangular portion of the chromatogram shown in Figure 12. This segment represents a seventy (70) second portion of this chromatographic analysis. Figure 14 shows the fluorescence emission spectra taken at 10 second intervals over this time frame (each spectrum represents a one second scan of the effluent stream). The spectral window covers 115 nm, from 295 nm to 410 nm. Identification of these components could be accomplished by computer if libraries of fluorescence (and/or absorption) spectra were in existence (as in the case of GC-MS and GC-FTIR systems).

This approach has proven useful in the analysis of environmental samples for the presence of hazardous contaminants. Figure 15 shows three chromatograms; the lower chromatogram is a trace enrichment of uncontaminated sea water; the middle chromatogram is of a methanol extract of a Bunker C fuel oil; the upper chromatogram is a trace enrichment of contaminated sea water after a one day oil/water contact time. The trace enrichment chromatograms were obtained by pumping the two sea water samples through Whatman guard columns (2.1 x 70 mm) packed with CO:PELL ODS and analyzed (as described under the experimental section) using a 2 segment water to methanol gradient. The OMA system was used to record both the UV absorption and fluorescence spectra of the separated eluates at peak maxima's only. A total of 145 absorption and fluorescence spectra were obtained during the HPLC analysis of the contaminated sea water sample. This represents water soluble fractions of the oil since no agitation of the oil/water mixture occurred. This capability allows for the rapid identification of soluble PAH's by comparison with published spectral data.

Conclusions

Optoelectronic image devices can be used to increase the versatility of standard HPLC absorption and fluorescence detectors by providing spectral information of the HPLC effluent stream "on-the-fly" during a chromatographic analysis. In addition, conventional multiple fixed wavelength absorption or fluorescence chromatograms can also be obtained by plotting narrow bandwidths within the monitored spectral windows. Further, the OMA system can effectively be used to ascertain chromatographic peak purity during the elution of a band by continuously monitoring its spectrum from leading edge, through peak maximum, to tailing edge. The capability of the OMA system to monitor a wide spectral window, rather than a narrow band, increases not only the amount of data generated, but also the utility of that data itself.

Current methods of identifying PAH's separated by HPLC techniques become increasingly impractical as the samples become more complex; stop-flow techniques are suitable only for

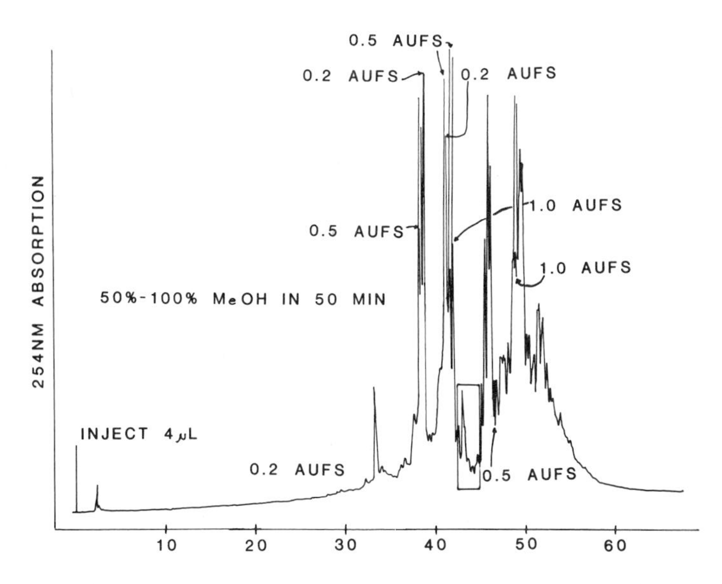

Figure 12. HPLC absorption chromatogram of a marine diesel fuel oil

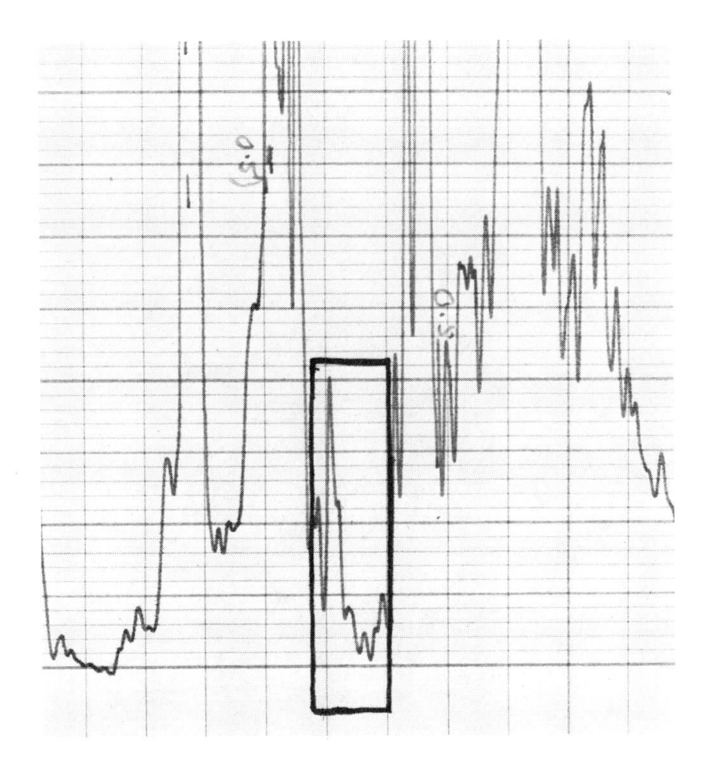

Figure 13. Enlargement of a seventy (70) second portion of the chromatogram shown in Figure 12

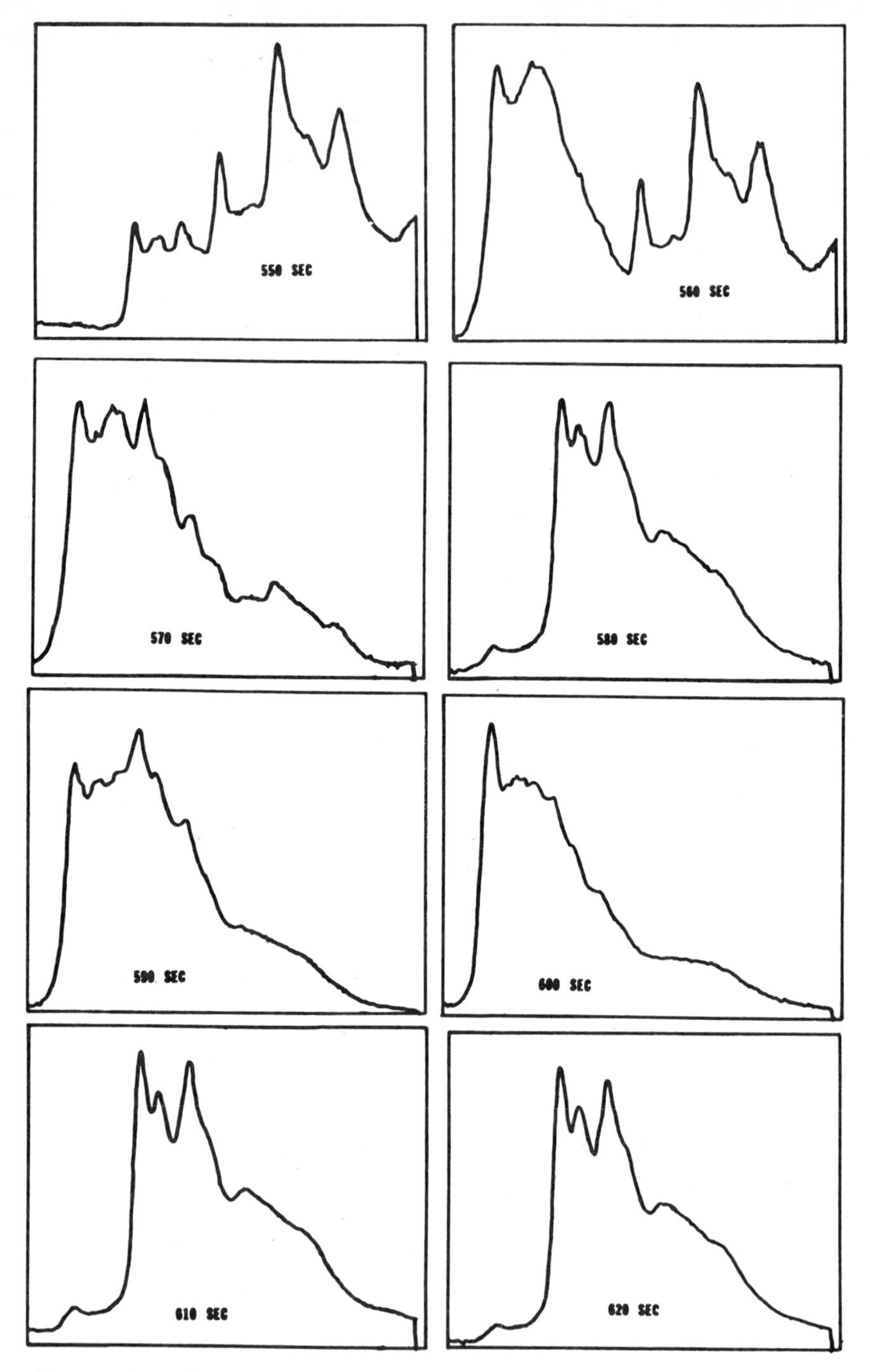

Figure 14. Eight fluorescence spectra taken at 10 second intervals during the 70 second portion of the chromatogram shown in Figure 13. Each spectrum was 32 OMA (1 second) accumulations.

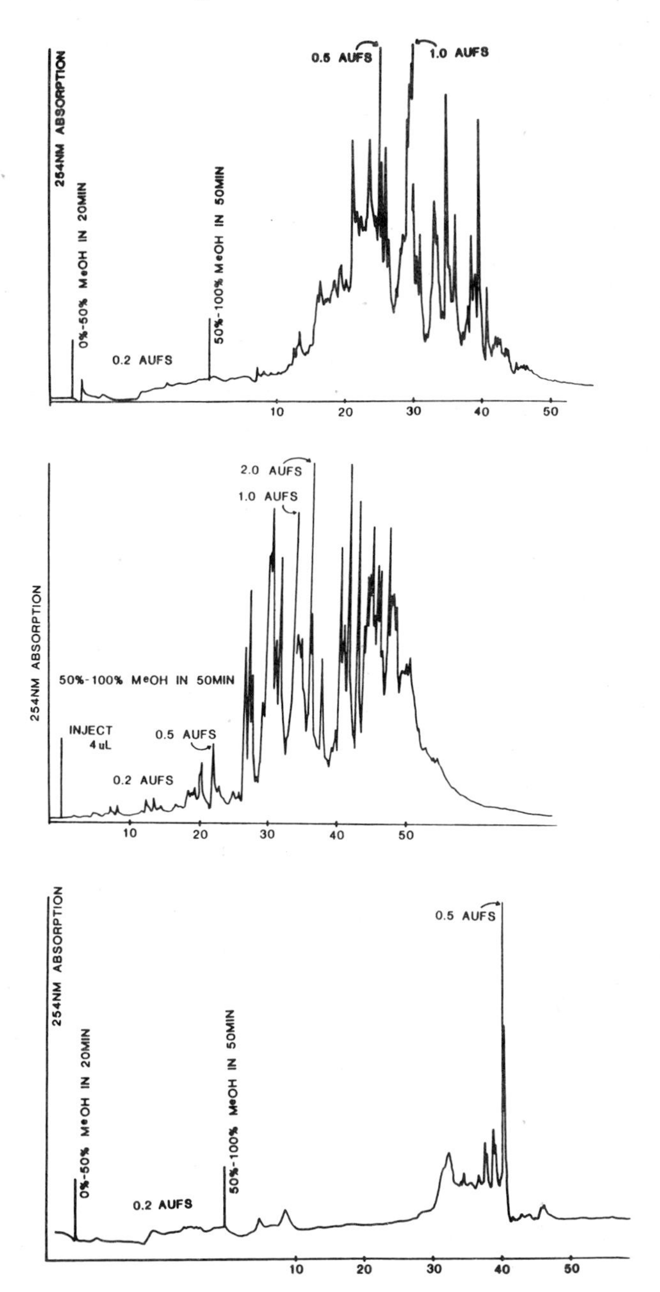

Figure 15. Three HPLC absorption chromatograms: lower is trace enrichment chromatogram of clean (uncontaminated) sea water; middle chromatogram is a methanol extract of a Bunker C oil; upper chromatogram is a trace enrichment chromatogram of sea water after 1 day contact with Bunker C oil.

relatively simple mixtures.

Present research efforts are being directed toward developing a polychromator system utilizing an OMA detector to record both absorption and fluorescence spectra of an HPLC effluent from a single flow cell. This will allow for the near-simultaneous recording of both the absorption and fluorescence spectra of an eluate. Since only one flow-cell will be utilized, any degradation in separation resulting from band broadening (attributable to the flow-cell) will be eliminated. This is not the case when several flow-cells are used in series (19). Studies currently in progress indicate that the use of multiple flow-cells (in tandem) not only causes an increase in band broadening but also increases peak skewness. This results not only in a decrease in detectability but also a loss in chromatographic resolution.

In the analysis of environmental samples, optoelectronic image devices allow for real time spectral acquisition and rapid identification by comparison to published spectra. It is not unrealistic to project that within 5 to 10 years suitable spectral libraries will be available for identifying HPLC eluates by computer search routines similar to those presently in use with MS and FTIR systems.

The opinions or assertions contained herein are the private ones of the writers and are not to be construed as official or reflecting the views of the Commandant or the Coast Guard at large.

LITERATURE CITED

1. F. Eisenbeiss, H. Hein, R. Joester, and G. Naundorf, Chromatogr. Newsletter. 6, 8 (1978).

2. C. G. Creed, Research/Development, Sep. 40 (1976).

3. D. Kasiske, K. D. Klinkmuller, and M. Sonneborn, J. Chromatogr., 149, 703 (1978).

4. S. A. Wise, S. N. Chester, H. S. Hertz, L. R. Hilpert, and W. E. May, Anal. Chem., 49, 2306 (1977).

5. A. D. Thruston, J. Chromatogr. Sci. 16, 254, (1978).

6. W. E. May, and S. P. Wasik, Anal. Chem., 50, 997 (1978).

7. R. D. Conlon, Anal. Chem., 41, 107A, (1969).

8. A. E. McDowell, and H. Pardue, Anal. Chem., 48, 1815 (1976).

9. A. E. McDowell and H. Pardue, Anal. Chem., 49, 1171 (1977).

10. L. N. Klatt, Abstracts, 173rd ACS National Meeting, New Orleans, LA, March 1977.

11. R. E. Dessy, W. G. Nunn, C. A. Titus, and W. R. Reynolds, J. Chromatogr. Sci., 14, 195 (1976).

12. M. J. Milano, S. Lam, and E. Gruska, J. Chromatogr. 125, 315 (1976).

13. J. R. Jadamec, W. A. Saner; and Y. Talmi, Anal. Chem. 49, 1318, (1977).

14. W. A. Saner, G. E. Fitzgerald, and J. P. Welsh, Anal. Chem. 48, 1747, (1976).

15. J. J. Kirkland, "Modern Practice of Liquid Chromatography" Wiley-Interscience, New York, 1971, p. 101.

16. U. S. Governmental Contract DOT-CG-81-78-1963 awarded to Farrand Optical Co., Inc., Oct. (1978).

17. Y. Talmi, D. C. Baker, J. R. Jadamec, and W. A. Saner, Anal. Chem., 50, 936 A (1978).

18. E. D. Pellizzari, and C. M. Sparacino, Anal. Chem., 45, 378, (1973).

19. T. J. Porro, R. D. Conlon, J. L. Dicesare, Abstracts, 29th Pittsburgh Conference, Cleveland, Ohio, Feb. 1978.

RECEIVED February 5, 1979.

6

A Dual-Beam Photodiode Array Spectrometer System for Liquid Chromatographic Separation Methods Development

W. G. NUNN[1] and R. E. DESSY[2]

Virginia Polytechnic Institute & State University, Chemistry Department, Blacksburg, VA 24061

W. R. REYNOLDS

National Center for Toxicological Research, Jefferson, AR 72074

A multiwavelength, dual beam optical system with 256 detectors operating in a free spectral range of 200 to 800 nm has been designed and implemented for use with a liquid chromatograph. Also, to facilitate the use of this detector an extensive computer software system has been written which allows the user almost unlimited freedom in the way that the data taken over the bandwidth of the detector may be plotted or displayed for visual examination. The linear photodiode arrays used as detectors have been shown to have a significant response in the ultraviolet region of the spectrum.

Automation and computerization of laboratory equipment have had a profound effect on the manner in which three important areas of chemistry have been developed and used:

1. The addition of a computer to multiple gas-chromatograph installations permitted rapid data analyses and report generation.
2. The application of Fourier transform methods to nuclear magnetic resonance experiments improved the signal-to-noise ratio and permitted extraction of data heretofore inaccessible.
3. The use of a computer with high-speed high-resolution mass spectrometers allowed vast amounts of data to be collected rapidly and manipulated easily.

In all of these cases, the instrument was designed long before the computer was attached. Increasingly, instruments will be designed from the beginning with automation and computerization in mind. The form of the instrument will be determined by the needs of the chemist for proper data, correlated to the needs of the computer.

The purpose of this article is to describe an automated unit for liquid chromatography (LC) which utilizes state-of-the-art digital electronics in the instrument and in the associated computer equipment. It will describe the development of the system

[1] Current Address: Union Carbide Chemicals and Plastics, South Charleston, W. VA. 25303

[2] Request for reprints.

0-8412-0504-3/79/47-102-135$08.25/0

for the interested chromatographer as well as provide the case history of a specific laboratory automation project for the general scientist.

Multiwavelength Detection

Liquid chromatography has been hindered by the lack of a universal detector-and as yet no equivalent for the GC/MS system has been described. For several years it has been evident that UV/VIS spectroscopy could provide a viable detector if multiwavelength detection principles were employed.

Many varieties of rapid scanning spectrometer systems are available. The first generation units relied on moving mechanical parts to scan the spectrum. These are typified by the rotating mirror or vibrating galvanometer types commercially available. The second generation instrument utilized Vidicon tubes of some sort. These eliminated the construction and maintenance problems associated with mechanical spectrometers, but the high cost of Vidicon systems, and their tendency to show memory and blooming makes them interim solutions only. The stage is obviously set for a third generation instrument using linear photosensitive arrays as the detector for a rapid scanning/multiwavelength spectrometer for liquid chromatographic use. An excellent review of multielement detectors has been published by Talmi.[1]

The classical silicon photodiode linear array manufactured by Reticon was the first detector marketed successfully. Similar solid state linear array detectors based on charge coupled devices, or charge injection devices may also be of interest. Typical of the families of detectors, the Reticon detectors are built in a number of elements/array sizes. Commercially available units have anywhere from 128 to 1024 elements/array. Each individual element in the array is 1 x 1 mil to 1 x 100 mil in area, and are spaced on approximately 1 mil centers. The spectrometer system discussed in this article was built using Reticon-type devices.

The detector schematic is shown in Figure 1.

1. As light strikes the surface of the detector, hole pairs are created and migration occurs toward the capacitor element shown.

2. As the light continues to strike the detector surface this action leads to a gradual discharge of the capacitor.

3. Over the integration time (the time light strikes the array) the charge on the capacitor drops an amount equivalent to the amount of integrated light falling on the detector.

4. When the element is read out a solid-state device called a multiplexer attaches the detector to a voltage source which charges the capacitor back up to a standard potential.

5. A signal, corresponding to the current-flow necessary to recharge the voltage source, is sent down a wire called the

video line.

6. The multiplexer then causes the voltage source to be connected to the next element in the detector, and the process is repeated.

The signal from the recharging of the capacitors is sent down the video line as a series of peaks where each peak corresponds to a capacitor, photodiode pair. The signal seen on the video line is illustrated in upper trace figure 2, where figure 3 is the signal striking the array.

The response of an array to light is wavelength dependent. As can be seen in figure 4 the array has the greatest response to near IR and the smallest to radiation in the ultraviolet. A true double beam spectrometer requires separate optical paths for sample and reference, and involves simultaneous comparison of the two. It is possible to construct a pseudo-double beam spectrometer, employing only one detector and optical path, taking advantage of the capabilities of a computer system attached to the detector.

All that is needed to make such a detector into a MULTI-WAVELENGTH/RAPID SCANNING spectrometer for liquid chromatographic purposes is to disperse the light exiting from an LC cell onto the surface of the photodiode array by means of a monochromater.

In order to properly condition the serial pulse train exiting from the common video line of the detector for input to a computer system, it is normal to run it through an integrate, sample/hold amplifier system. Each pulse is integrated over a major fraction of its width, leading to a reduction in noise by the analog integrating operation. This integral is "sampled" and the potential "held" at the end of the integration period, so that the output of the system really looks like Figure 2 bottom. This can be compared to the output that might be expected from a standard photometer unit in a regular spectrometer (Figure 3). Under normal conditions this could be displayed directly onto an oscilloscope, and a rapid scanning spectrometer has been constructed.

It is obvious that with the large data throughput a computer will be necessary to take advantage of all the data available. Therefore the output shown in Figure 2 is input to an analog/digital converter, and digitized; i.e., converted from analog domain to digital domain. This provides a digital number that can be accepted by a computer and stored.

A shutter and pure solvent in the sample compartment of this pseudo-double beam spectrometer permits acquisition of both a dark current (0% T) and an emmisivity/responsivity (100% T) data array. These consist of digitized responses from each of the pixels in the array under conditions where the integration time and the speed of read-out is identical to that planned for the measurement of the spectrum of a sample. The dark-current data will provide information as to the shot-noise and other inherent

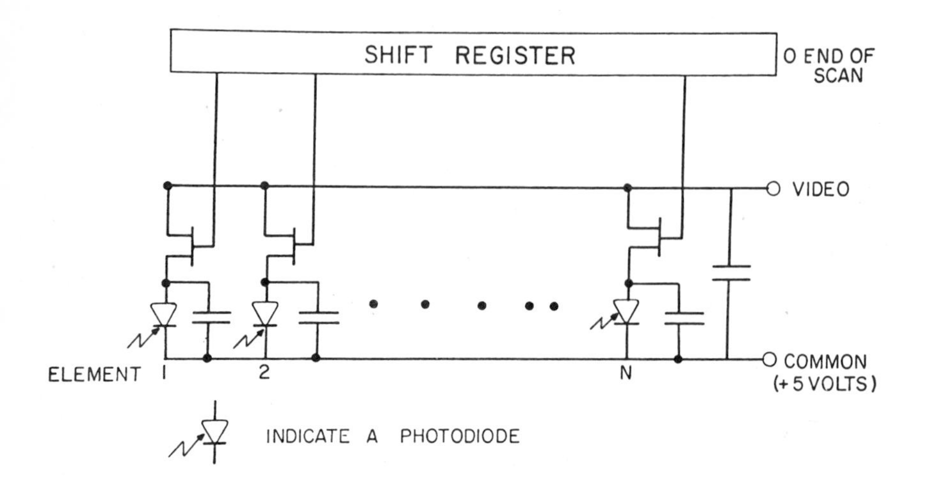

Journal of Chromatographic Science

Figure 1. Equivalent circuit for a Reticon linear photodiode array (4)

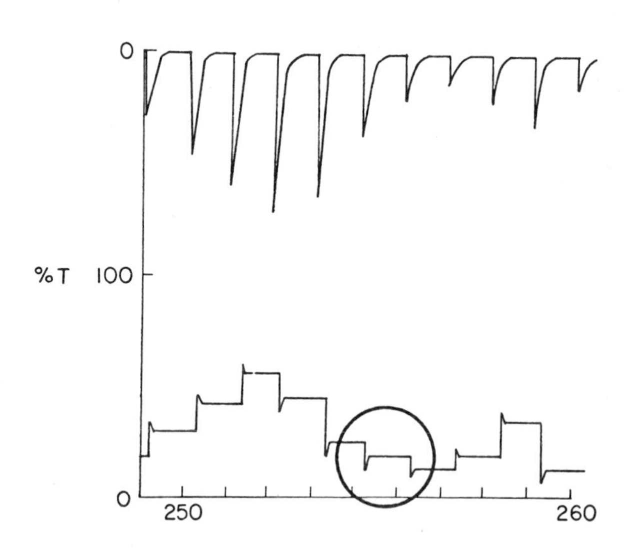

Journal of Chromatographic Science

Figure 2. The output of the Reticon linear photodiode array (upper trace). The output of the CASH-1B integrate, sample, and hold (lower trace) (4).

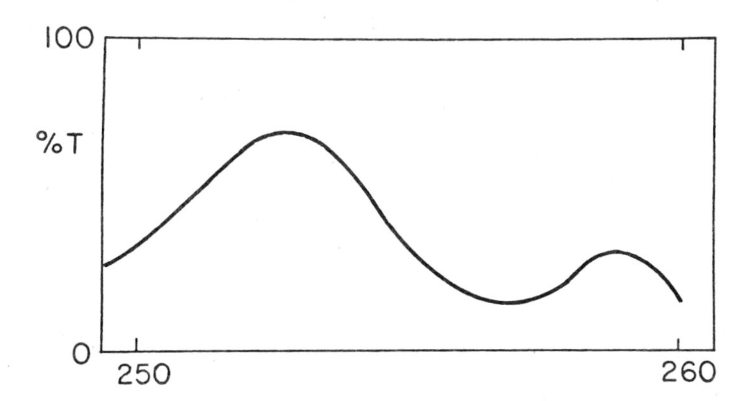

Journal of Chromatographic Science

Figure 3. A spectrum falling on a 10 element section of a Reticon linear photodiode array (4)

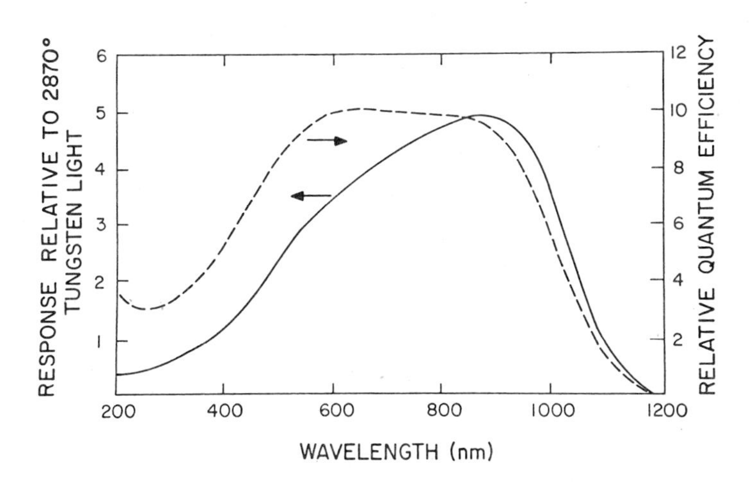

Journal of Chromatographic Science

Figure 4. Spectral response and relative quantum efficiency of the 256 EC/17 linear photodiode array (4)

noise in a non-illuminated spectrum. The 100% T data will characterize the emmisivity of the light source and the responsivity of the detector. This will permit compensation for the varying responsivities of the pixels as will be discussed. It is possible to choose a light source whose emission complements the detector response, so that a relatively flat 100% T curve is obtained. These data arrays are stored in computer memory, and a sample subjected to measurement. With the three arrays in memory it is a simple matter to calculate absorbance values for the material under examination.

This pseudo-double beam spectrometer requires that the source be stable over the measurement of the three required arrays. It also consumes a large amount of computational time forbidding the very rapid acquisition of spectra.[4]

Although such spectrometers have been built and used in our laboratory, the intent of this article is to describe the true double beam version we have constructed for the National Center for Toxicological Research.

The sample and reference arrays work in identical fashion and are driven by a common clock; thus when the sample array is outputting a signal corresponding to a certain element, the reference array is also outputting its corresponding array element. The clock that is used to drive the arrays is a two-phase crystal clock operating at twenty kHz. The two phases are ninety degrees out of phase with the first phase being used to drive the arrays. The second phase is delayed by 25 microseconds and is used as an external start signal for the computer's analog-to-digital converter.

In the rapid scanning environment of liquid chromatography continuous operation of the device is unnecessary. One thousand spectra/second provides more data than can either be used or handled by a computer. In practice therefore, it is usual to initiate data collection only periodically. The concepts involved are as follows. During a dead period, when the detector is not being used, the light striking the detector's surface slowly leads to saturation of all the elements. In order to prepare for the gathering of spectral information, the array must be "dummy read". This means a read pulse is applied which starts the drive electronics, and all elements in the array are recharged back to their starting charge state. The light that strikes each element of the array during the time period before the next start pulse is integrated as described previously.

The integration or exposure time of the arrays is controlled by the clock and a series of counters. The minimum integration time at room temperature of an array running with a 20 kHz clock is 15 milliseconds; the maximum integration time is 205 milliseconds. The minimum time is limited by the scan time of the array; the maximum time by thermal charge.

Signals provided by the arrays are an end-of-scan pulse and a beginning-of-scan pulse. The end-of-scan (EOS) pulse occurs immediately after the last element of the array has been switched onto the video line. It is used by the front-end processor which will be discussed. The beginning-of-scan (BOS) signal is used to start the process by which each element is read and put onto the video line. This signal is also used in the front-end processor.

Analog Front-End Processor. The sample and reference video signals as well as the BOS and EOS pulse are transmitted via coaxial cables to a front-end analog processor (Fig. 5). The first stage of the front-end processor is a 10 kHz low pass filter to remove noise that is the result of FET switch ringing as illustrated in figure 6. After the sample and reference signals have been filtered the signals are placed into voltage amplifiers. The amplifier used with the reference signal may be used in either a unity or variable gain configuration, controlled by a two position switch to the front panel. The amplification is variable from a gain of 0.5 to approximately 2.0. The variable amplification is used to balance the sample and reference signals.

The output from the unity gain followers is input to two additional amplifiers. The first is a differential amplifier which subtracts the reference signal from the sample signal. The output of an array is a transmittance signal and if the reference is taken to indicate one hundred percent transmittance then the output of the differential amplifier will have a direct correspondence with transmittance. The second amplifier into which the sample and reference signals are input is a log-ratio-amplifier. The output of the amplifier can be considered as absorbance.

Within the front-end processor is an integrator that will integrate the output of the log-ratio-amplifier over the period between the beginning and end-of-scan pulses. This is the equivalent of total ion current in GC/MS; the value in LC/UV,VIS is termed a total absorption chromatogram or TAC.

The front-end processor also provides a visual warning flag when the reference array saturates. This is done by comparing the signal level received from the reference array with a manually set upper limit. Saturation of the reference array is not a problem when the detector system is run with a reverse phase or any single solvent system. The problem becomes very real when gradient elution systems are employed.

Optical Design. The most common design for an ultra-violet spectrometer is the Czerny-Turner modification of the Ebert mount for plane grating. This type of mount was discounted because the detectors being used require the fastest optical system possible (f/3.0 or faster). The easiest way to simplify the optical system is by replacing the plane grating with a concave one. A concave grating with a focal length of 200 mm and an aperature of f/3.0

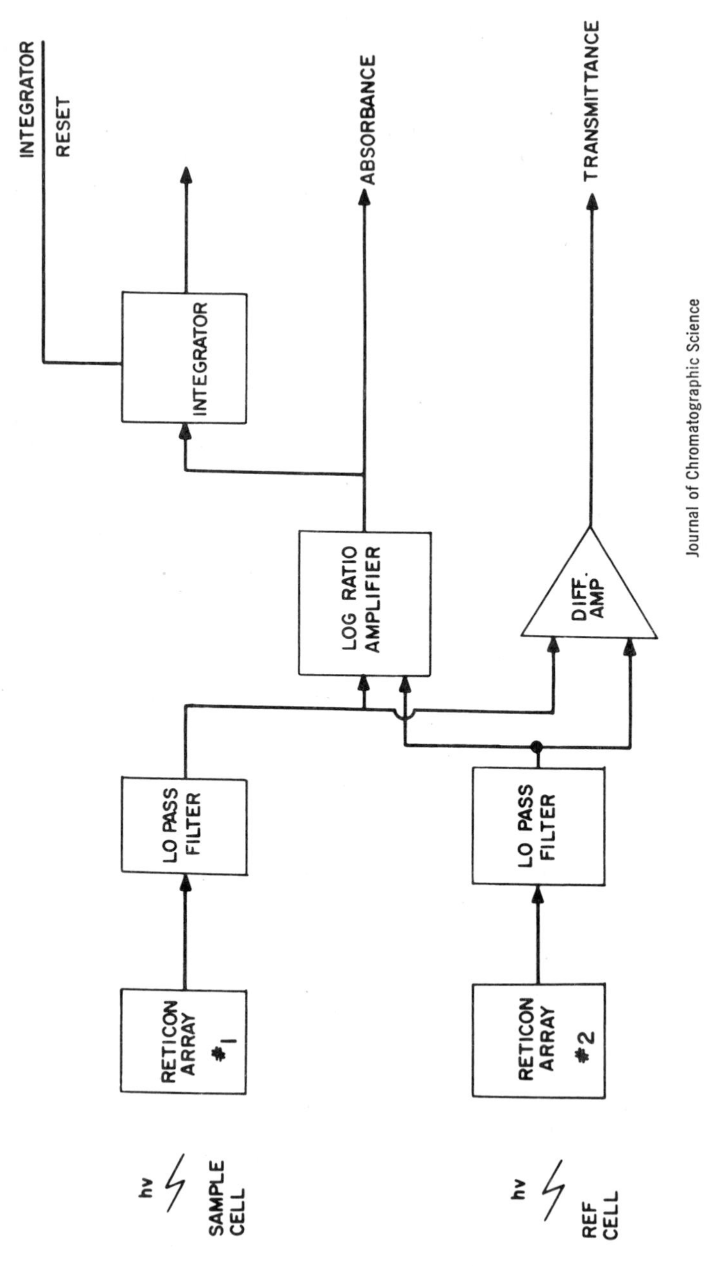

Journal of Chromatographic Science

Figure 5. The general structure of the analog front-end processor (4)

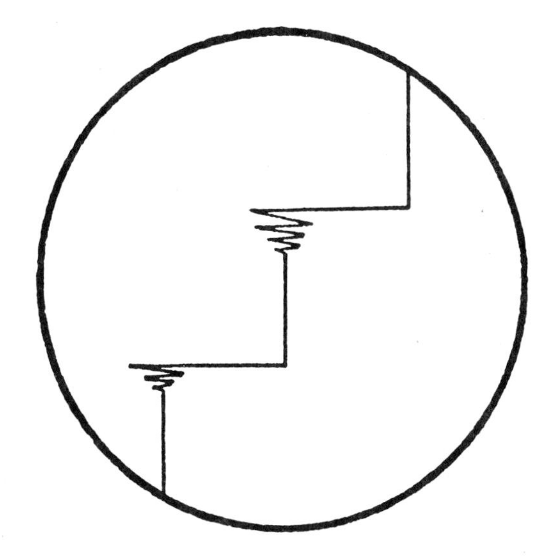

Journal of Chromatographic Science

Figure 6. Typical noise found in the output of the CASH-1B integrate, sample, and hold (4)

was specifically designed by J-Y Optical (Instruments S. A.) for use with linear photodiode arrays. The final optical path used is shown in Figure 7.

The light source is a deuterium lamp with a power output range of 30 to 60 watts. As provided by Oriel it includes a 35 millimeter Supersil quartz condenser set used as a condenser. A beam splitter is placed in the light beam such that it is between the focal point of the condenser and the condenser. The light beam is divided into two beams which will be used as a sample and reference beam. After the sample and reference cells, quartz lenses are used to focus on entrance slits.

The spectrographs are composed of a cast aluminum housing which contains an entrance slit, a front surface folding mirror, and a concave grating. The grating was designed to have a focal length of 200 mm and a diameter of 70 mm. This will yield an f-number of approximately 3. The line spacing is 75 lines/millimeter resulting in a linear dispersion of 1.2 nanometer per one thousandth of an inch.

Computer Hardware. The use of a computer for data acquisition and control is mandatory because of the clock frequency used by the Reticon array (20 kHz) and the volume of data that it is capable of outputting. A PDP-8e computer made by Digital Equipment Corporation, with 12 K words of memory was employed. An Extended Arithmetic Element (EAE) instruction set was installed.

Two RK05 moving head cartridge disk drives provide mass storage capabilities of 3.2 million words. The most economic solution to long term storage is magnetic tape. A 9 track, 800 bits per inch, 45 inches per second tape drive was used.

The ADC converter had an analog input range of 0 to +5 volts and a digital range of 0 to 1024 (10 bits). The D/A converters used for scope display were 10 bit bipolar converters. Two additional pieces of hardware were commercially unavailable. The first item was an extended range fixed period clock with a resolution of 0.01 seconds and a range of 167,772.16 seconds. In use, this clock is started at the beginning of a chromatographic run; then as each spectrum is taken for storage, the time at which it was taken is read from the day clock.

The second hardware unit was an interrupt, skip-check control unit for the Reticon arrays. This unit allows the computer to see the end-of-scan and beginning-of-scan pulses generated by the arrays and allows the computer to have an on/off control of the external clock which is used to start the analog to digital converter.

Applications Software

Several commercial single beam versions of this type of array detector are available. They are oriented toward the

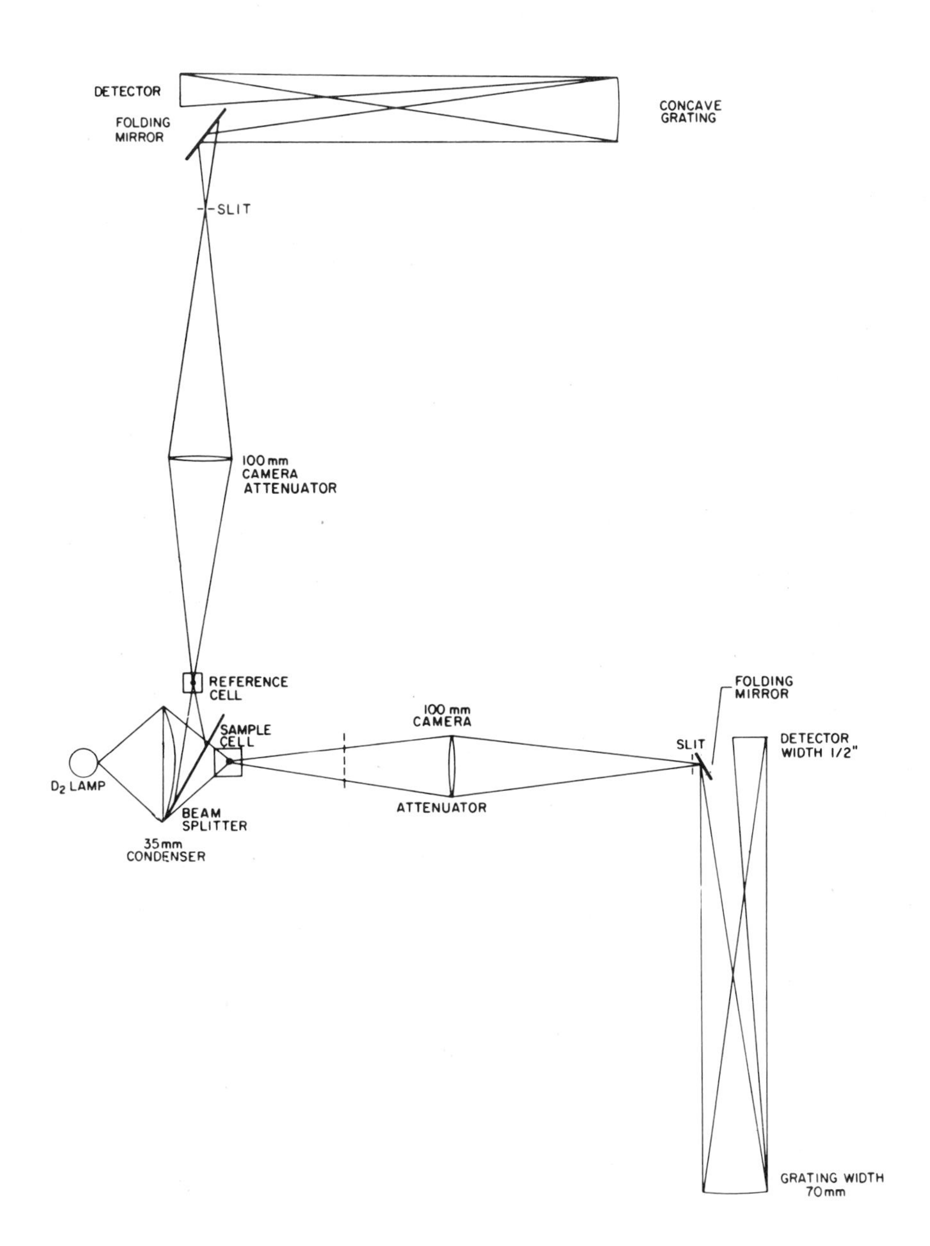

Journal of Chromatographic Science

Figure 7. Ray diagram for the optical bench (4)

single event-rapid event experiment, and have very limited moving storage capability. Essential to any widespread application of these spectrometers is an integrated set of applications software. Without this key item provided and supported by a commercial source, the area will not reach its proper development and application.

The specific target installation for the double beam spectrometer described is the research laboratory of a large government laboratory engaged in the detection and identification of metabolites in the urine of mice being fed potential carcinogens. Over 400 metabolites can be separated in such urine samples. The project involved characterization of each of these by UV/VIS spectroscopy. The ultimate goal was to attempt to correlate oncological events with certain "descriptors" obtained by observation of the UV/VIS record. At the outset, it was impossible to define the exact regions of the spectra that would be important or how they should be displayed best for the operator. It was essential that all raw data be stored first on disk, and second on back-up magnetic tape so that the user could replay any given experiment in a variety of interactive modes. Therefore, software was developed which would permit the spectrometer to be set up by personnel relatively unskilled in computer operation. After the data was collected it could be scanned by "cinematographic" like techniques, viewing each successive spectra in a forward rapid scanning mode; stopping display at a frame of interest; and reversing the display. Certain sections of the spectra could be integrated to provide the equivalent of running the experiment with a narrow band pass filter, allowing comparison of an Absorbtion Band Chromatogram (ABC) in contrast to the TAC, which is an integral of the Total Absorbtion Chromatogram. The ABC could be constructed from a single pixel, or the ensemble of all pixels, at which point the ABC is equivalent to the TAC.

Any of these displays could be presented on a CRT with interactive cursors for determination of wavelength or maxima, and any display could be directed to a hard copy digital plotter.

This constitutes a minimum set of software programs that should be provided by any vendor.

Typical computer/user dialogues are shown in figures 8 and 9. Several important entries will be discussed.

A request for "SPECTRAL RATE:" is made.* When a non-averaging method is used, any number may be given as input to the request for spectral rate. The command decoder will then request "ENDING TIME:". The response to this will determine the time at which data acquisition will be automatically terminated. Data

---

*The proper response is dependent upon the data acquisition method used. The means to select a specific method will be discussed. If an ensemble averaging method is used, then the spectral rate is the number of spectra to be averaged.

```
.R ZZOO
MODE  ?0
VPI & SU MULTIPLE WAVELENGTH DETECTION SYSTEM


THIS SYSTEM IS COMPOSED OF XXX SUBPROGRAMS WHICH
ACQUIRE DATA FROM A DUAL BEAM MULTIPLE WAVELENGTH
DETECTOR IN A CONFIGURATION FOR USE WITH A HIGH PRESSURE
LIQUID CHROMATOGRAPH.


THE MODE OF OPERATION IS SELECTED BY ENTERING
THE NUMBER CORRESPONDING TO THE OPERATION DESIRED
IN THE FOLLOWING LIST IN RESPONSE TO 'MODE?'


THE MODES OF OPERATION ARE:
0.  DESCRIPTION OF SYSTEM.
1.  DATA ACQUISITION.
2.  EXAMINATION AND PLOTTING OF INDIVIDUAL SPECTRA.
3.  VIEW FROM TIME A TO TIME B (WITH INTEGRATION)
4.  TRANSFER DATA FROM MAGTAPE TO DISK
5.  TRANSFER OF DATA FROM DISK TO MAGTAPE FOR STORAGE.
6.  DETAILED INSTRUCTIONS FOR SYSTEM OPERATION.
7.  GENERATION OF PATTERN RECOGNITION DESCRIPTORS.
8.  SYSTEM ALIGNMENT AND ADJUSTMENT.



*******************************************************
* ALL INPUT FROM THE KEYBOARD IS ENDED BY HITTING     *
* THE RETURN KEY.  OTHER ACTIONS CAUSE ERRORS         *
*******************************************************
MODE   ?
```

Figure 8. Overall system description given by the primary monitor

```
.R ZZOO
MODE  ?1


DATA ACQUISITION MODE

DESCRIPTION OF COMMANDS, Y OR N:  ?Y

COMMAND SET

FILENAME:------(MUST BE 6 CHARACTERS.)

COMMENTS:
              (MAY BE 3 LINES OF 72 CHARACTERS EACH.
              THEY MAY BE TERMINATED AT ANY POINT
              BY TYPING AN -@-.)

SPECTRAL RATE:
              SPECTRA/MINUTE =
              1/(SPECTRAL RATE * 50 MILLISEC.)

ENDING TIME:
              (TIME AT WHICH RUN IS TO BE ENDED,
              GIVEN IN MULTIPLES OF A THOUSAND SECONDS,
              I.E. 1=1000 SECONDS.........15=15,000 SECONDS.
              A RESPONSE OF ZERO -0- WILL BE TAKEN AS
              ENDING TIME = INFINITY.)

METHOD:
              A.  SINGLE SPECTRA
              B.  ENSEMBLE AVERAGE WITH HARDWARE BACKGROUND
                  SUBTRACTION
              C.  ENSEMBLE AVERAGE WITH HARDWARE AND
                  SOFTWARE BACKGROUND SUBTRACTION
              (IN METHODS B AND C THE VALUE OF SPECTRA/MINUTE
               IS USED AS THE NUMBER OF SPECTRA TO BE AVERAGED.)

EXECUTE, Y OR N:
              (Y WILL START DATA ACQUISITION
               N WILL CAUSE A RETURN TO SYSTEM MONITOR.)

DATA ACQUISITION MAY BE STOPPED AT ANY
TIME BY SETTING BIT 11 EQUAL TO ONE
```

Figure 9. Description of input to data acquisition command decoder

acquisition may also be terminated from the terminal.

The command decoder will then request "THRESHOLD:". The threshold is used by the data acquisition programs to determine whether or not data is to be saved. If the threshold is set to 15, the data acquisition program will compare 15 with the value of the spectral integrator (TAC). If the spectral integrator is less than 15 then that spectrum will be rejected as containing baseline data. Thus storage of zero information is avoided.

The final piece of information required by the command decoder will be prompted by the request "METHOD:". The response to this query will determine what method of data acquisition will be used. The allowable responses are:

A - single spectrum acquisition
B - ensemble average
C - ensemble average with the background subtraction.

The final obvious action will be to print "EXECUTE -- Y or N:". If an "N" is entered the command decoder will terminate itself and the primary monitor will be started. A response of "Y" will cause the acquisition of spectral data to begin.

Methods of Data Acquisition. Any of three methods of data acquisition may be selected. The first method is the single spectrum acquisition. The mass storage devices will be zeroed and a hardware stopwatch is started.

When it is time to acquire a spectrum the current elapsed time is recorded, the spectrum is stored in a temporary buffer, and the value of the spectral integrator is compared to the manually set threshold. If the value is less than the threshold then this spectrum is ignored. At this point the program begins to count and skip spectra according to the number given to the query, "SPECTRAL RATE". When the appropriate number of spectra have been skipped the process will repeat itself. If at some point in this loop the value of the spectral integral is greater than the threshold the spectra will be stored on one of the mass storage devices. Spectra will continue to be saved until the value of the integration falls below that of the threshold.

In the following discussion of data acquisition by methods B and C the logic order of events is the same as used in method A. Method B is an ensemble averager that uses the number entered for spectral rate as the number of spectra to be averaged. The summation of spectra is divided by that number to give an average. Signal to noise ratio improvement equal to the square root of the number averaged is achieved.

Method C of the data acquisition routines is also an ensemble averager; however, a software routine has been added to do background subtraction. At the beginning of the run the sample and reference cell must contain pure solvent only. The background subtraction in method C works by taking the first ensemble and subtracting it from each of the following ensembles before they are stored on a mass storage device. This compensates for beam splitter non-equalities and other aberrations in the physical arrangement.

Examination of Spectral Data. Control of the system will return to the primary monitor when data acquisition has been concluded. At this point if a 2 is given in response to the query "MODE?", then the secondary monitor will be started so that it can oversee the use of the x-y point-plot-display and a Calcomp plotter.

The first action of the secondary monitor will be to print the que "SCOPE, PLOTTER MONITOR, DESCRIPTION AND INSTRUCTION SET?--YES OR NO?", as shown in figure 10. When the response is "NO" it will go directly to the next query "SCOPE, PLOTTER, OR EXIT--S,P, OR E?"

Upon a response of "S", it is assumed that the spectral data is to be examined. An abbreviated list of the scope commands is printed and the display of the spectra data will begin. Figure 11 continues the scope commands that are printed.

The range of the spectral data displayed on the scope is 230 nanometers at the left edge of the screen to 537 nanometers at the right edge. The number in the upper most left hand corner is the time at which the spectra was taken. Directly below this number is a second number which represents the wavelength. This wavelength is tied to a movable cursor which may be positioned with the linefeed and backspace keys at any point in the spectrum. If the display of spectral data is moving either forward or backward in time the display of the wavelength will be turned off. Only when the scope is displaying a single spectrum continuously will the wavelength display be activated.

In the command list for the spectrum display program is the "P" command. This command is used to tag the spectrum which is currently being displayed for plotting on the Calcomp plotter.

In the normal sequence of events, control would be passed to the plotting programs. These programs will be discussed later.

If a "P" is typed in response to the query "SCOPE, PLOTTER, OR EXIT" then control will be given to an assembly language program that is designed to format the spectral data so chromatographs may be plotted.

The first action of the program will be to ask "SINGLE, INTEGRAL, OR EXIT -- S,I, OR CTRL/D?". When an "S" is typed the program will go into the single wavelength mode and a chromatograph of signal amplitude versus time may be generated. The program will give queries for wavelength, starting time, and ending time.

If an "I" is entered, an integral will be performed. The program will ask for a starting and ending wavelength as well as the starting and the ending time. After the chromatograms have been formed, whether by the single or integral wavelength method, a request will be made as to the type of filtering that is to

```
.R ZZOO
MODE  ?2

SCOPE, PLOTTER MONITOR
DESCRIPTION AND INSTRUCTION SET?--YES OR NO?YES

THIS PROGRAM SERVES AS A COORDINATOR OF
THE USE OF THE OSCILLOSCOPE AND CALCOMP PLOTTER.  IT
WILL RUN IN TWO MODES, SCOPE AND PLOTTER


SCOPE MODE     COMMAND SET
               CINE FORWARD IN DATA SET
?              HOLD CURRENTLY DISPLAYED SPECTRA
               CINE BACKWARDS IN DATA SET
C              RETURN TO SCOPE, PLOTTER MONITOR
P              TAG CURRENT SPECTRA FOR PLOTTING
E              EXIT, PLOT ANY TAGGED SPECTRA AND RETURN TO SYS.
               MON.

***********************************************

*THE ABOVE COMMANDS DO NOT ECHO TO THE PRINTER*

***********************************************

THE NUMBER IN THE UPPER LEFT OF THE SCREEN IS
THE TIME AT WHICH THE SPECTRA WAS TAKEN TO THE NEAREST
ONE-HUNDREDTH OF A SECOND.
```

```
PLOTTER MODE

THE PLOTTER FUNCTIONS BY ASKING A SERIES OF QUESTIONS

COMMAND SET

SINGLE WAVELENGTH OR AN INTEGRAL OR WAVELENGTHS?--YES OR NO

SINGLE MODE
WAVELENGTHS?
STARTING TIME?
ENDING TIME?
EXECUTE--YES OR NO

INTEGRAL MODE
STARTING WAVELENGTH?
ENDING WAVELENGTH?
STARTING TIME?
ENDING TIME?
EXECUTE--YES OR NO

AN ANSWER OF 'O' TO THE 'ENDING TIME' QUESTION
WILL SET THE ENDING TIME TO THAT OF THE LAST SPECTRA TAKEN.

**********************************************

*USE C TO INTERRUPT PLOTTING AT YOUR OWN RISK*

**********************************************
```

Figure 10. Command set description given by secondary monitor

```
SCOPE MODE


                    MOVE FORWARD
?                   HOLD CURRENT SPECTRA
                    MOVE BACKWARDS
CTRL/C              RETURN TO SCOPE, PLOTTER MONITOR
P                   TAG CURRENT SPECTRA FOR PLOTTING
E                   PLOT ANY TAGGED SPECTRA & RETURN TO SYS. MON.

SCOPE, PLOTTER MONITOR
DESCRIPTION AND INSTRUCTION SET?--YES OR NO?
```

Figure 11. Non-echoing commands for spectral display program

be used in removing any high frequency or periodic noise. The types of filters are listed in Table I with the response that causes its activation.

TABLE I

A List of the Digital Filters Which May Be Used

Response	Filter type
0	Do not filter
1	7 point Savizky-Golay filter[2]
2	13 point Savitzky-Golay filter
3	21 point Savitzky-Golay filter
4	Tukey Exploratory Filter[3]

It should be noted that these programs do not make use of standard logic in the way that they handle the data. The normal sequence would be to bring as much data into memory as possible and move the filter through the data. However, because of the size of the data base this is not feasible. It is necessary to move the data through the filter.

After the chromatographic data has been filtered a query of "PREVIEW, PLOT, OR EXIT--V,P, OR E?" will be made. A response of "E" will return control to the secondary monitor, while typing a "V" will cause the execution of a program that displays the chromatograph on the x-y point plot display. The behavior of the display may be controlled by the commands listed in figure 12. The only purpose of this method is to allow the previewing of the chromatograph before it is plotted on the Calcomp Plotter.

Typing either the command "CTRL/P" or the command "P" in response to the query "PREVIEW, PLOT OR EXIT?" will cause the execution of a peak picker. It works on the basis of determining the mean noise level of the data according to the equation

$$X = \sum_{i=2}^{N} | P_i - P_{i-1} | /N$$

After the noise level has been calculated then the difference between two adjacent data points will be compared to the noise level. If the difference is greater than the noise then the program will assume that a peak has begun. At this point an integral is begun to determine the area under the peak. The end point of the peak is determined in the reverse manner. At the end of each peak the starting, center, and ending times of the peak are printed as well as the area under the peak.

Calcomp Plotter, Use and Control. As can be seen from the command list for plotting spectral data in figures 13 and 14 any of several programs may be chosen to give the desired plot. For example, if in plotting spectral data the program "USPEC.LD" is chosen then all of the spectra previously tagged for plotting

```
 PLOTTER PREVIEW PROGRAM

 COMMAND SET (NON-ECHOING)

   <      MOVE FORWARD IN TIME
   >      MOVE BACKWARD IN TIME
 ?        HOLD CURRENT DISPLAY
 ^ C      RETURN TO SCOPE,PLOTTER MONITOR
 ^ P      TO PLOTTER ROUTINE
 ^ F      ACTIVATE FILTER ROUTINE FOR ONE PASS
 ^ D      TURN DISPLAY ON
 ^ N      TURN DISPLAY OFF

 SCOPE, PLOTTER MONITOR
 DESCRIPTION AND INSTRUCTION SET?--YES OR NO?
```

Figure 12. Non-echoing commands for plotter preview program

```
SPECTRUM PLOTTER

INSTRUCTIONS, Y OR N   ?Y

THERE ARE THREE PROGRAMS WHICH MAY BE USED
TO PLOT A SPECTRUM.  THEY ARE:

SPEC.LD        PLOTS ALL SPECTRA, NO GRID
SPECG.LD       PLOTS ALL SPECTRA WITH A GRID
UNSPEC.LD      PLOTS ALL SPECTRA UNSCALED

IN RESPONSE TO THE PERIOD TYPE THE FOLLOWING INSTRUCTIONS

.R FRTS
*XXXX.ZZ/G     WHERE XXXX.ZZ IS THE SPECTRUM PLOTTER TO BE USED
*BLOCK1.DA/1
*PLOTZ1.DA/2
```

Figure 13. Instruction for using spectrum plotter

```
CHROMATOGRAPH PLOTTER

INSTRUCTIONS,  (Y OR N)  ?Y

IN RESPONSE TO THE PERIOD, TYPE IN
FOLLOWING INSTRUCTIONS

.R FRTS
*CHRMG.LD/G
*BLOCK.DA/1
*OUTPUT/2
```

Figure 14. Instruction for using chromatograph plotter

will be plotted in an unscaled format. If on the other hand, either of the programs "SPEC.LD" or "SPECG.LD" is chosen the spectral data will be individually scaled. "SPECG.LD" will overlay the plot with a set of grid lines spaced at one inch intervals while "SPEC.LD" will not.

The two programs for plotting chromatographs, "CHRM.LD" and "CHRMG.LD" are identical in their methods of treating the data. Both programs are designed to scale the data. Both programs will generate plots of varying length up to a maximum of forty inches.

Transfer of Data From Disk to Magnetic Tape. Transfer of the spectral data from disk to magnetic tape is accomplished by responding to the primary monitor's que with a 5. Each time this mode of operation is entered two files will be written to magtape. The first file will contain one record of five hundred twelve bytes, where a byte is six bits. The information written will be the sample name and comments which were given to the data acquisition command decoder. The files are terminated with an end of file mark.

Control will be passed to a new program whose function is to transfer spectral data from the disk to the magtape. One spectrum is contained in each record of 512 bytes.

Results

Detector Performance and Conclusions. The performance of the detector was checked by connecting it to a Spectra-Physics Model 3500 liquid chromatograph. The LC is set to do bonded phase chromatography with a spherisorb ODS column and a 3:1 methanol, water solvent system.

Signal to Noise Ratio. The nature of the data collected and the different ways in which it may be handled yield 3 types of signal to noise ratios. They are the signal to noise ratio for an individual spectrum; the signal to noise ratio of a chromatogram at a given wavelength, and the signal to noise ratio of a chromatogram over a spectral bandwidth.

The signal to noise ratio for an individual spectrum is given in Table II. The methods of acquisition were either A (single spectrum acquisition) or B (ensemble averaged spectrum).

TABLE II

Signal to Noise Ratios for an Individual Spectrum

Method	SNR	No. of Spectra Averaged
A	174	0
B	206	2
B	253	4
B	271	8

The signal to noise figures for ensemble averaging indicate that some noise source other than thermal noise is active. The source of this noise was ultimately found to be the computer bus and the read-out electronics. These signal to noise ratios can be improved greatly by use of the "S" Series arrays which have much larger areas and dynamic ranges of 90,000/1, as well as by using read-out electronics which minimize switching noise. Commerical equipment is available to perform this function.

The signal to noise ratios for chromatograms are given in Table III. In this table "Method" refers to the means by which the spectral data were taken,"SNR_c"is the signal to noise ratio of a chromatogram generated by specifying a single wavelength, and "SNR_{c20}" is the signal to noise ratio of a chromatogram generated by integrating 20 array elements or 24 nanometers.

TABLE III

Signal to Noise Ratios for Chromatograms

Method	SNR_c	SNR_{c20}	No. Averaged
A	348	906	0
B	438	1006	2
B	576	1217	4
B	869	1765	8

Effects of Post Run Digital Filtering. In an effort to improve the signal to noise ratio a 21 point Savitzky-Golay[2] digital filter was installed in the software system. However, this filter proved to have an adverse effect upon peak space and amplitudes. The effect is illustrated in figures 15 and 16 which are plots of the effect of the digital filter width upon peak area and peak height respectively. The filter has its greatest effect upon peak area. This response of a signal to filtering is typical of all methods of filtering when the number of data points in the full width at half height of the peak divided by the filter width is less than 1.3.

The behavior of the Tukey[3] exploratory filter is excellent in that the change in signal to noise ratio approximates that of a 9 point Savitzky-Golay without the corresponding effects upon peak height and area. In operation, the Tukey filter is a 3 point median replacement series in which the filter window moves through the data replacing the center point of the three with the value which is numerically located between the other two. The results of such a filter are shown in figures 17, 18, and 19. Figure 17 is a set of test data; figure 18 is the result of filtering the test set with a 21 point Savitzky-Golay filter; and figure 19 is the same data filtered by the Tukey algorithm. While the signal to noise ratio of the Savitzky-Golay filter is better than that of Tukey, it has also caused a 30 percent drop in the signal amplitude while the Tukey filter gives an 8 percent

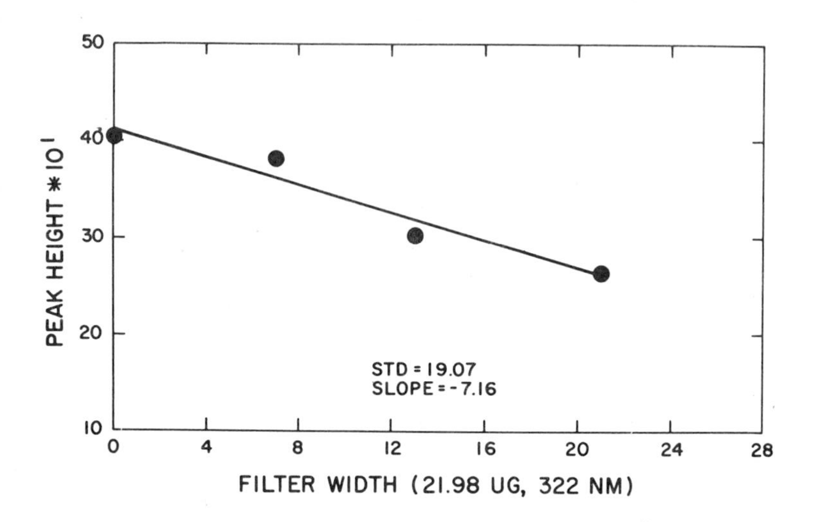

Figure 15. The effect of the Savitzky–Golay filters upon peak areas

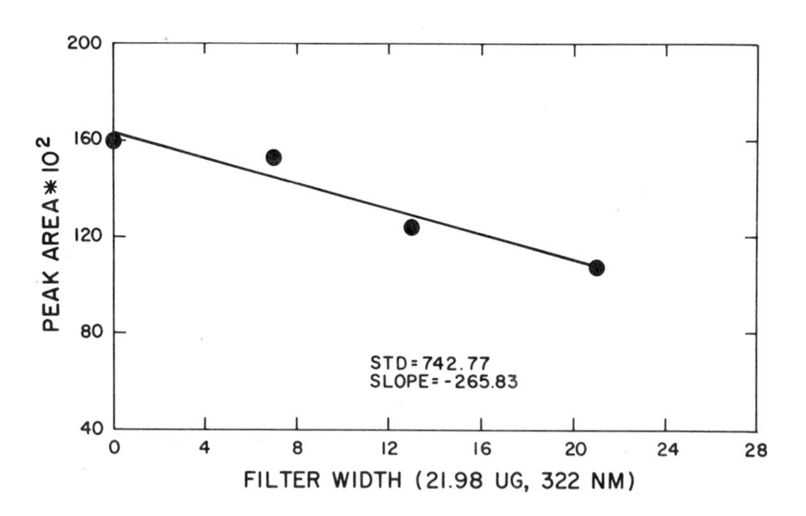

Figure 16. The effect of Savitzky–Golay filters upon peak heights

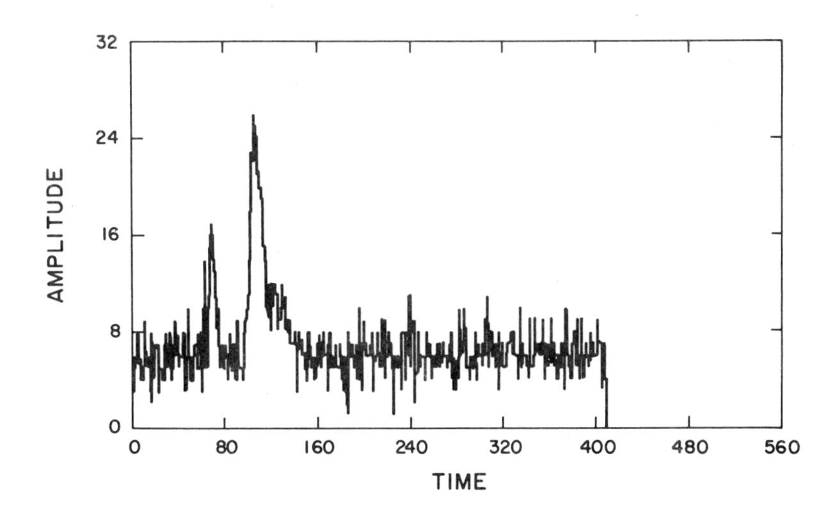

Figure 17. Unfiltered test data

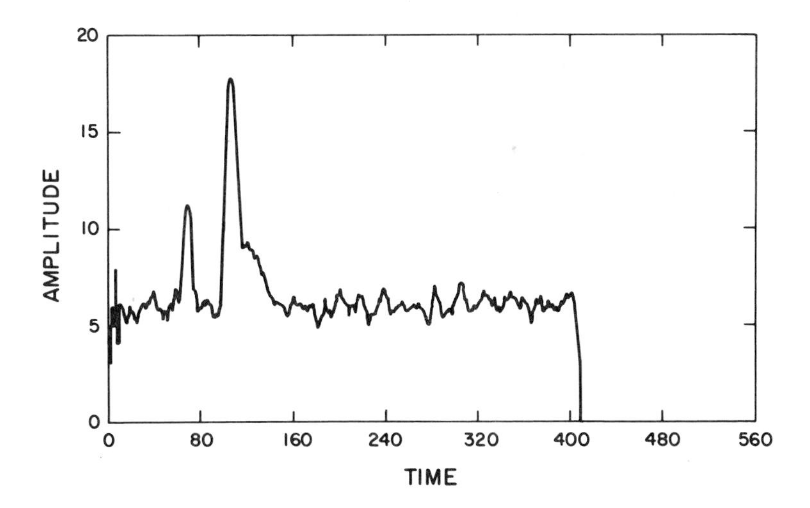

Figure 18. Test data after filtering with a 21-point Savitzky–Golay filter

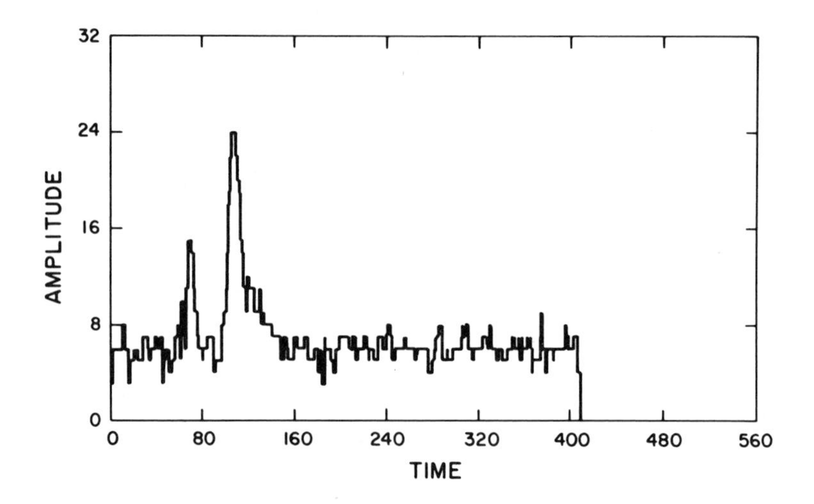

Figure 19. Test data after filtering with a Tukey exploratory filter

decrease. The comparison between the Tukey filter and other Savitzky-Golay filters at 254 nm for acenaphthalene is given in Table IV.

Detector Linearity and Detection Limits. The detector's response over a range of concentrations is given by figures 20, 21. The calibration curves for the detector when used with a liquid chromatograph should be linear. The wavelengths, detection limits, and slopes for typical compounds are numerized in Table V. The detection limit and slope are given for 254 nm to use as a reference to the wavelength which is normally used for detecting compounds eluting from a liquid chromatograph.

TABLE IV

Slopes of the Calibration Curves for Acenaphthalene After Filtering

Filter Type	Slope*
for Peak Heights at 254 nm	
no filter	4.54
7-pt. S-G	4.45
13-pt. S-G	3.54
21-pt. S-G	3.10
Tukey	4.60
for Peak Areas at 254 nm	
no filter	196.83
7-pt. S-G	191.39
13-pt. S-G	148.36
21-pt. S-G	133.24
Tukey	206.65

* Determined by linear, least squares.

TABLE V

Wavelengths Detection Limits, and Slopes for Acenaphthalene, Nitrobenzene, Acetone, and 2,6-Dichloro-4-nitroaniline

Compound	Wavelength(nm)	Detection Limit(ug)	Slope
Acenaphthalene	254	2.75	4.50
	322	1.37	18.20
Nitrobenzene	254	0.48	33.30
	265	0.25	37.40
Acetone	254	99.00	0.08
	269	49.50	0.12
2,6-Dichloro-4-	254	0.68	7.10
nitroaniline	361	0.34	24.20

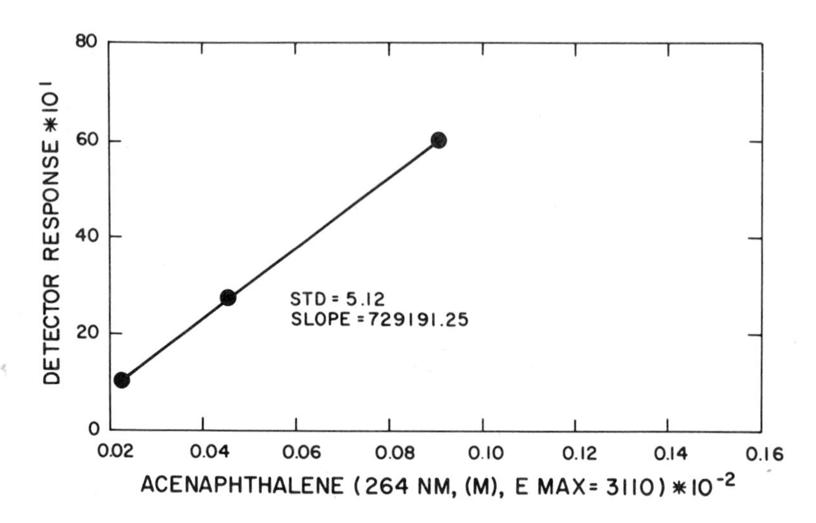

Figure 20. Detector response at 264 nm to concentration for acenaphthalene

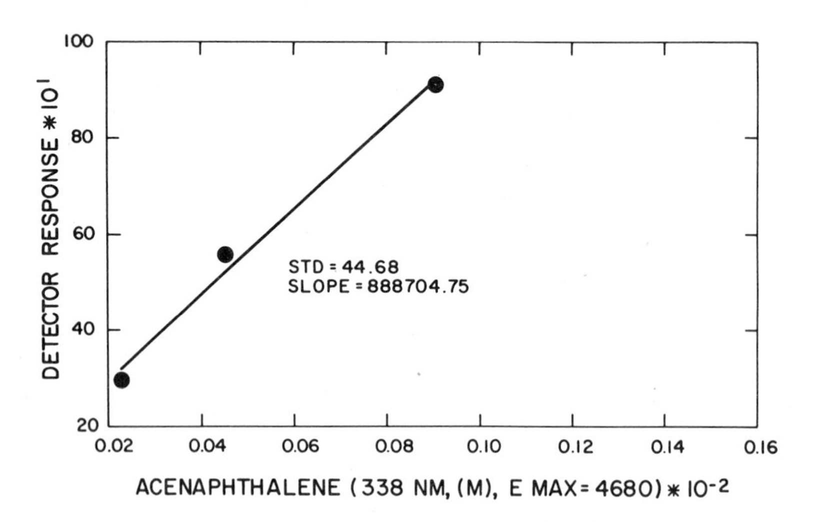

Figure 21. Detector response at 338 nm to concentration for acenaphthalene

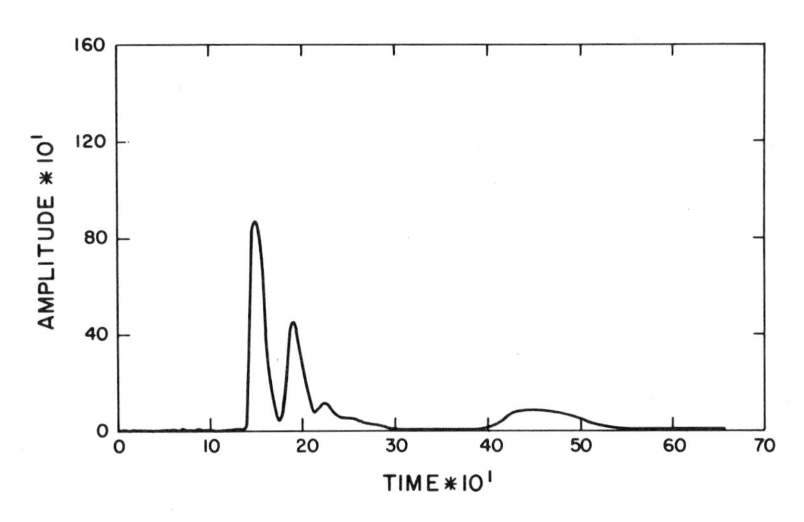

Figure 22. Chromatograph of unknown mixture monotored at 254 nm

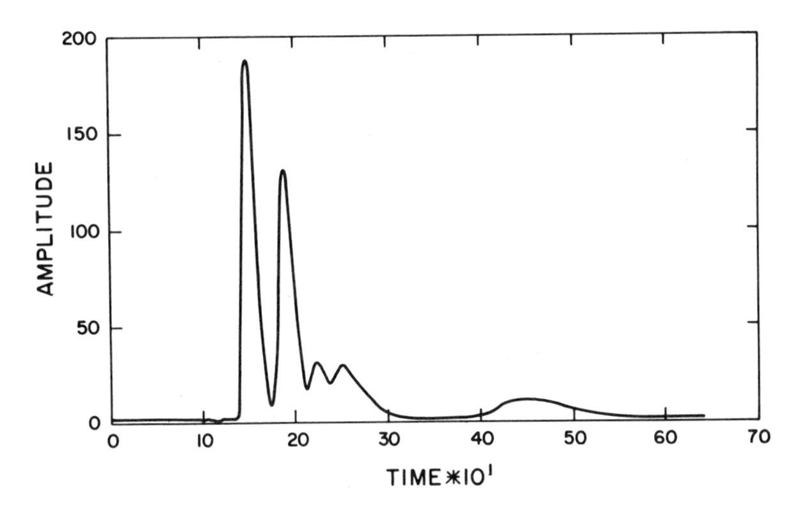

Figure 23. Chromatograph of total detector response to an unknown mixture

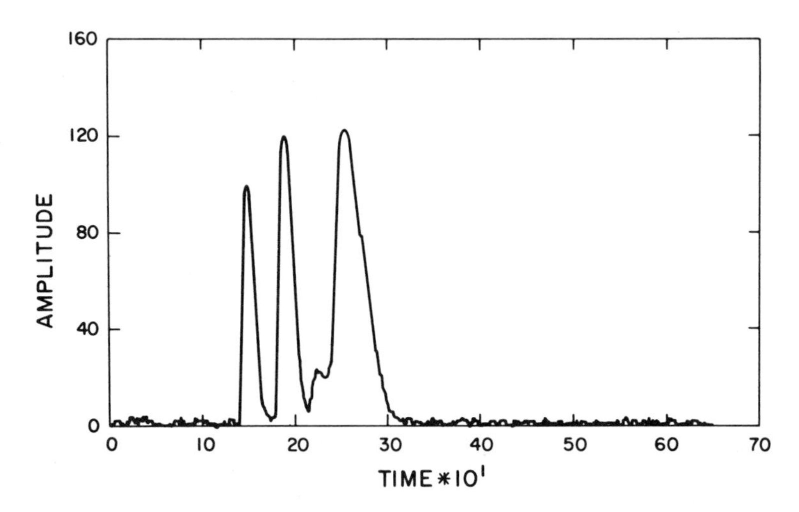

Figure 24. Chromatograph of an unknown mixture monitored at 316 nm

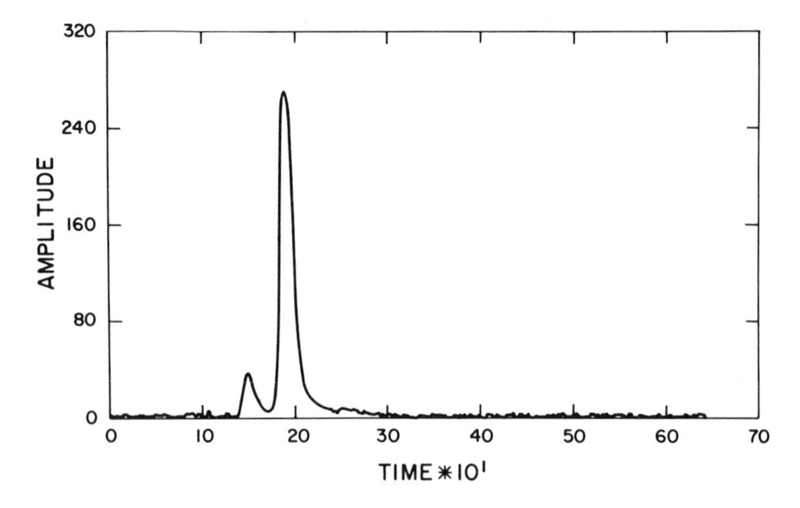

Figure 25. Chromatograph of an unknown mixture monitored at 343 nm

It is immediately obvious from the data presented that linear array detectors cannot compete with any single wavelength detector. However, consider the chromatograph shown in figure 22. This is a chromatogram of a complex mixture containing 5 compounds. It would appear from the chromatogram that this mixture contains only 4 components. If the integral of the free spectral range (ABC) is plotted against time then the chromatogram shown in figure 23 will result. From this it can be sėen that the tailing of the third peak in the 254 nm chromatogram was actually due to a compound which has a very low absorbance at 254 nm. If this peak represents the one of interest then its response may be further enhanced by selecting 316 nm as the wavelength at which to plot the chromatograph, (figure 24).

Finally, figures 24 and 25 demonstrate a common occurrence in any variable wavelength detector system---that is the disappearance of peaks. Depending upon luck and the wavelength chosen, any peak in the chromatograph may appear or disappear. It becomes mandatory that the wavelength at which the chromatograph was taken be stated, and this is the simple justification for the exploratory instrument as just described.

Acknowledgements. The spectrometer was designed for Dr. Warren D. Reynolds at the National Center for Toxicological Research under a HEW grant #222-75-2047. The Spectra Physics Model 3500 Liquid Chromatograph was an educational gift from Spectra Physics. Figures 1-7 are used with permission by J. Chrom. Sci., Vol.14, 194 (1976).

Literature Cited

1. Y. Talmi, Anal. Chem., 47, 658A (1975).
2. A. Savitzky, M.J.E. Golay, Anal. Chem., 36, 1627 (1964).
3. J. W. Tukey, "Exploratory Data Analysis", Chapter 7, Addison-Wesley, (1977).
4. R. Dessy, W. Nunn, C. Titus, W. Reynolds, J. Chrom. Sci., 14, 194 (1976).

RECEIVED January 5, 1979.

A Multi-Microcomputer Controlled, Vidicon, Stopped-Flow Spectrophotometer

ERIK M. CARLSON[1] and CHRISTIE G. ENKE

Chemistry Dept., Michigan State University, East Lansing, Michigan, 48824

Most spectrophotometric detectors used for stopped-flow kinetics monitor the course of a reaction at only a single wavelength. The ability to monitor the course of a reaction simultaneously over a range of wavelengths offers tremendous advantages in certain applications. One of the most important applications of rapid wavelength scanning techniques in stopped-flow kinetics is in the determination of the number and types of species present, particularly the detection of reaction intermediates and the subsequent investigation of the kinetics of the formation and decay of these intermediates (1,2). Rapid scanning techniques also allow two or more reactions to be monitored at different wavelengths simultaneously (3,4). Also, many standard kinetics investigations could benefit by the initial use of a rapid scanning system for establishing the optimum analysis conditions for later study with a simple and/or more sensitive single wavelength system (5).

A great many techniques have been developed which allow a range of wavelengths to be rapidly scanned, and a number of excellent reviews of these techniques can be found in the literature (6-10). However, only a few rapid scanning techniques have been applied to stopped-flow kinetics. These techniques can be divided into two general categories according to the method by which the wavelength is scanned. The first category consists of mechanical scanning systems in which the mechanical movement of a mirror (11-15) or grating (16) in the optical system causes the wavelength region of interest to be swept past a stationary detector. The need for mechanical scanning can be eliminated by focusing the dispersed spectrum on an array detector which allows the wavelength sorting to be performed electronically (1,4,17,18).

[1]Current Address: B.F. Goodrich Chemical Co., Technical Center, P.O. Box 122, Avon Lake, Ohio, 44012.

0-8412-0504-3/79/47-102-169$05.00/0

We had a number of goals in mind when we set out to design a new vidicon rapid scanning stopped-flow spectrophotometer. We wanted to design an instrument which was highly automated so that it would be simple to use. Versatility in the vidicon spectrophotometer was also desired so that it could be used in a variety of applications in addition to stopped-flow kinetics. As with any detector, the vidicon detector has a number of limitations, many of which have not yet been thoroughly explored. To facilitate the characterization of the detector and the determination and minimization of its limitations, we wanted to place a large number of the vidicon scanning parameters under computer control.

Instrument

A block diagram of the instrument is shown in Figure 1. The design of the instrument will be discussed primarily on the block diagram level. Details on the construction of the vidicon spectrophotometer (19), the multi-microcomputer system (20) and the stopped-flow mixing system (20) are presented elsewhere.

Multi-Microcomputer System. The instrument is controlled by four microcomputers, all of which are based upon Intel's 8080A microprocessor. Three of the microcomputers are slave microcomputers that are used for controlling the three major sections or functions of the instrument. The sequencing and coordination of the activities of the slave microcomputers are controlled by a fourth microcomputer. Each slave microcomputer is completely independent of the others during the execution of its assigned task. Therefore, even extensive alterations in the operation of one of the microcomputers have little or no effect on the others. Microcomputer number 1 of Figure 1 controls the instruments communication with the outside world. This includes interactions with the operator and a floppy disk mass storage device and communication with our PDP 11/40 minicomputer. Microcomputer number 3 controls the entire stopped-flow mixing sequence and determines when the data acquisition should begin. For diagnostic purposes, it can also monitor the velocity of the stopping syringe plunger during the course of a stopped-flow run.

Vidicon Spectrophotometer. When dispersed radiation is focused on the vidicon detector, an equivalent charge pattern is produced on the vidicon's silicon target. The readout of this charge pattern is performed by the sequential scanning of an electron beam along the wavelength axis of the target. A variety of parameters affecting the electron beam scanning pattern and the data acquisition system are under the control of microcomputer number 2. The wavelength window i.e., the

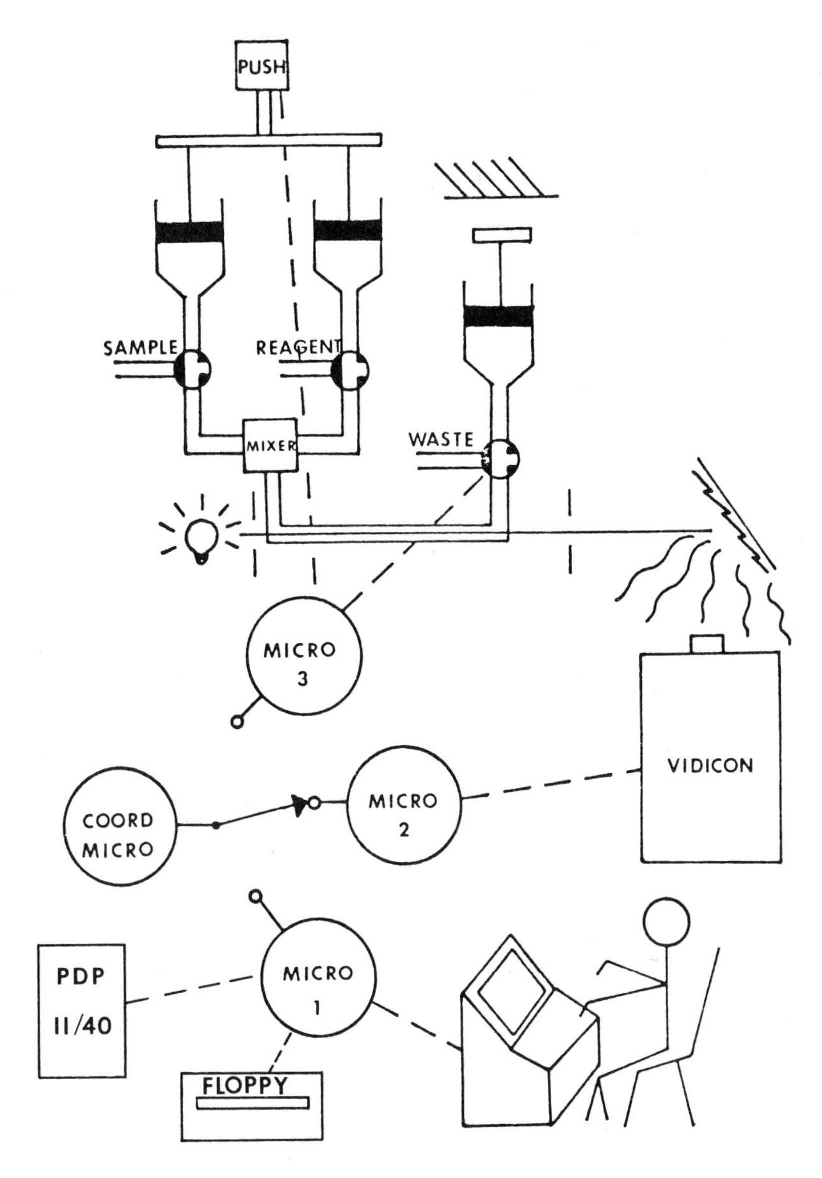

Figure 1. Block diagram of the vidicon rapid scanning stopped-flow spectrophotometer

wavelength range which can be simultaneously detected, of the vidicon target is approximately 290 nm. The spectrum focused on the vidicon is scanned vertically to obtain a single wavelength channel and horizontally through successive wavelength channels to produce a complete frame. The vertical scans are equally spaced across the frame and can vary in number from 16 to 4096. The rate at which each wavelength channel is scanned can be varied from 3.91 kHz to 1 MHz. However, the data acquisition system limits the maximum practical vertical scan rate to 100 kHz. The horizontal scan rate (or frame rate) is equal to the vertical scan rate divided by the number of vertical scans per frame. The electron beam current can be varied and the beam can also be disabled to vary the detector's charge integration time. The maximum data acquisition rate of 100 kHz is too high to be handled by a single microcomputer. For this reason a hardware adder circuit was designed which, under computer control, allows successive spectra or even entire stopped-flow runs to be acquired and averaged together.

Results and Discussion

Before any instrument can be used with confidence its operating characteristics must be well understood. The exceptional versatility of the vidicon rapid scanning stopped-flow system allowed a large variety of characterization experiments to be easily performed. A few of the more important experiments designed to help characterize the vidicon detector will be presented before the actual application of the instrument is discussed.

Scanning Frequency. The vertical scan frequency has a dramatic effect upon the intensities observed from the vidicon detector. To study this effect, the vidicon target was illuminated with a tungsten continuum and read out with 203 channels per frame at varying frequencies. Figure 2 shows the relationship between the relative intensity observed at the center of the target and the vertical scan frequency. The rapid decrease in observed intensity at higher frequencies is due primarily to two factors. Much of this decrease is due to the decrease in exposure time at higher frequencies. When the observed intensities are normalized to a constant exposure time, a maximum response is observed at about 33 kHz as seen in Figure 3. The decrease in intensity at frequencies above and below 33 kHz is mainly due to a decrease in the vertical drive amplitude. This decrease results in incomplete scanning of the upper and lower edges of the target and therefore, a decrease in intensity.

Resolution. The resolution of the vidicon spectrophotometer is limited by the vidicon detector. The resolution of the

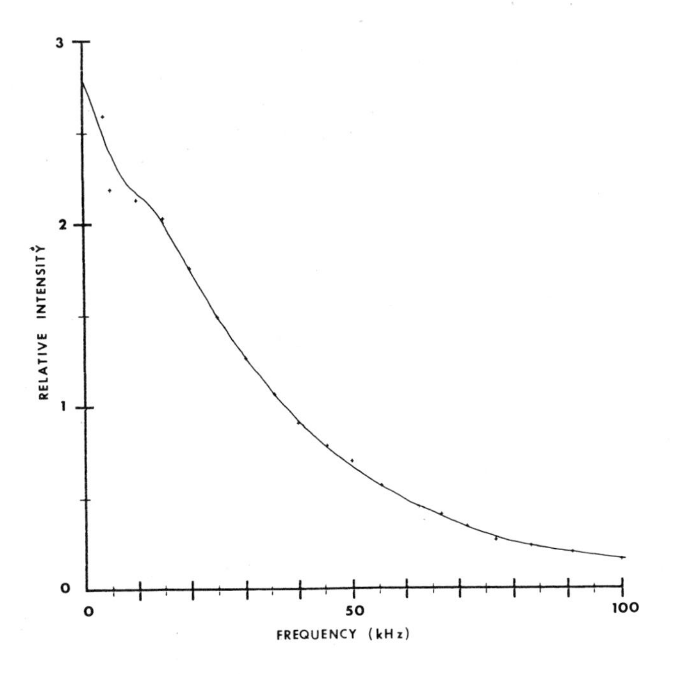

Figure 2. Relative intensity vs. frequency

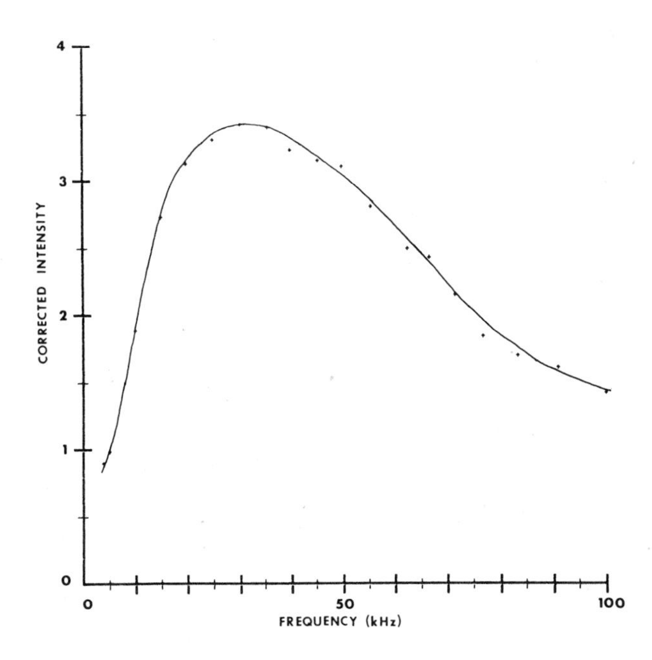

Figure 3. Relative intensity corrected for varying exposure time vs. frequency

vidicon detector is determined by the number of wavelength channels which are used per scan frame. The maximum resolution which can be obtained is limited by the electron beam width of the vidicon detector. To study the resolution of the vidicon detector, the target was illuminated with a tungsten continuum. Figure 4 shows the relationship between the observed intensity at a vertical scan frequency of 25 kHz, and the number of channels per frame. As the number of channels per frame increases the exposure time increases proportionally. Normally an increase in exposure time results in an increase in observed intensity. However, the intensity is relatively constant from about 65 channels/frame to over 400 channels/frame. The number of channels per frame is also inversely proportional to the effective target area scanned per channel. Therefore, the signal intensity increase due to the increased exposure time is exactly cancelled by the decrease in the effective target area per channel. This results in the signal intensity being relatively constant over a wide range of frequencies.

The decrease in intensity at very high and very low resolution is more easily understood if the data of Figure 4 are expressed in terms of the intensity as a function of the channel separation. The channel separation is determined by dividing the width of the scanned portion of the vidicon target (12.8 mm wide) by the number of channels. This relationship is shown in Figure 5. The rapid decrease in intensity at small channel separations is due to the increasing overlap of adjacent channels. A much less dramatic decrease in intensity is also observed when the channel separation becomes relatively large. This is due to the increasing probability of electron-hole recombination when relatively extensive charge migration is required. The intersection of the region of adjacent channel overlap and the region of constant intensity should give a good indication of the electron beam width. The minimum beam width, as determined by this technique, was found to be approximately 30 μm (approximately 427 channels). Although this is significantly less than the 51 μm (21) and 66 μm (22) beam widths which have been reported for similar instruments, it is very close to the 25 μm beam width recently cited (10) as being typical of vidicon detectors. It should be noted that at the maximum resolution of 427 channels, adjacent channels are not completely isolated from each other. This is due to inter-channel cross-talk or "bleed" which is unavoidable.

Lag. As the electron beam travels across the vidicon target not all of the charge stored there is read out. The percentage of the total charge which is left behind is defined as the lag. Lag seriously degrades the response time of the vidicon detector and, therefore, it is the feature which most severely limits the applicability of vidicon detectors to fast kinetics. Lag measure-

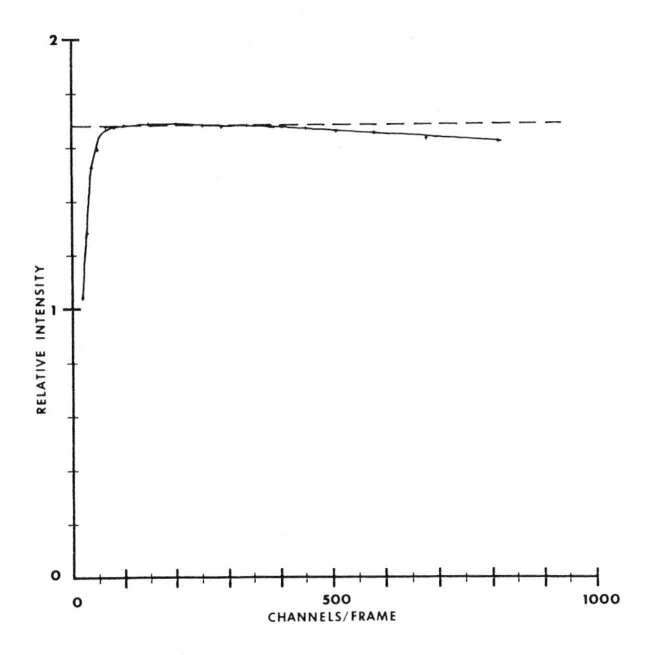

Figure 4. Relative intensity vs. resolution

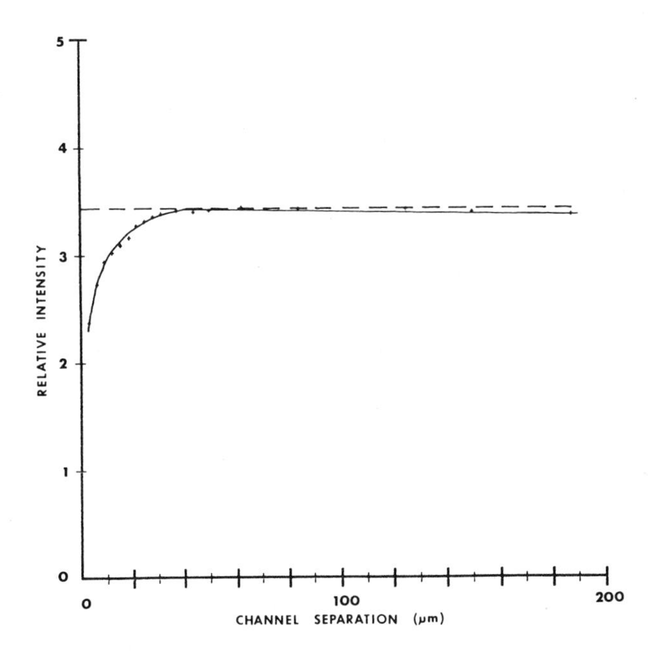

Figure 5. Relative intensity vs. channel separation

ments have been made on our system by the following procedure: First the target was illuminated by placing a red LED a few inches from the target. A number of frames were scanned with the LED turned on. The LED was then turned off and the signal decay was observed until a constant signal was obtained. The lag was then defined in the following manner:

$$\% \text{ Lag} = \frac{S_1 - S_D}{S_{ILL} - S_D} \times 100$$

where S_1 is the signal measured one frame after the LED has been turned off, S_{ILL} is the average signal obtained while the LED is on and S_D is the average dark signal. At a vertical scan frequency of 15.87 kHz and a resolution of 272 channels per frame, the resulting lag was 12.0% after one frame and 4.9% lag after three readout frames.

Lag is dependent upon the magnitude of the signal read out from the vidicon target. Normally, lag tends to improve at higher signal levels. However, as the signal level approaches saturation, the lag increases rapidly. The resolution which is selected also has a significant effect upon the observed lag. Decreasing the channel separation decreases the saturated area between the channels, therefore decreasing the relative lag. There is a dramatic increase in the lag as the vertical scan frequencies increases. This is partly due to the decreased intensity and the decreased beam residency time with increasing frequency. The beam current also has a significant effect on the lag with generally lower lag at higher beam currents. Although lag is a serious problem in the vidicon spectrophotometer, its effects can be minimized by the careful selection of the scanning conditions.

Electron Beam Current. The electron beam current is determined by the negative voltage which is applied to Grid 1 in the vidicon tube. The beam current is decreased by making the Grid 1 voltage more negative. In the current system the Grid 1 voltage can be varied from about +4 V to -110 V. To determine the optimum beam current, the vidicon target was illuminated by a tungsten continuum. The resolution was set at 511 channels per frame. The relationship between the intensity observed at the center of the target and the Grid 1 voltage at various vertical scan frequencies is shown in Figure 6. The rapid decrease in intensity at large grid voltages results from a reduction of the beam current to a point where the current can no longer read out all the available charge stored on the target. To minimize lag, the beam current should be substantially greater than the minimum required for steady-state readout.

Biuret Reaction. The particular capabilities of the stopped-flow vidicon system have been used to help explain some unusual behavior in the biuret reaction. The biuret reaction is the basis for the standard clinical chemistry technique for determining the total protein content of human blood serum (23). It involves a complexation reaction, in alkaline solution, between the cupric ion (Cu^{2+}) and the peptide bonds of the protein. In the standard biuret technique, the reaction is allowed to go to completion and then the absorbance of the copper-protein complex is measured at 55 nm. This technique tends to be rather slow since the reaction, although very rapid over the first few seconds, does not go to completion for at least 20 to 30 minutes.

Recently, Wai-Tak Law and S. R. Crouch at Michigan State University have been investigating a more rapid rate method for total serum protein using the biuret reaction in a standard stopped-flow spectrophotometer (24). The reaction was monitored by following the growth of the absorbance of the copper-protein complex at 550 nm. The rate curve for this reaction was found to be rather unusual. After a short induction period, the rate increases rapidly until it reaches a peak at just over 100 msec. After this peak, the rate falls off irregularly over a long time period. The reaction was initially investigated with the vidicon rapid scanning stopped-flow system by centering the wavelength window of the vidicon detector at the absorbance maximum of the copper-protein complex (550 nm). It was soon discovered that an isobestic point existed at about 690 nm. The wavelength window was then moved to cover the region from about 550 nm to 850 nm. Figure 7 shows selected spectra from the biuret reaction with human serum protein. Figures 8 and 9 show the absorbance change with time which occurs at wavelengths of 575 nm and 752 nm. Both curves show that the reaction does not proceed by a simple first order or pseudo first order mechanism.

After comparing spectra it was determined that the species which tends to decrease in absorbance during the reaction was the cupric tartrate complex found in the biuret reagent. Its absorbance is significant even down to wavelengths of slightly below 530 nm. The complications caused by the absorbance of the cupric complex at 550 nm appear to be a substantial cause of the unusual rate curve observed in the early part of the reaction.

Conclusions

Our experience with experiments performed thus far with the vidicon system have shown that it is a powerful tool. The structure of the system allows new types of operations to be easily designed and rapidly implemented, while modifications of

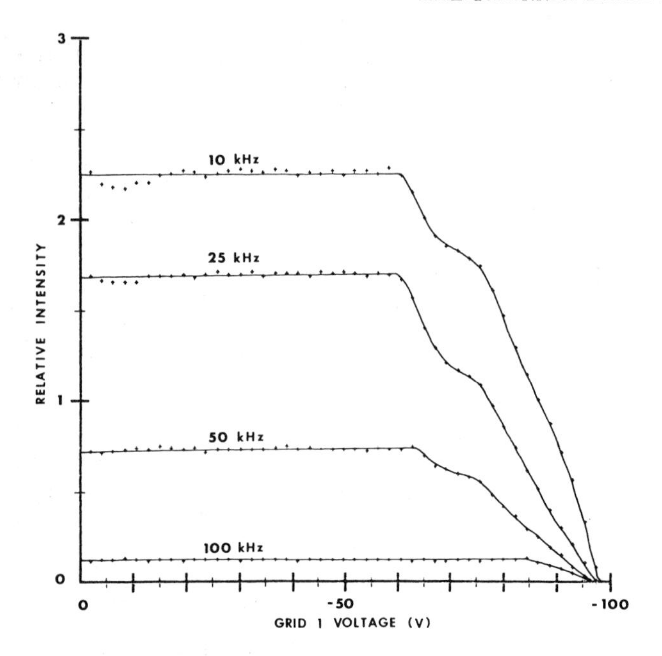

Figure 6. Relative intensity vs. Grid 1 voltage at various frequencies

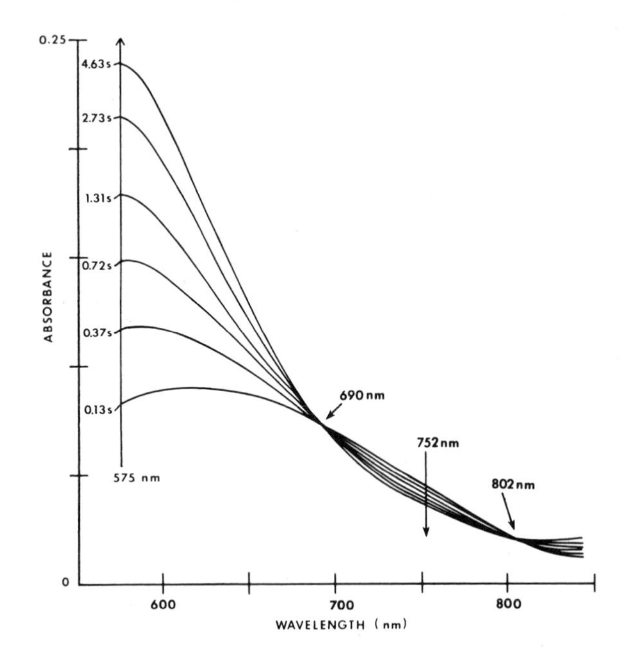

Figure 7. Absorption spectra at various times during the biuret reaction with human serum

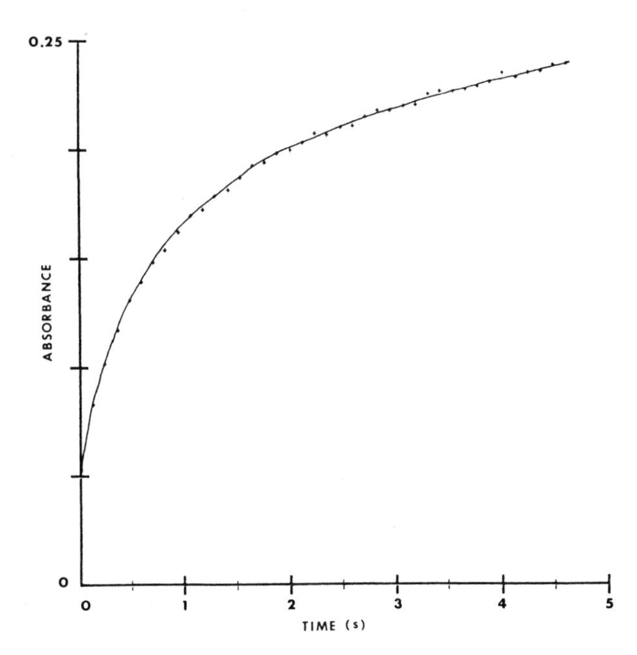

Figure 8. Absorbance (575 nm) vs. time for the biuret reaction with human serum

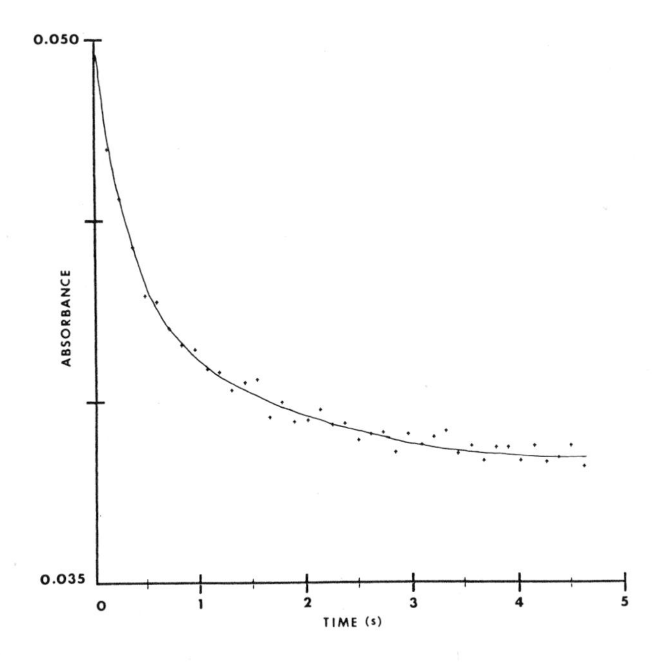

Figure 9. Absorbance (752 nm) vs. time for the biuret reaction with human serum

existing functions can be accomplished without the need for extensive alterations. Placing many of the vidicon's scanning parameters under computer control has not only enabled characterization experiments to be performed rapidly and easily, but also allows the system to optimize these parameters for any given situation. The high sensitivity (the total absorbance change in Figure 9 is about 0.01), rapid scanning capabilities and ease of use make the vidicon system extremely useful for investigating stopped-flow kinetics.

Literature Cited

1. M.J. Milano and H.L. Pardue, Anal. Chem., 47, 25 (1975).
2. R.B. Coolen, Ph.D. Thesis, Michigan State University, 1974.
3. M.J. Milano and H.L. Pardue, Clin. Chem., 21, 211 (1975).
4. G.M. Rider and D.W. Margerum, Anal. Chem., 49, 2098 (1977).
5. T.A. Nieman, F.J. Holler, and C.G. Enke, Anal. Chem., 48, 899 (1976).
6. G.C. Pimentel, Appl. Opt., 7, 2155 (1968).
7. R.E. Santini, M.J. Milano, and H.L. Pardue, Anal. Chem., 45, 915A (1973).
8. Y. Talmi, Anal. Chem., 47, 658A (1975).
9. Y. Talmi, Anal. Chem., 47, 697A (1975).
10. Y. Talmi, Amer. Lab., 10, 79 (1978).
11. J.L. Dye and L.H. Feldman, Rev. Sci. Instrum., 37, 154 (1966).
12. N. Papadakis, R.B. Coolen, and J.L. Dye, Anal. Chem., 47, 1644 (1975).
13. R.B. Coolen, N. Papadakis, J. Avery, C.G. Enke, and J.L. Dye, Anal. Chem., 47, 1649 (1975).
14. R.M. Wightman, R.L. Scott, C.N. Reilley, and R.W. Murray, Anal. Chem., 46, 1492 (1974).
15. M.R. Hollaway and H.A. White, Biochem. J., 149, 221 (1975).
16. G.J. Faini, R.J. Resa, and J. Lee, in Flavins and Flavoproteins, T.P. Singer, Ed., Elsevier Scien. Pub. Co., Amsterdam, Neth., 1976, pp. 82-86.
17. M.J. Milano, H.L. Pardue, T.E. Cook, R.E. Santini, D.W. Margerum, and J.M.T. Raycheba, Anal. Chem., 46, 374 (1974).
18. T.A. Nieman and C.G. Enke, Anal. Chem., 48, 619 (1976).
19. J.E. Hornshuh, Ph.D. Thesis, Michigan State University, 1978.
20. E.M. Carlson, Ph.D. Thesis, Michigan State University, 1978.
21. H.L. Felkel, Jr., and H.L. Pardue, Anal. Chem., 49, 1112 (1977).
22. T.A. Nieman and C.G. Enke, Anal. Chem., 48, 619 (1976).
23. N.W. Tietz, Fundamentals of Clinical Chemistry, W.B. Saunders Co., Philadelphia, PA, 1976, pp. 298-304.
24. Wai-Tak Law, Ph.D. Thesis, Michigan State University, 1978.

RECEIVED March 22, 1979.

ULTRASHORT LIGHT SPECTROSCOPY

8

Video Imaging Systems in Picosecond Laser Spectroscopy

F. PELLEGRINO and R. R. ALFANO

Picosecond Laser and Spectroscopy Laboratory, Physics Department,
The City College of The City University of New York, New York, NY 10031

Most physical processes occurring in nature outwardly appear peaceful and serene. On the submicroscopic level, however, molecules and atoms are actually involved in a riot of activity. Most of the fundamental energy transfer processes occur on a subnanosecond time scale. In order to obtain direct information on this ultrafast time scale new clocking techniques with picosecond time resolution are required. The mode-locked laser provides the ultrashort pulses which form the heart of the clocking mechanism. The recent development of these picosecond time resolution methods have greatly enhanced the study of ultrafast molecular and energy transfer processes. Application of Video imaging systems to this field has allowed for the convenient as well as more detailed acquisition and analysis of the spectroscopic and time-resolved data. New information has been gained on the photosynthetic process, the photovisual process, condensed state matter and chemical physics which has led to a more complete understanding of these important natural events. Some of the measurements obtained with the aid of Video Imaging systems will be presented in this paper.

0-8412-0504-3/79/47-102-183$05.00/0

Picosecond Time Resolution Techniques

The techniques that have been developed to probe the kinetics of energy transfer processes in materials on a picosecond time scale can be divided into three general categories. They are; the optical Kerr gate, the excite and probe technique, and the streak camera technique.

Optical Kerr Gate

The optical Kerr gate(1) basically consists of a Kerr active liquid situated between two crossed polarizers. Under the action of the intense electric field associated with laser pulses emitted from an Nd: glass laser the molecules of the Kerr active liquid experience an induced birefringence. This causes light passing through the Kerr cell at that time, and initially linearly polarized by a polarizer plate, to become elliptically polarized on passing through the liquid and thus enabling it to pass through an analyzer. A light signal can thus pass such a gate only while it is coincident with the intense laser pulse which opens the gate, and may be detected by a photomultiplier tube or video imaging system. The intense laser pulse can be used to carve out successive portions of the temporal profile of a light emitting event such as the fluorescence emitted from a dye. The intensity of the observed signal passing through the gate is determined by such factors as the intensity of the laser pulse and the relaxation time of the molecules of the Kerr active liquid. The resolution of the Kerr gate is typically on the order of 10 ps. Techniques which are currently being used to study fluorescence kinetics on a picosecond time scale preferentially employ either the optical Kerr gate or the streak camera. With its characteristic picosecond time resolution and high dynamic range the Kerr gate is an ideal tool for fluorescence measurements on a subnanosecond time scale. The optical Kerr gate has been used to measure dye fluorescence, fluorescence from photosynthetic systems and molecular orientation decays.

Excite and Probe Technique

Another technique which makes use of the ultrashort mode-locked laser pulse is the excite and probe technique.(2-3) In this method two pulses impinge on the sample. After primary excitation by an intense pump pulse, a weaker probe pulse enters the sample region that has been excited. The probe pulse may be used to monitor such processes as bleaching, induced Raman light scattering or absorption changes induced by the strong exciting pulse. The delay time between the arrival of the pump and probe pulse is easily obtained by moving a prism in the delay path. In order to measure a significant spectrum of absorption on a picosecond time scale in a single shot, a picosecond probe pulse with a broad spectral width is required. Such a picosecond continuum pulse can be obtained by passing an intense monochromatic picosecond pulse through certain materials which possess an intensity dependent nonlinear index of refraction.[4] This technique can be used to measure optical phonon lifetimes, singlet-triplet intersystem crossing rates, dephasing times, electron transport processes, and the generation of new species in chemical reactions.

We have used a Reticon photodiode array and an Optical Multi-channel Analyzer to measure optical density changes induced in photovisual materials using this technique. The Reticon is a device which incorporates a linear high density monolithic array of silicon photodiodes with integrated scanning circuits for serial readout. The array consists of 128 to 1024 photodiodes typically spaced by one or two mils with an aperture of one or seventeen mils. Each silicon photodiode has associated with it a storage capacitor on which to integrate the reverse photodiode current. The readout can be externally or internally controlled to enable easy system interfacing. The spectral response of the Reticon is that of a typical silicon photodiode extending from 0.2 μm to 1.1 μm, with sensitivity comparable to 3000 speed Polaroid film. The dark output signal buildup will contribute about 1% of the saturated output signal for a 40 ms scan of the array. The dynamic range is typically 100:1 at room temperature and can be made as high as 1000:1 if the array is cooled to 0°C and the dark output signal subtracted with the aid of a computer. The noise buildup can be further decreased by increasing the scan rate of the array. The major disadvantage of this system lies in the lack of adequate gain which is required for measuring low light level signals. However, this disadvantage may be overcome by the addition of an image intensifier stage with a typical gain of 10^3. We have used the Reticon to measure the fluorescence from dyes in one and two photon fluorescence measurements and also the S.R.S. spectra of liquids. The Reticon optical scanning system is enabled by a central control system which was designed to synchronize laser firing and computer data acquisition. The central control system consists of a programmable sequence generator which is used to enable both a program timing generator and laser firing mechanism.

Streak Camera

The technique which affords the convenience of both ease of operation along with fast data reduction capability for measuring optical transients incorporates a streak camera and video system. In a streak camera, photoelectrons emitted by light striking the photocathode at various times are deflected by an applied voltage ramp which causes the electrons to be transversely streaked across a phosphorescent screen at the same time that they are accelerated through the anode. Thus, photoelectrons released at a certain function of time from the photocathode will strike the phosphorescent screen at a corresponding function of position, causing a track to be produced whose spatial intensity profile is directly proportional to the incident temporal intensity profile of the light emitting event being investigated. The phosphorescent track may be analyzed by photographic techniques or electronically sampled by a video system or photodiode array. There are several important reasons which make the streak camera and video system a highly desirable system. While the Kerr gate yields only one data point of the intensity decay profile for each laser shot, the streak camera produces the entire decay curve for the same single shot. The streak camera thus provides the longest continuous display of events. Recording only a small portion of the temporal characteristics from a light emitting event can and indeed has resulted in misleading results. It is therefore essential to observe as large a portion of the time domain of a physical event as is experimentally possible. Also, since the delay time in the Kerr gate experiment is varied by changing the optical path length of the gate activating pulse by moving a prism, the time range which can be studied is generally limited to about one ns while the range of the streak camera extends from a few ps to several ns. Kerr gate operation requires extensive data normalization which is necessitated by the fact that light transmission through the gate depends nonlinearly on the intensity of the gate activating pulse. Typically 300 to 500 laser shots are required in a Kerr gate measurement to obtain a complete decay profile. The streak camera too must be initially calibrated and periodically monitored for such factors as streak rate linearity (which affects both time base and intensity calibrations), jitter in triggering of the sweep deflection subsequent to excitation, and time resolution.

Picosecond techniques make extensive use of new devices such as the low-light level video camera based optical multichannel analyzer (OMA) by Princeton Applied Research or Temporalanalyzer by Hamamatsu which along with the streak camera have greatly facilitated the measurement of fluorescence kinetics. In our experiments using these devices we have encountered some problems which the experimenter must overcome. The major problems consist of 1)the lag of the video TV tubes (RCA SIT camera tube 4804 and Vidicon specifications); 2)the proper triggering of the tube scan; 3)the limited intensity dynamic range of the streak camera; and 4)the nonlinearity of the streaking rates of the streak camera. The term lag is used to refer to the residual signal charge left on the target face of the Silicon Intensified Target (SIT) or Vidicon tube after three scans of the tube target face. Although many scans are needed to remove all the signal charge from the tube face, some investigators have used only one scan. This effect would normally not cause a problem were it not for the fact that the lag is a non-linear function of the incident intensity. For a SIT tube the lag (5) varies by 400% over a tenfold range of incident illumination, thus causing possible inaccurate reading of the signal data. Since the scan of the tube should be initiated after the signal arrives at the target face, correct electronic triggering of the tube and laser is also required in order to prevent an over-representation of certain portions of the display region. The tube reading should commence after the signal has arrived at the target face and must be initialized to the beginning of the display. The streak camera can be used to measure changes in intensity ranging from a factor of 10 to 300 (depending on the particular camera used) in a 10 ps time interval. This dynamic range is rather limited when compared to that of the optical Kerr gate which is typically $\gtrsim 10^3$. The streaking rates of the camera are easily calibrated by using laser pulses which are optically delayed by a known separation. The streak rate calibration data can then be used to correct the streak data both in time and in intensity. This can be accomplished by measuring the average streak rate at a particular position of the output slit of the streak camera, which can in turn be easily referenced to a channel number on a Vidicon photodiode array. Obtaining a calibration curve for streak rate as a function of channel number allows one to calibrate the various streak rates and intensity. It is easily seen that for a constant input light signal a higher intensity will be registered over those channels where the streaking rate is slower and a correspondingly lower intensity will be registered over those channels where the streaking rate is faster. Therefore, by merely multiplying the intensity observed as a function of channel number by the streaking rate as a function of channel number, one is able to deconvolute the intensity dependence from the streaking rate.

Recent advances in microcircuitry have made the computer an integral part of most, if not all data acquisition and analysis systems. Signal averaging of data enhances the signal to noise ratio available in most video or photodiode array based imaging systems by allowing for background subtraction and averaging the random noise fluctuations arising from thermodynamic effects or shot-noise characteristics. We have used a PDP 11/03 minicomputer to provide data storage and analysis for the streak camera - OMA system and a Reticon photodiode array detector. Since the output signal from the streak camera which we have used (Temporaldisperser from Hamamatsu Corp.) is subject to an inherent jitter on the order of 50 ps, it is essential to determine a time reference position for each data set so as to correctly average corresponding portions of different sets of data. This has been accomplished by allowing a portion of the ps laser excitation pulse to strike the camera entrance slit prior to the arrival of light from the event being observed. Since the streak camera resolution is comparable to the laser pulse duration, a reference mark is thus obtained on the output slit relative to which signal averaging and intensity calibrations of pump light may be performed. In realtime a Fortran operating program synchronizes data output rates from the video system and provides data storage on floppy disk. The realtime signal is displayed within 10 sec of laser excitation. At this time signal scaling, background subtraction, pump pulse intensity calibration and preliminary curve fitting procedures are performed so as to allow the operator to monitor key laser system and sample parameters in order to both optimize the system and allow elimination of possible artifacts arising from abnormal laser operation. Since the turn-around time for these procedures is exceeded by the required system recovery time for single shot laser operation, (typically 1-2 minutes) the fast data reduction and analysis becomes a critical feature of the experiment. In particular, in cases where signal averaging is required, the operating program allows for simultaneous monitoring of averaged data and individual raw data so as to provide the operator with a better perspective on the benefit of further averaging. By averaging 100 curves it is possible to improve the signal to noise ratio by a factor of 10. Thus the Fortran operating program provides powerful scientific subroutines to be effectively applied in realtime so as to enable the experimenter to make critical decisions at a more informed level than was previously obtainable.

Some Measurements Obtained with Video Imaging Systems

In order to appreciate more fully the impact that video imaging systems have had on measurements in Picosecond Spectroscopy some data obtained with the above techniques will now be presented covering various areas of interest in Physics, Chemistry, and Biology.

Physics

In order to fully understand the physics of the liquid state, a knowledge of the rotational motion of molecules is required. Direct measurements of the time dependence of the Kerr effect associated with the orientational motion of anisotropic molecules in neat and mixed liquids have been recently obtained through the use of picosecond laser techniques. Fig.1 shows the intensity profile measured as a function of time for the optical Kerr effect in Nitrobenzene at 25°C. The decay time measures the molecular reorientation of the molecules of nitrobenzene. The data was obtained with an Optical Multi-channel Analyzer (OMA) with a single shot picosecond laser optical Kerr gate. The input to the Kerr gate consists of an oblique wave front obtained by scattering a 5300 A, 6-picosecond laser pulse through a milky solution at right angles to the axis of the gate. The scattered light, which is variously delayed with respect to the 1.06μm gate activating pulse thereby probes the temporal evolution of the induced transitory birefringence of the Kerr active sample solution in a single laser shot.[6]

A measurement of the Kerr relaxation times in succinonitrile (SN) as a function of temperature is shown in Fig. 2. The Kerr relaxation times measured show the effect of temperature on the rotational motion of the SN molecules as they undergo a change from the liquid to the plastic crystal phase. The data obtained from the Kerr gate measurement is shown along with a best fit curve from depolarized Rayleigh scattering [7] (dotted line), and a best fit curve from dielectric relaxation measure-

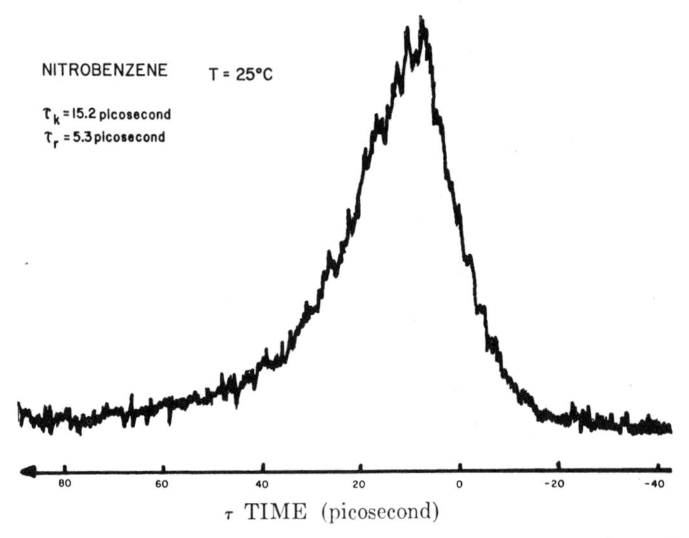

Chemical Physics Letters

Figure 1. Intensity profile of optical Kerr effect of NB at 25°C vs. time. The zero time is arbitrary and the peak transmission of the Kerr effect is about 10%. The rise time is 5.3 ps and the decay time is 15.2 ps. This decay time corresponds to a molecular orientation time of 30.4 ps (6).

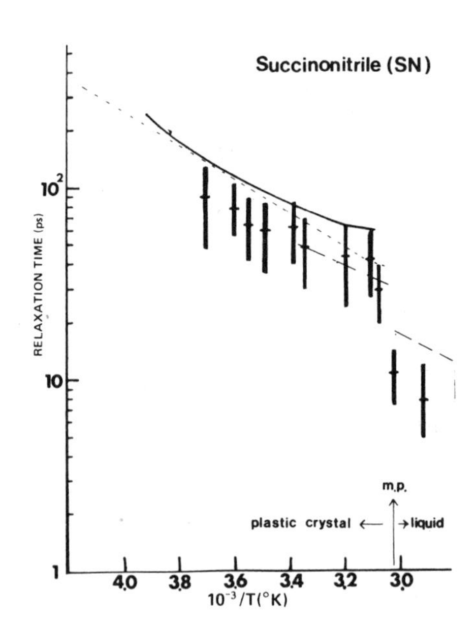

Physical Review

Figure 2. Reorientational relaxation time of SN vs. the inverse of the temperature (9).

ments[7,8] (dashed and solid lines). The important feature of this curve is the jump in the relaxation time at the phase transition.[9]

The photoluminescence kinetics from Gallium Arsenide (GaAs) at 100K was measured with a Hamamatsu streak camera coupled to a PAR OMA. The hot photoluminescence intensity (7200 to 8500 Å) as a function of time is displayed in Fig.3. The decay time of hot luminescence is ~25ps. The electrons are photo-generated by a single 0.53μm 6ps pulse to an energy state greater than E_G + 0.3 ev. At this pump energy, the luminescence kinetics should reflect the intervalley transfer of electrons from Γ, to and from the upper valleys along the L and X directions. The electron transfer from $\Gamma \rightleftarrows L$ is responsible for the Gunn effect. The luminescence intensity profile versus time in Fig.3 shows a complex profile, particularly in the rise portion, which may indicate the electron transfers from $\Gamma \xrightarrow{k1} X,L \xrightarrow{k2} \Gamma$. Since $k1 > k2$, a transfer time $k2^{-1}$ of approximately 4ps is estimated from the data presented in Fig. 3.

Chemistry

Environmental factors such as polarity, viscosity, hydrogen bond donor strength, PH and temperature can readily affect the optical properties of dye molecules in solution. The subnanosecond fluorescence kinetics from erythrosin, a fluorescein derivative, is shown in Fig. 4. The fluorescence lifetime of erythrosin was found to decrease linearly as the concentration of water increased in a water-acetone mixture, as may be seen from Fig. 5. The fluorescence lifetime of erythrosin in acetone was found to be 2.4 ns, and it reduces linearly to 75 ps as water is added. In erythrosin, past research studying the effect of halogenation of fluorescein dyes have suggested that the decrease of fluorescence yield from fluorescein to eosin and erythrosin is due not only to an increased intersystem crossing rate but also to an increased internal conversion rate. These results together with some unpublished data which suggested an even weaker triplet yield for erythrosin in water were the basis for Umberger[10] to suggest that the fluorescence quenching of erythrosin in water is mainly the result of an enhanced internal conversion by protonation. For erythrosin, at PH 9 the triplet yield was determined to be 1.07 ± 0.13, and the fluorescence yield at 0.02. Varying the solvent, the triplet yield varies. In methanol, the triplet yield is reported to be 0.6. Since the fluorescence yield in acetone is about 0.55, the maximum

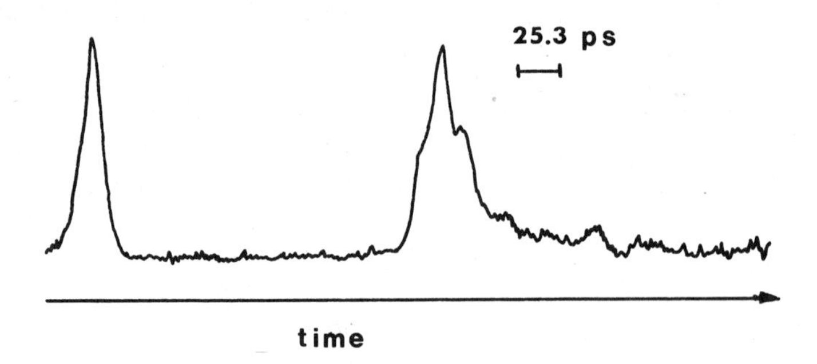

Figure 3. Hot photoluminescence intensity vs. time from GaAs. The pulse on the left is a calibrating 0.53 pulse arriving at the camera prior to the photoluminescence emission from GaAs.

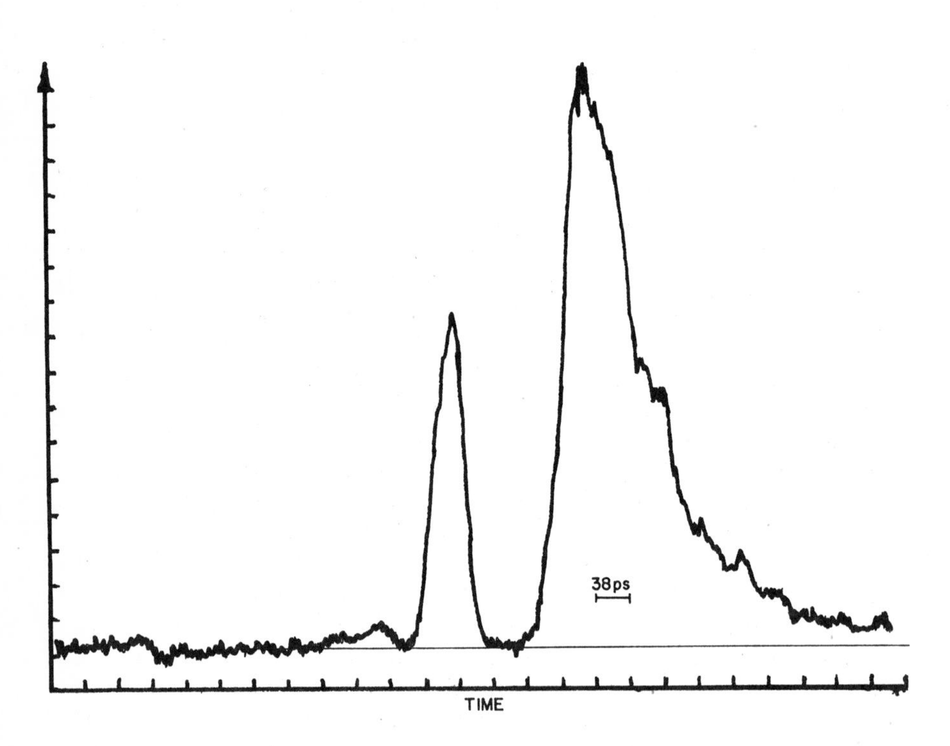

Journal of Chemical Physics

Figure 4. Fluorescence kinetics of erythrosin in water measured by the streak camera–OMA system. The decay is a single exponential with a decay time of 78 ps (18).

possible triplet yield in acetone is only 0.45. Therefore, we believe the fluorescence quenching in acetone-water mixture of this experiment and in the series of solvents studied by Umberger is the consequence of the variation of the inter-system crossing rate.

Biology

The photosynthetic process forms the basis for life on our planet, and has through the years been a subject of great interest to investigators from all scientific fields. The recent availability of ultrashort laser pulses has enabled the direct measurement of fundamental kinetic properties such as the fluorescence lifetime. In the photosynthetic process it is currently believed that a unit consisting of approximately 300 chlorophyll molecules acts as harvester and processor for the light energy which falls upon it. The energy is transferred among the chlorophyll molecules by a dipole-dipole resonance mechanism which finally brings the captured energy to an energy sink or reaction center where the primary oxidation-reduction reaction which is responsible for harnessing the energy in an energy rich bond takes place. Fig.6 shows a measurement of the fluorescence intensity as a function of time for a spinach leaf excited by a 0.53 μm, 6 ps laser pulse, as measured with a streak camera-OMA system. The fluorescence decay possesses a double exponential nature with a fast component of approximately 100ps and a slower component with a 252 ps lifetime. The intensity of excitation in this experiment was 1.3×10^{13} photons/cm^2 in a single pulse experiment. Lifetime measurements as a function of incident photon flux[11,12] have shown the fluorescence lifetime from higher green plant photosystems to depend sensitively on intensity $> 3 \times 10^{13}$ photons/cm^2 per pulse, with the intensity dependence being attributed to exciton annihilation effects.[13,14] The present single pulse results obtained without the benefit of signal averaging are in agreement with earlier measurements at $\sim 2 \times 10^{14}$ photons/cm^2 per pulse measured in an experiment utilizing a train of 100 laser pulses.[15] More experiments at lower intensities are evidently needed in this fundamental area of research for a more complete and precise determination of the primary energy transfer kinetics.

A great deal of fundamental information about vision has been obtained through absorption spectroscopy.[16] The primary event in vision is the photo-chemical formation of bathorhodopsin from rhodopsin and isorhodopsin. Rhodopsin is the

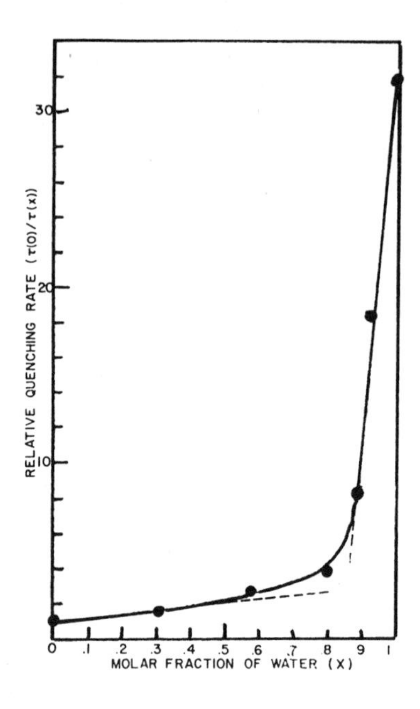

Journal of Chemical Physics

Figure 5. Relative quenching rate of erythrosin fluorescence $\tau(0)/\tau(X)$, *as a function of molar fraction of water (X)* (18).

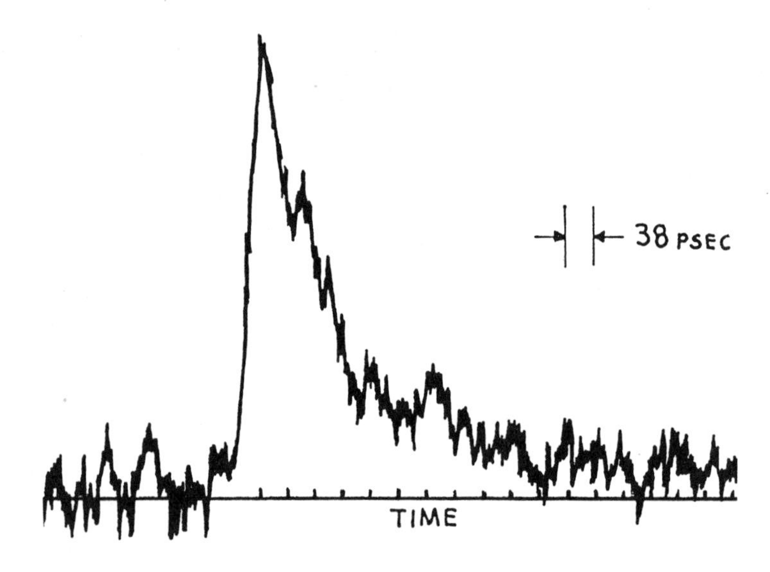

Figure 6. Fluorescence kinetics from spinach measured with streak camera–OMA system

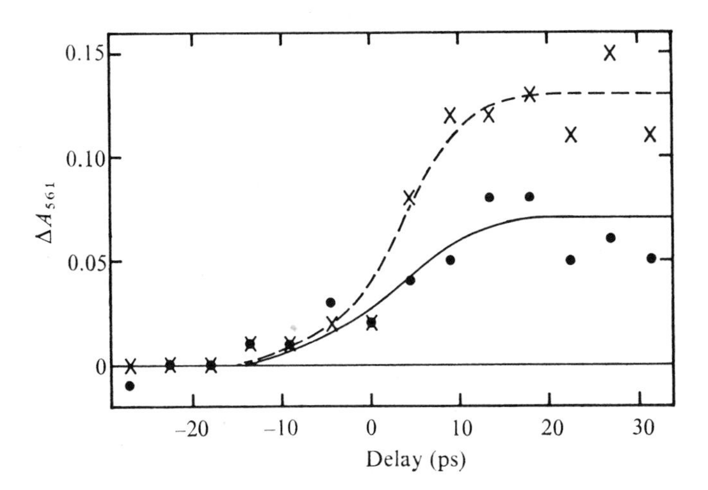

Figure 7. Laser-induced absorbance changes at 561 nm as a function of time in detergent solubilised bovine rhodopsin (×) and isorhodopsin (●) at room temperature. Bathorhodopsin is the only intermediate during the bleaching of bovine rhodopsin known to absorb strongly at 561 nm. The energy of the 530-nm pump pulse was about 10^{-4}J; the energy of the 561-nm probe pulse was about 10^{-7}J. The beam sizes were about 1 mm² for the pump and 0.5 mm² for the probe. The samples (about 1.5 mL) were held in 0.5-cm cuvettes. The concentrations were about 4 A cm^{-1} at the absorption peaks near 500 nm; the ratios A_{400}:A_{500} were about 0.3; and ratios A_{530}:A_{500} were about 0.7 for rhodopsin and 0.5 for isorhodopsin. Each data point shown is the average of six (rhodopsin) and nine (isorhodopsin) laser shots. Typical mean standard deviations are ±0.03. The zero time is located using a 0.5 cm CS_2 Kerr optical shutter at the sample site. The half width at half maximum for the CS_2 shutter prompt response curve is about 6 ps.

visual pigment in disk membranes of vertebrate rod cells,[17] which are found in the retina of the eye. The time dependence of the laser-induced absorbance[3] changes for the conversion of rhodopsin or isorhodopsin to bathorhodopsin are shown in Fig. 7. From the figure it can be seen that the photo-chemical formation of bathorhodopsin occurs in less than 9 psec. This measurement has led to the important interpretation that bathorhodopsin is an isomerized product of at least one of the primary pigments.[3]

This research is supported by NSF, NIH, and CUNY FRAP grants.

References

1. Duguay, M. and Hansen, H., Appl. Phys. Lett. 15, 192 (1969); Shimizu, F. and Stoicheff, P. P., IEEE J. Quantum Electron. 5, 544 (1969).

2. Struve, W. and Rentzepis, P. M., Chem. Phys. Lett. 29, 23 (1974).

3. Netzel, T. L., Rentzepis, P. M. and Leigh, J., Science 182, 238 (1973).

   Green, B. H., Monger, T. G., Alfano, R. R., Aton, B., Callender, R. H., Nature 269, 179 (1977).

4. Alfano, R. R. and Shapiro, S. L., Phys. Rev. Lett. 24, 592, 585, 1217 (1970).

5. R.C.A. Camera Tube 4804 Specifications, R.C.A. Electronic Components, Harrison, N. J. 07029, "Electro-Optics Handbook", R.C.A. Technical Series EOH-11 (1974).

6. Ho, P. P. and Alfano, R. R., Chem. Phys. Lett. 50, 74 (1977).

7. Bird, M. J., Jackson, D. A., and Pentecost, H. J., in "Proceedings of the Second International Conference of Light Scatterings in Solids"(Flammarion, Paris,1971),p.493.

8. Williams, D. E. and Smyth, C. R., J. Am. Chem. Soc. 84, 1808 (1962).

9. Ho, P. P. and Alfano, R. R., Phys. Rev. A17, 1161 (1978).

10. Umberger, J. Q., J. Phys. Chem. 71, 2054 (1967).

11. Campillo, A. J., Kollman, V. H. and Shapiro, S. L., Science 193, 227-229 (1976).

12. Mauzerall, D., Biophys. J. 16, 87092 (1976).

13. Breton, J. and Geacintov, N. E., FEBS Lett. 69, 86-89 (1976).

14. Geacintov, N. E. and Breton, J., Biophys. J. 18, 1-15 (1977)

15. Yu, W., Pellegrino, F., and Alfano, R. R., Biochim. et Biophys. Acta 460, 171-181 (1977).

16. Wald, G., Annual Review of Biochem. 22, 497 (1953); Science 119, 887 (1954); In Structure of the Eye, (Smelser, G. K., ed.) Academic Press, 101 (1961).

17. Wald, G., Science 162, 230-239 (1968).

18. Yu, W., Pellegrino, F., Grant, M. and Alfano, R. R., J. Chem. Phys., 67, 1766-1773 (1977).

RECEIVED January 17, 1979.

Coupling an Ultraviolet Spectrograph to a SC/OMA for Three Dimensional (λ,I,t) Picosecond Fluorescence Measurements

G. W. ROBINSON, T. A. CAUGHEY, R. A. AUERBACH, and P. J. HARMAN

Department of Chemistry, Texas Tech University, Lubbock, TX 79409

Little is known about the "molecular scale of time". Chemical research in the past has had its accent on highly varied spectroscopic methods, but these have been mainly for the study of spatial and frequency resolution. This spectrum of spectroscopies is incomplete without the inclusion of time. The availability of ultrashort pulses of energy and their application to molecular problems are therefore expected to form an important extension to the field of molecular spectroscopy. During the next decade the creation of new frontiers in chemistry through studies based on such techniques is inevitable.

Even though subpicosecond spectroscopy is rapidly developing along the lines of mode-locked argon-ion pumped dye lasers (1,2), to date most subnanosecond experiments of chemical and biological interest have been carried out using Nd+3/glass or Nd+3/YAG solid state lasers as excitation source (3,4). The efficient production of 2nd, 3rd, and 4th harmonics of the output of these lasers is now routine, and, in photochemical experiments, can provide excitation energy in the visible (~530 nm), the near ultraviolet (~353 nm) and the farther ultraviolet (~265 nm) spectral regions.

Before 1975 such studies were mainly based on the detection of time-resolved transient absorptions produced by an ultrashort energy pulse (5,6). As in a conventional flash photolysis experiment, the exciting pulse produces transients and a probe pulse detects them as a function of a delay time. For detection to be possible, a large fraction of the parent molecules must be converted to the transient species and an intense absorption band of this species must occur in a suitable region of the spectrum. High excitation power is often required and nonlinear optical effects can distort the results (7).

The development of the ultrafast streak camera (8) in the early 1970's provided a continuous time base for the detection of transient photon signals within the picosecond timescale. Almost immediately the usefulness of image detectors became apparent. Instead of recording streak camera events on film, coupling of the streak camera through an image intensifier to an optical

0-8412-0504-3/79/47-102-199$05.00/0

multichannel analyzer became the standard technique in the study of molecular emission. This provided a digital, as opposed to a photographic (analog), record of the transient event, and allowed a rapid, convenient, and precise analysis of the large quantity of data necessary to characterize these molecular emission processes.

More recently, research emphasis has shifted to streak cameras with ultraviolet sensitivity. This new advance allows picosecond emission spectroscopy to unshackle itself from the large dye molecules common to the visible wavelength region, and to begin addressing problems of more chemical physics interest, viz. small molecules, energy transfer, and diffusion theory. The present paper describes such an apparatus using a mode-locked Nd+3/glass laser as excitation source. The primary advance is the coupling of an ultraviolet-visible spectograph to the transient detection system so that both wavelength and time are simultaneously resolved in a given single shot experiment. The paper then presents some data illustrating the capabilities of such an apparatus.

Streak Camera Imaging

The Nd+3/phosphate glass laser source, the pulse selecting system, and the harmonic generators for the production of single short pulses of light at 527 nm, and 351 nm, and 264 nm have all been adequately described in the literature (9,10). Such pulses, whose wavelength may be crudely tuned (11), or made continuous (12) by various methods, can be used as excitation sources in a transient fluorescence experiment. Usually the pulse is focussed into a sample cell as a pencil of radiation with a diameter less than 2mm. Fluorescence light emerging from the sample cell is collected by a lens system whose aperture matches the limiting aperture of the detection system (f/3). The sample cell and collection lenses are made of nonfluorescing fused quartz (suprasil I).

Commercially available ultrafast streak cameras are equipped with a slit and an achromatic lens system for focussing an image of this slit onto the photocathode of the streak camera. Even if the entrance window of the streak tube and the photocathode substrate are made of ultraviolet transmitting material (suprasil I or sapphire), the transmission of the achromatic lenses rarely extends to wavelengths much shorter than 350 nm. High aperture ultraviolet transmitting achromatic lenses are extremely expensive and are achromatic over an inadequate wavelength range, or have so many elements that reflection losses become a grave concern. Light collection systems with reflection optics, such as a Cassegrainian, are achromatic and are commercially available at a fairly low cost, but these systems are usually designed for long focal length applications, whereas the present application requires 1:1 imaging at high aperture. Furthermore, for three dimensional (λ,I,t) detection, use of either of these types of light collection systems requires a supplemental wavelength dispersing element, such as a monochromator or interference filters, giving rise to additional light loss.

High aperture spectrographs are designed precisely for the applications that are required here. Thus, to avoid some of the problems and inconveniences of the lens or mirror input systems, we have coupled a small f/3 spectrograph (American ISA, UFS-200) directly to the streak camera. In this arrangement the spectrograph provides both the wavelength dispersion and slit imaging, the streak camera gives the time dispersion, and the image-intensifier/optical-multichannel-analyzer comprises the read-out assembly.

Figure 1 is a schematic diagram of the excitation and detection system. Photons emitted from the experiment are collected by an external lens system and are focussed onto the slit of the spectrograph. This instrument has an essentially flat focal plane over the wavelength range 200-800 nm, obviating the necessity for a wavelength dependent focussing adjustment. The spectrograph input therefore can directly provide an achromatic slit image on the photocathode of the streak camera over this entire wavelength range. There is no need for an auxilliary ultraviolet transmitting light collection system.

The requirement for combined temporal and wavelength dispersion in a streak camera is that the wavelength be dispersed perpendicular to the streak direction along a slit image at the photocathode. This is accomplished by rotating the grating 90 degrees from its normal orientation. In this configuration what would normally be termed "slit width" contributes to the time resolution while the wavelength resolution is related to the slit height. In the current setup the input slit is 1000 microns in height and 50 microns in width.

Unfortunately, simply rotating the grating is not sufficient to give a well-defined slit image on the photocathode of the streak camera. The reason for this is a severe wavelength dependent astigmatism that smears the slit image horizontally, totally degrading the time resolution of the system. In any astigmatic optical device, however, there are two focal surfaces, *tangential* and *sagittal*, with the astigmatic aberrations perpendicular to one another (13). The use of the saggital focal surface, instead of the usual tangential focal surface, preserves the imaging quality in the horizontal (time) direction to within the 50 micron slit width. The astigmatism has thus been rotated from the horizontal time regime into the vertical wavelength regime. Use of a narrower slit is unnecessary since the relatively poor electron focussing capability (120 microns) of our Hadland streak tube is the limiting time resolution factor. In the arrangement described here the sagittal focal surface intersects the tangential focal surface at an angle of 23 degrees, both surfaces being essentially flat near the optic axis. The spectrograph therefore

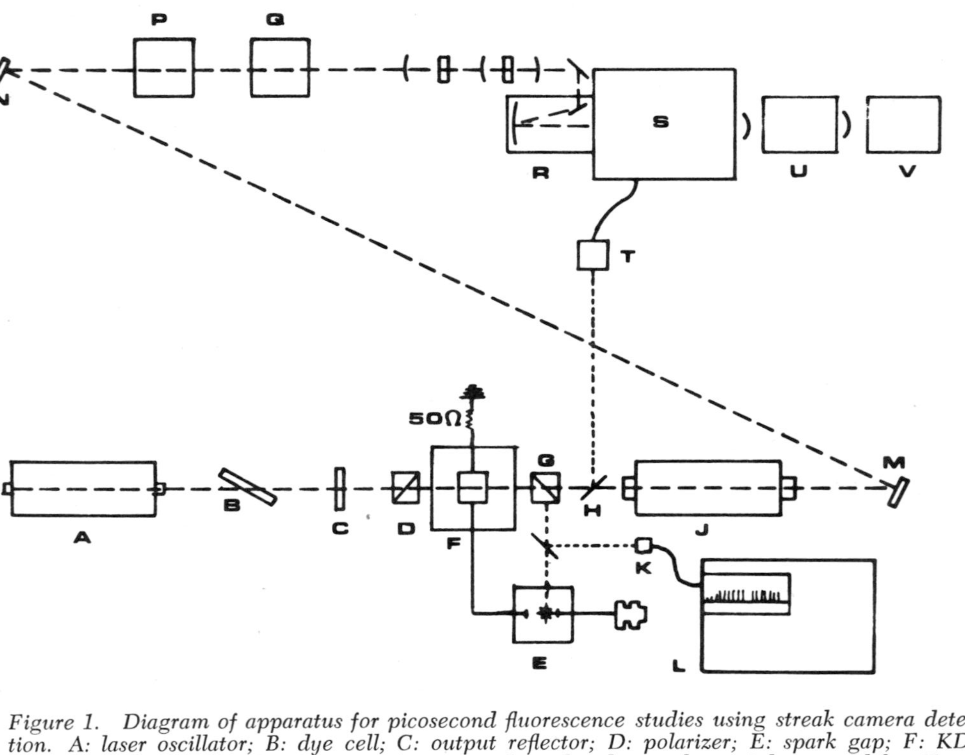

Figure 1. Diagram of apparatus for picosecond fluorescence studies using streak camera detection. A: laser oscillator; B: dye cell; C: output reflector; D: polarizer; E: spark gap; F: KDP pockels cell; G: polarizer (crossed with D); H: clear glass beamsplitter; J: laser amplifier; K: pin photodiode; L: transient digitizer; M,N: 1054 nm reflectors; P: 2nd harmonic generator; Q: 3rd or 4th harmonic generator; R: spectrograph; S: streak camera; T: biplanar photodiode; U: image intensifier; V: OMA.

must be physically mounted at this angle with respect to the streak camera (see Fig. 2). At the present time, the loss of vertical resolution caused by the astigmatism is immaterial since the practical wavelength resolution of the system is essentially limited by the inability to operate the OMA with more than approximately ten wavelength tracks in the 2-D mode. This restriction on the number of tracks arises both because of the limitation in the dynamic range of the OMA and the weak signal levels that result when the available input photons are divided among so many tracks. In the present setup the resolution is roughly 20 nm.

In addition to rotating the grating and tilting the spectrograph body, a third minor modification of the spectrograph was required. The camera photocathode is recessed 24 millimeters inside the input window of the streak tube. This is beyond the range afforded by the normal distance between the body of the spectrograph and its focal plane. In order to focus the dispersed fluorescence on the photocathode, the focal plane of the spectrograph was shifted outward from the body by moving the input slit of the spectrograph 5-10 mm closer to the grating. The range of wavelengths that can be detected in a single streak camera sweep is determined by the dispersion of the spectrograph and by the 6 mm useful height of the photocathode. A wavelength range of approximately 175 nm has been measured using the emission lines from a low pressure mercury arc.

Different wavelength settings are selected by adjustment of a micrometer screw that moves the entire spectrograph body vertically relative to the streak camera. A flexible light tight cover consisting of a single layer of black "Ultrasuede" is used to shroud the space between the spectrograph and the streak camera. A disadvantage of this wavelength setting system is that at each new micrometer setting, all the external input optics to the spectrograph must be repositioned and aligned. A much better system for wavelength adjustment is to fix the spectrograph and rotate the grating in a vertical plane using a micrometer drive, but as yet this has not been tried.

Effect of Polarized Light

Whenever the transient light emission to be detected occurs on the same timescale as molecular rotation, and if polarized laser excitation is used, it is essential to pay attention to the polarization properties of the emitted light (14). Depending on the molecular weight and the viscosity of the surrounding medium, interference between molecular rotation and light emission can strongly distort data in the subnanosecond regime. Resolution of the emitted light into components parallel ($\alpha = 0°$) and perpendicular ($\alpha = 90°$) to the polarization of the exciting light, or observation at the "magic angle" ($\alpha = \tan^{-1}\sqrt{2} = 54.7°$) is required. When the emission to be detected lies in the visible region, it is the normal practice to use a fixed polarization of

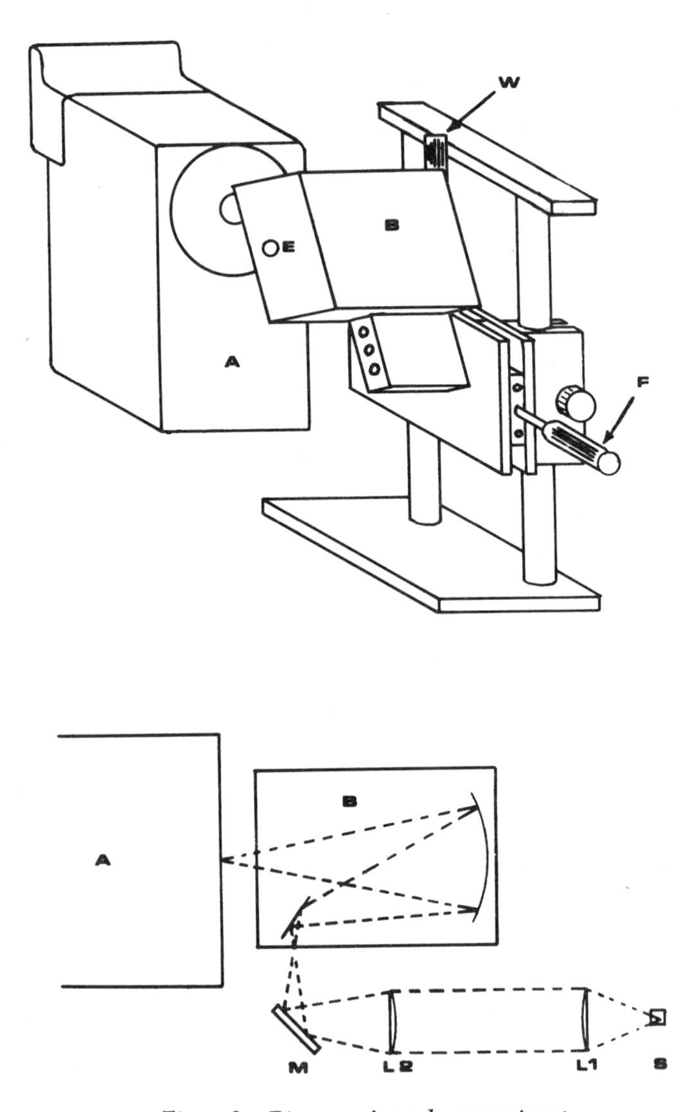

Figure 2. Diagram of streak camera input

the exciting light and adjust the angle of a polarizer-analyzer so that it is either at 0°, 90°, or 54.7° relative to the polarization of excitation. This polarizer-analyzer is positioned between the sample cell and the detector, and a high aperture can be maintained by using ordinary camera polarizing filters, which are available in large diameters. When the light to be detected lies in the ultraviolet region such high aperture devices with reasonable transmission and polarization properties are not available. Relatively low aperture Glan-Taylor polarizers made from high quality calcite have to be used. Another serious problem, which would arise in the present detector configuration, is that dispersion gratings themselves have a polarization bias and can distort the relative intensities of different polarizations reflected from them.

Because the exciting light is a well-collimated "beam" of highly polarized monochromatic light, both of the above problems can be solved simultaneously. One merely has to fix permanently the angle of a small Glan-Taylor polarizer-analyzer directly in front of the spectrograph slit. The angle of polarization of the exciting light can then be varied using a crystal quartz half-wave plate. This technique ensures a constant polarization bias for the spectrograph and avoids the use of costly crystal polarizers.

Image Detection

The streak camera provides a streaked image of the input slit across the face of an output phosphor at the rear of the streak tube with horizontal distance along the phospor faceplate representing time, and phosphor brightness indicating the fluorescence intensity. When the spectrograph is used as input optics to the streak camera, wavelength is dispersed vertically on the phosphor screen to give three-dimensional (λ,I,t) detection capability in a single shot experiment. An EMI three-stage image intensifier tube (IIT) is coupled optically to the streak camera output with a f/1 Tachonar lens to provide a reduced image on the IIT output phosphor. The intensified image is then focussed by an oscilloscope lens onto the silicon target area of a Princeton Applied Research Corporation 1205-A/D optical multichannel analyzer (OMA) fitted with the 2-D option. The OMA target is electronically scanned in a horizontal direction (time) through the 500 channels and sequentially stepped vertically (wavelength) through a preset number of tracks to read out the intensity information developed and stored at the detector.

Although the laser is repetitively charged for firing on its own internal cycle (currently 55 seconds), the actual firing pulse of the laser is synchronized to the internal clock of the OMA. This is to enable the streaked image on the camera phosphor to appear during the 768 μsecs retrace interval between OMA target scans.

Data Retrieval

Intensity information from the 500 channels of the OMA is transferred in digital form from the OMA memory to a Digital Equipment PDP-11/34 computer through a parallel bit interface. Each BCD coded OMA datum is transferred as one sixteen bit word into the 32 kiloword computer memory. Only the first three BCD characters are transferred, since the real time read out of any channel must be less than 783 counts due to the A/D conversion limitations of the present OMA. Data transfer from the OMA to the computer is sufficiently fast to keep up with the real time digitization rate of the OMA, 500 channels in 32 msec. However, decoding the data into binary form and adding it to previous scans of the same track are too slow to be carried out during real time. Such data manipulation is done after data transfer to the computer memory and before transfer to disk storage. Data accumulation in the (λ,I,t) mode is then limited by the size of the computer memory. Storage space is not a significant problem as frequent use is made of disk storage when manipulating these large data blocks.

Typically, the OMA target is divided into five tracks or vertical regions and data are accumulated from four scans of each track. This requires a total of 10 kilowords of computer memory for initial data storage. Due to detector "lag", several passes of the electron beam over the silicon target are needed to completely recharge it. Under our conditions four scans of each track are sufficient to read out most (95%) of the signal. Although the first track read in 2-D operation is selected at random, the OMA-computer interface recognizes a "selected track" flag while collecting data. This flag identifies the wavelength sequence of tracks and provides a means of matching up tracks when background subtraction is performed to ensure a flat baseline for each wavelength region. In operation, computer programs for data accumulation, background accumulation, background subtraction and data display are run sequentially under preprogrammed control.

Data Calibration

The raw data stored on disk in the computer must be corrected for the non-constant sweep rate of the streak camera. Sweep rate calibration is accomplished with the use of Fabry-Perot etalons as fixed interval pulse generators. Both air spaced and solid quartz elatons are used, with surfaces coated for approximately 97% reflectivy at the laser wavelength. A single laser pulse propagating normal to such an etalon produces pulses of gradually decreasing intensity spaced at twice the time of flight between the coated surfaces (see Fig. 3). Sweep rate per channel *vs* channel number is fit by a power series up to a quadratic term. On certain sweep speeds (but not the one shown in Fig. 3) deviations in sweep rate can be very large, up to 30% across the 500 channels. Fits with a 1% standard deviation are obtained and are reproducible to within this standard deviation for at least several weeks. Each data file is appended with this calibration information, which is used to scale the data accurately with time. Figure 4 illustrates the typical type of nonlinearity between channel number and item relative to the start of the recorded sweep.

Noise and Signal Averaging

The poor dynamic range of the streak camera, together with the A/D conversion capability of the OMA limits the signal that can be utilized. High signal levels in the streak camera cause space charge effects that result in distortion of the streak and consequent loss of time resolution. Low signal levels are therefore advisable, but photon statistics at such low light levels usually result in poor signal-to-noise ratios. Thus, signal averaging of many shots has proven to be absolutely necessary to obtain curves smooth enough for reliable statistics.

Most of this photon statistical noise is generated at the input to the image intensifier stage. An example illustrates this. Assume that a single channel on the OMA screen has a digitized signal read off by the OMA electron beam of 100 counts. As the specified sensitivity of the silicon intensifier tube detector head of the OMA is 15 photons/OMA count, based on an average P11 phosphor, the 100 count signal represents 1500 photons incident on the OMA. The lens that images the IIT output screen on the OMA has a f/1.4 aperture with approximately 90% transmissivity. Thus the 100 counts/channel read at the OMA corresponds to 28,600 photons emitted by the phosphor screen of the IIT. Since the image intensifier is typically used with an amplification of about 10^3, the corresponding number of photoelectrons emitted by the IIT photocathode is therefore about 29. The signal-to-noise ratio, assuming Poisson statistics, is 5.4. This is the weak link in the detector chain. Virtually no statistical noise contribution will occur directly from light input to the streak camera (SC) as there is no amplification in that device. However, the low input signals into the IIT are a result of low SC output and inefficient lens coupling between the SC and the IIT. Fiber optic coupling can partially alleviate the latter problem, but the former is limited by low SC dynamic range.

The averaging of several transients is complicated by jitter in the triggering pulse and the firing circuitry of the camera, which causes shot to shot time variations of the signal on the OMA target. At present, signals are averaged by eye matching of the curves on a Tektronix 4027 graphics terminal. This requires scaling the curves to the same apparent intensity to ensure the best time matching. A less ambiguous technique involves the use of a prepulse (as in Fig. 5). The prepulse is a fraction of the

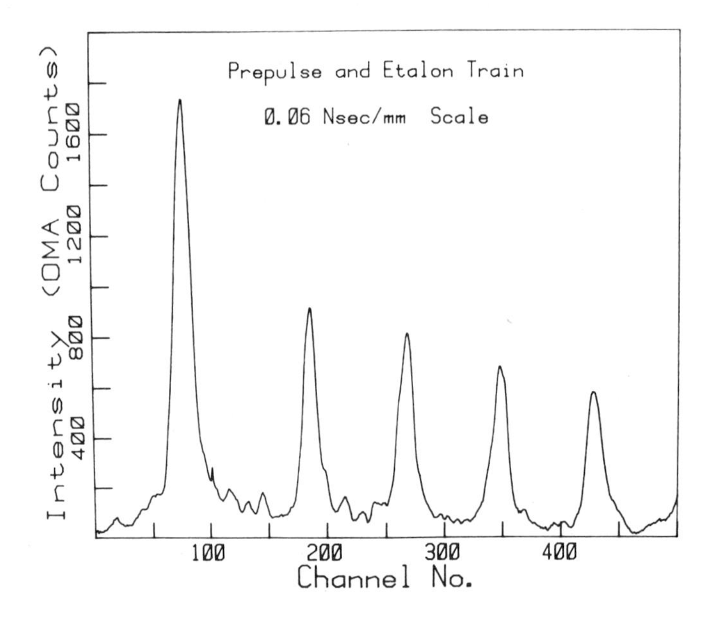

Figure 3. Etalon train. Full scale is approximately 0.8 nsec. The first peak on the left is a prepulse. The abscissa is not exactly linear with time (see Figure 4).

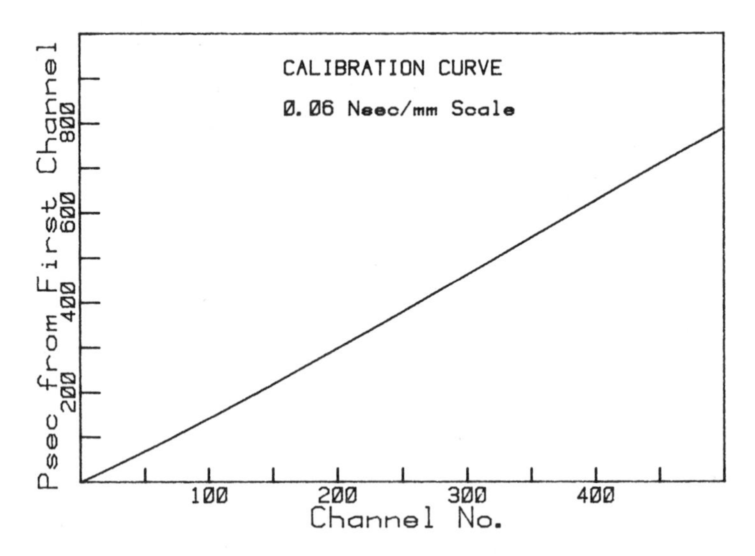

Figure 4. Sweep rate calibration for 0.06 nsec/mm scale on streak camera

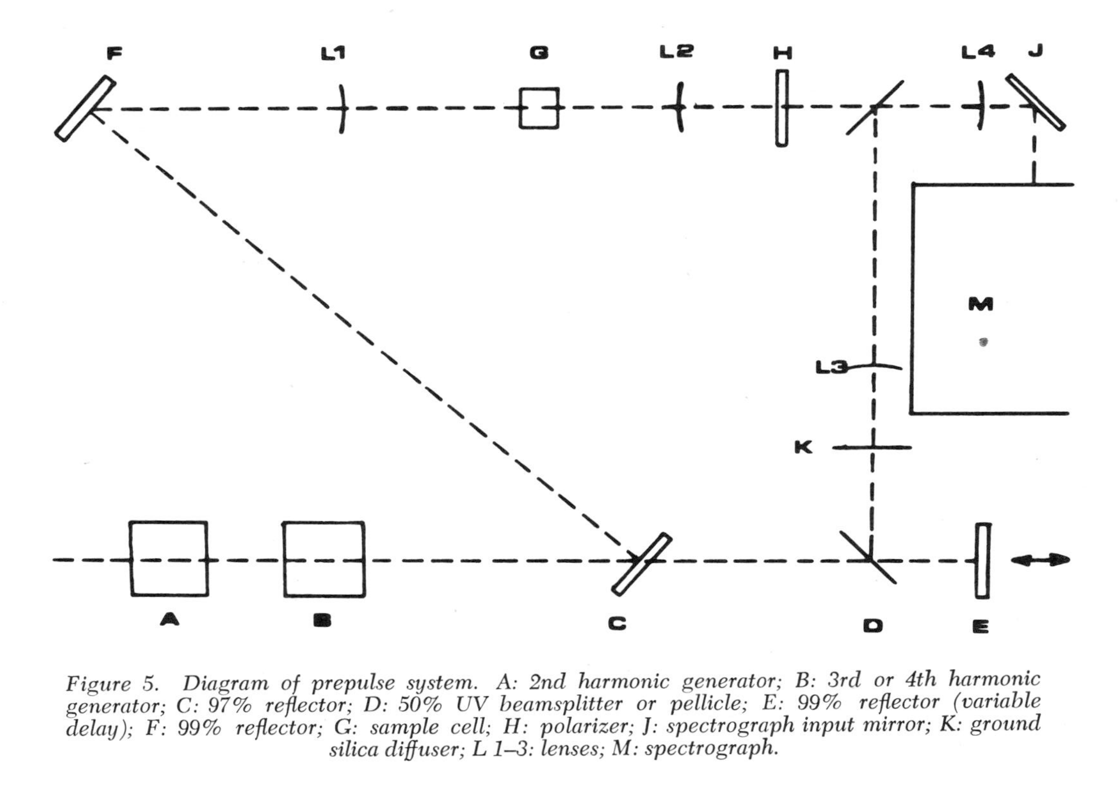

Figure 5. Diagram of prepulse system. A: 2nd harmonic generator; B: 3rd or 4th harmonic generator; C: 97% reflector; D: 50% UV beamsplitter or pellicle; E: 99% reflector (variable delay); F: 99% reflector; G: sample cell; H: polarizer; J: spectrograph input mirror; K: ground silica diffuser; L 1–3: lenses; M: spectrograph.

laser beam which arrives at the photocathode of the streak camera a fixed time before the emission signal. This pulse, whose peak position is easily determined, defines a zero time for the fluorescence and gives an estimate of the intensity of the laser shot. The transients can then be averaged with less recourse to human objectivity.

Systems Performance

To illustrate the operation of the system, L(-) Tryphophan dissolved in water at a concentration of 10^{-4}M and buffered with 5mM THAM to pH7, has been studied. It has recently been reported (15) that there are two lifetimes, which change their relative weighting as a function of observational wavelength. In Fig. 6 a single transient curve is illustrated. This is the fluorescence emitted after excitation by a single laser shot that has been wavelength dispersed by the spectrograph, streaked, and recorded on the OMA. The wavelength of the tracks ranges from ~310 nm in the bottom track to 430 nm in the top track. Each track has been successively offset by 100 counts for reasons of clarity. The ordinate, while linear in channel number, is not exactly linear in time (see Fig. 4). Full scale is approximately 10 nsec.

In Fig. 7 an average of twenty transients similar to that in Fig. 6 is presented. The curves were matched by the procedure described above and are displayed as the sum of all 20 curves. Once again the curves are offset for reasons of clarity. The signal-to-noise ratio is dramatically improved by this procedure. Even so, the wavelength dependence of the fluorescence decay time remains a subtle effect. Obviously, one must bias the data on the ultraviolet tail of the fluorescence spectrum relative to the fluorescence maximum near 360 nm in order to bring out this effect more clearly.

The data in the above figures may be improved by using more intense excitation. A new oscillator rod and a new amplifier rod have recently been installed and this should improve intensity and reduce the statistical noise. It should also be possible to achieve better imaging from the spectrograph and lens coupling systems. For example, the rounded effect at the peak of the curves in Fig. 7 is caused by rather wide linewidths (about 10 channels FWHM). This will be reduced in future studies partly by better imaging and partly by deconvolution.

Abstract

A small flat-field spectrograph (American ISA, UFS-200) having sensitivity from 200-800nm is used for slit and input optics to a Handland-Photonics 675 II (U.V.) streak camera (SC) for simultaneous dispersion of wavelength and time in the picosecond regime. The SC is further coupled through an EMI 3-stage

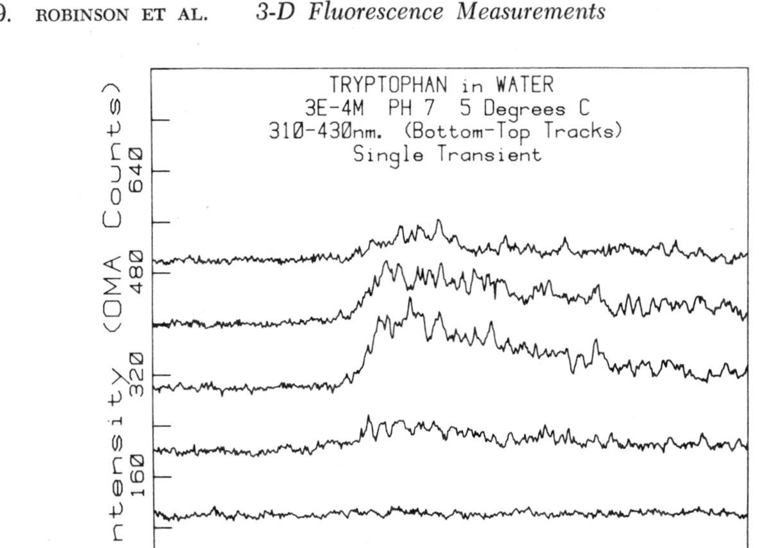

Figure 6. Time and wavelength resolved fluorescence of tryptophan (3×10^{-4}M) in water at 5°C excited by a single 263 nm picosecond pulse. Wavelength range is from 310 nm in the lower track to 430 nm in the upper track. Full scale on the time axis is approximately 10 nsec. The abscissa is not exactly linear with time (see Figure 4).

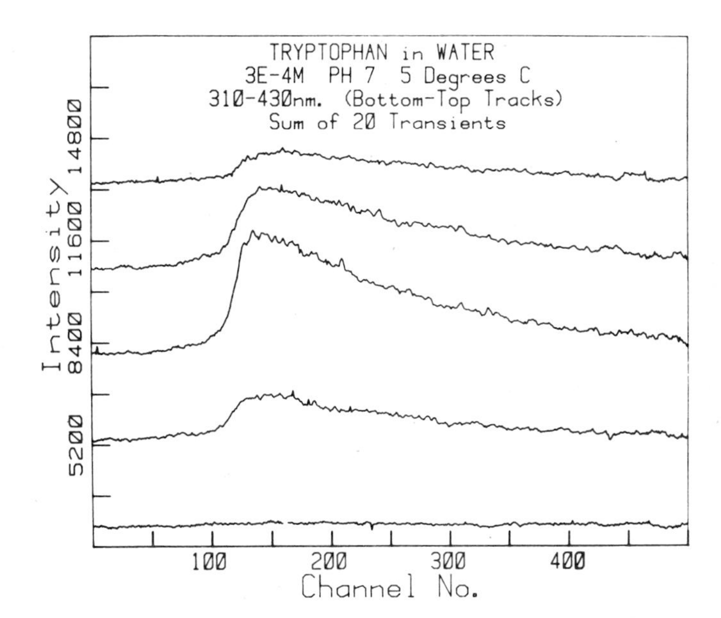

Figure 7. Time and wavelength resolved fluorescence of tryptophan (3×10^{-4}M) in water at 5°C. This curve is an average of 20 single shots each one similar to that in Figure 6.

image intensifier to a Princeton Applied Research 1205-A/D optical multichannel analyzer (OMA) fitted with the 2-D option — time = channels, wavelength = tracks. Digitized fluorescence data are rapidly retrieved using a dedicated Digital Equipment PDP-11 computer, interactive data analysis being aided by a Tektronix 4027 graphics terminal and a Hewlett-Packard 7221A digital plotter. In order to achieve the three dimensional (λ,I,t) aspect of the detection, the spectrograph must create a well-focussed slit image on the photocathode of the SC with wavelength dispersion along the direction of this slit image. This is accomplished by using the spectrograph in an unconventional configuration — slit height of the spectrograph perpendicular to the grating rulings and use of the sagittal, rather than the tangential, focal surface of the corrected concave grating. Wavelength resolution (presently only 20 nm) is limited by the slit height, the astigmatic lengthening of the actual slit height in the direction of the wavelength dispersion, and limitations of the 2-D characteristics of the OMA. Wavelength range (~175 nm) is limited by the diameter of the streak camera photocathode (6-7 mm). Temporal resolution depends on the quality of the slit image perpendicular to the slit height and has been found to be commensurate with the electron imaging quality of the SC. Thus, the maximum temporal resolution (~2 psec) of the detection system can be achieved in this configuration. Signal-to-noise is limited by dynamic range, the noise arising mainly from photon statistics associated with low allowable input signals to the SC. Future improvements in this system will depend upon the availability of a number of components: a high aperture, flat-field spectrograph designed specifically for this application; and more advanced 2-D SC/OMA's providing larger viewing formats, better spatial resolution, broader dynamic range, and a decrease in the number of electron/phosphor stages in the overall system.

Acknowledgements

The Robert A. Welch Foundation is gratefully acknowledged for providing the means through which the picosecond laboratory at Texas Tech University was initially set up. Continued support from the Welch Foundation for this research program is also acknowledged. Salary support from the U. S. National Science Foundation (CHE77 — 21913) for PJH and from the National Institutes of Health (GM-23765) for RAA and TAC is also gratefully acknowledged.

Literature Cited

1. C. V. Shank, E. P. Ippen: App. Phys. Lett. 24, 373 (1974).
2. R. K. Jain, C. P. Ausschnitt: Optics Lett. 2, 117 (1978).

3. D. von der Linde: IEEE. J. Quant. Electron. QE-8, 328 (1972).
4. G. S. Beddard, G. Porter, C. S. Treadwell: Nature 258, 166 (1975).
5. P. M. Rentzepis: Adv. Chem. Phys. 23, 184 (1973).
6. T. J. Chuang, K. B. Eisenthal: Chem. Phys. Lett. 11, 368 (1971). G. T. Evans, M. Fixman: J. Phys. Chem. 80, 1544 (1976).
7. H. E. Lessing, E. Lippert, W. Rapp: Chem. Phys. Lett. 7, 247 (1970).
8. R. Hadland: Survey of British Electro-Optics, Taylor and Francis, Ltd. (1975).
9. G. R. Fleming, J. M. Morris, G. W. Robinson: Aust. J. Chem. 30, 2337 (1977).
10. G. W. Robinson, T. A. Caughey, R. A. Auerbach: In Adv. in Laser Chem. A. H. Zewail, ed., Springer Series in Chem. Phys. (Springer, New York), (1978).
11. G. R. Fleming, I. R. Harrowfield, A. E. W. Knight, J. M. Morris, R. J. Robbins, G. W. Robinson: Optics Comm. 20, 36 (1977).
12. T. L. Netzel, W. S. Struve, P. M. Rentzepis: Ann. Rev. Phys. Chem. 23, 473 (1973).
13. M. Born, E. Wolf: Principles of Optics (Pergamon Press, Oxford 1970 Ch. 5).
14. G. R. Fleming, J. M. Morris, G. W. Robinson: Chem. Phys. 17, 91 (1976).
15. D. M. Rayner, A. G. Szabo: Canad. J. Chem. 56, 743 (1978).

RECEIVED January 22, 1979.

10

Time Resolved Resonance Raman Spectroscopy in Photochemistry and Photobiology

M. A. EL-SAYED

Department of Chemistry, University of California, Los Angeles, CA 90024

Lasers have found a number of applications in spectroscopy, photochemistry and photobiology. One of the most useful applications has been the use of picosecond lasers to study fast photochemical and photobiological processes using picosecond laser flash photolysis techniques in the optical region (1,2). Indeed, the time dependence of many fast photophysical, photochemical and photobiological processes has been measured by following the optical absorption or emission of fast appearing transients or fast disappearing photochemically labile systems. Most unfortunately, the optical spectra observed for these transients are generally broad and yield very little or no structural information, only rate information. In most studies made, the identity of the transients is not assigned from their observed spectral properties but rather assumed from previously proposed mechanisms. If the vibrational spectra (e.g., in Raman spectroscopy) are recorded in time, more structural information will indeed be obtained.

Time dependent Raman spectroscopy is a field in its infancy. Bridoux and Delhaye (3) were the first to discuss the use of short pulses and multichannel detection for recording the Raman spectra. The first Raman spectrum for short lived species was reported in 1975-76 for p-terphenyl anion (4a) and $FeCO_3$ (4b). The use of picosecond pulses to minimize the interference of fluorescence with the Raman spectrum was also demonstrated (5) at about that time. The use of vidicon detection in Raman spectroscopy was demonstrated (6) in 1976. The first resonance Raman spectrum taken for a photobiological system (bacteriorhodopsin) in the nanosecond time scale was (7) in 1977. The resonance Raman spectra of bacteriorhodopsin have also been measured in the microsecond (8,9,10) and in the millisecond (11) time domain. Recently the time resolved resonance Raman spectra of photolyzed hemoglobin derivatives have been reported (12).

In this article, we would like to point out that time resolved resonance Raman spectroscopy (TRRR) is a powerful tool which, with the use of lasers as radiation sources and vidicon

0-8412-0504-3/79/47-102-215$05.00/0

detection, could yield both structural and dynamical information of short lived intermediates in photolabile systems. We discuss here a number of different methods that can be used to obtain these spectra for different photochemical decomposition schemes. The different methods use different types of lasers and the suitability of each method depends on the lifetimes of the transients being studied.

PRINCIPLES

A. Resonance Raman Spectrum. A normal (nonresonance) Raman spectrum of a sample results from an inelastic scattering of an incident light source (e.g., a laser) at frequency ν_0, where $h\nu_0 \neq \Delta E$, the electronic transition energy of the sample. In this case, the scattered radiation is modulated by the different vibrational frequencies (ν_i) of the sample giving rise to the Raman spectrum of the sample at frequencies of $\nu_0 \pm \nu_i$ (the + and - give rise to antiStokes and Stokes Raman bands, respectively). The scattering cross section depends on how much a particular vibration changes the polarizability of the vibrating molecules.

As $h\nu_0$ becomes resonant with one of the electronic transition energies of the molecule, the Raman bands resulting from the vibrations whose force constants or equilibrium parameters change upon this particular electronic excitation are greatly enhanced (by factors of a million in some cases). These vibrations thus show up strongly in solutions at low concentrations (using a cooled vidicon and proper laser wavelength, a good resonance Raman spectrum has been obtained in a few seconds at concentrations as low as 10^{-5} M for bacteriorhodopsin (13)). The other vibrations that are not affected by the electronic excitation do not show up at these low concentrations. This has the advantage that if we have two species in solution (or two transients with similar rise and decay times) it is possible to obtain the Raman spectra of one species and then the other by simply tuning the laser frequency to the absorption region of one and then moving it to the absorption maximum of the other. This is particularly important in studying structural changes of chromophores in the presence of the dense vibration spectra of the proteins. By tuning the laser source to the absorption maximum of the chromophore, the Raman spectrum obtained is the enhanced spectrum of that chromophore with little interference from the dense vibration modes of the protein or the water itself. For a quantitative discussion of resonance Raman spectroscopy (14) and its application to biological systems (15), the reader is referred to other papers.

B. The Different Types of Photolabile Systems. In the following, we will discuss the different systems which upon absorbing laser radiation at a specific frequency (the photolysis radiation) produce transients whose resonance Raman spectra are to be recorded. This can be accomplished by dispersing and recording the scattered radiation of the photolysis radiation itself (in the experiments where the photolysis laser is also the probe laser) or by dispersing and recording the radiation of another laser (the probe laser) at another frequency and pulsed at a different delay time after the photolysis pulse. First, we will discuss the different types of photolabile systems and then we will discuss the different types of experimental arrangements.

Some of the processes that a photolabile system can undergo after the absorption of a light pulse are:

i) formation of one product $A \xrightarrow{h\nu} B(A^*)$

ii) more than one product $A \xrightarrow{h\nu} B + C + ..$

iii) sequential decomposition $A \xrightarrow{h\nu} B \rightsquigarrow C \rightsquigarrow D$

iv) branching decomposition $A \xrightarrow{h\nu} B$, $B \rightsquigarrow C$, $B \rightsquigarrow D$

v) cyclic processes $A \xrightarrow{h\nu} B \rightsquigarrow C \rightsquigarrow D \rightsquigarrow E \rightsquigarrow A$

vi) bimolecular processes $A \xrightarrow{h\nu} A^*$

$A^* + B \rightsquigarrow (AB)^* \rightsquigarrow C$

In all the above processes, only the first one ($\xrightarrow{h\nu}$) is a photochemical change while the rest ($\rightsquigarrow$) are nonradiative chemical changes. It should be mentioned that the first step does not have to be photochemically induced for the methods discussed here to be applicable. Heat pulses or electric field pulses could provide the initial perturbation that changes A into the other intermediates that are to be identified by using a probe Raman laser.

In the above photochemical systems we have assumed that only A absorbs a photon for the sake of simplicity. At very high laser power densities one should expect that the new intermediates could also be photochemically transformed to other intermediates or products and that some of the latter processes in the above changes could be due to photochemical changes. In these cases the lifetimes of the different species should be power dependent and their time dependent concentrations will have different from linear dependency on the power of the initial photolytic or the probe lasers.

Optical flash or laser photolysis experiments in which the optical absorption spectrum of the system is recorded as a function of delay time after a short photolysis laser pulse could differentiate between the different schemes above. Different schemes will give different time dependent optical absorption spectra. The differentiation is simplest when the absorption spectra of A and its photoproducts are in different spectral regions.

The different schemes above can also be distinguished by using TRRR techniques. At the moment this technique might take more effort than the optical methods. However, it can be done with more accuracy since vibrational Raman bands are better resolved than optical absorption bands. A detailed study of the observed change of the resonance Raman spectrum with time and with probe laser frequency should, in principle, enable one to distinguish between the different schemes given above. This will be possible if the photoproducts in a certain scheme are produced with different rates or have different optical absorption maxima (and thus different resonance Raman enhancement profiles).

As an example, scheme i) gives a new transient Raman spectrum in which all the observed vibrational bands have the same rise time and the same enhancement profile. In scheme ii) all the new bands should have the same rise time but the relative band intensity of the new spectrum should change upon changing the probe laser frequency (if B and C have different optical absorption profiles). Scheme iii) predicts changes in the relative intensity of the new bands with both the laser probe frequency as well as the time of delay between the photolysis and probe laser pulses. The difference between scheme iii) and iv) is that in iii) the bands of C and D could have different rise and decay times while in iv) they all should have similar rise times. Schemes iii) and v) are similar except that A in iii) disappears permanently upon laser exposure while in v) A regains its concentration and no permanent photochemical damage takes place. In scheme vi) the rise time of the vibrational bands of the $(AB)^*$ transient (an excimer or an exciplex) should depend on the concentration of B.

It is thus clear that TRRR has a number of degrees of freedom at its disposal (delay times, probe laser frequency and the power of the photolytic laser) which when used together could identify the spectra and the kinetics of the different transients formed in a photochemical or photobiological change.

As was pointed out earlier, the techniques discussed here can also be used to obtain the vibrational spectra of intermediates formed as a result of any pulsed initial perturbation. Thus in the discussion above, the process involving $h\nu$ (the first step) could be the initial perturbing pulse. The photolysis laser source in the discussion in this article should be replaced by the perturbing source. The length of the perturbing pulse, if too long, could set a limit on the time resolution of the experiment, just as in the case of photochemical changes.

C. The Basic Elements of the Experimental Setup. The basic elements of TRRR experiments are: a photolysis source; a laser probe source (whose scattered radiation by the photolabile sample contains the vibrational spectra of the photodecomposed sample and its transients); a dispersing instrument (e.g., a spectrometer) and an optical multichannel analyzer (OMA) system used as a detector.

1. Laser systems and time variation. A number of methods can be employed, using either pulsed or c.w. lasers as photolytic and probe sources to determine the RR spectrum of the transients with time. These are discussed below.

i. Pulsed lasers. Two pulsed lasers can be used to provide both a photolysis and probe pulse separated by a variable time delay. The pulse duration of the longest pulse could set a limit on the time resolution of the experiment. It is conceivable that this technique could be used in the picosecond time regime. One laser setup could also be used, in which the fundamental or one of the harmonics of a YAG or ruby pump laser is used as the photolysis pulse and one of the other harmonics or the fundamental could be used as the probe laser. One pulsed laser with a dye laser system can also be used in which the pump or its harmonics becomes the photolytic pulse and the dye laser light can be used as the probe for the different intermediates. The shortest time delay in the pulsed laser experiments is limited either by the pulse width (in the picosecond time range) or by the shortest time the probe pulse can be delayed from the photolytic pulse (in the picosecond time range). The convenient long time delay could be accomplished by sending the probe pulse around the laboratory a few times (producing a delay time in the nanosecond range).

It is also conceivable that one laser pulse could be used as both the photolysis and the probe laser. By studying the RR spectrum as a function of power, the Raman spectrum of the species formed during the pulse duration and enhanced at the laser frequency used for photolysis will be observed. It is conceivable that the amplified picosecond pulses produced from the mode locked-cavity dumped techniques (16) could be used to determine the RR spectra of species formed in the pico- and hopefully in the sub-picosecond time scale.

ii. c.w. lasers.

a. am-modulation techniques. A c.w. laser can be transformed into a pulsed laser for kinetic studies by amplitude modulation techniques. A simple modulation technique uses a rotating disk with one (8,9) or two slits in it (9,11). In the one-slit experiments, studying the RR spectra as a function of the slit width and laser power can resolve the spectra of the different transients appearing during the pulse width and whose Raman scattering is enhanced around the photolysis laser frequency. One disadvantage of this technique resides in the fact that the photolysis pulse is also the probe pulse. This limits the use of the enhancement profile technique to identifying only those transients whose absorption maxima are not too far from that of the parent photolabile species.

Due to the fact that lasers can be focused into a very small volume, small slits can be used together with a fast rotating disk to make the time resolution in the one-slit experiment in the tens of nanoseconds when using very sensitive detection techniques and samples with good Raman enhancements. This technique will probably be most useful in the microsecond time regime. Fig. 1 shows the results of this technique when used in the measurement of the time development of the bands characteristic of the intermediates produced in the bacteriorhodopsin photosynthetic cycle (8). Using optical flash photolysis (17) techniques, the rise time of the intermediate having a Raman band at 1570 cm^{-1} is known to be in the microsecond time scale.

In the experiment using a rotating disk with two slits (9,11), one (large) slit could produce the photolysis pulse while a narrow slit placed at variable distance from the first slit (thus producing different delay times) could be used to produce the probe pulse. Another rotating chopper with only one slit (synchronized with the probe slit) could be placed (9) in front of the spectrometer entrance slit. This prevents detection of Raman scattering from the photolysis slit. With the present laser powers and OMA detection, this technique might prove useful in the milli- to microsecond time scale. In all the above experiments, a large volume of the photolabile sample is used such that the permanent photoproducts do not interfere with the primary change under examination. The chopper rotation speed and slit width should be adjusted such that the time dependence of the Raman spectra is not limited by the diffusion of the scattering molecules from the laser focus volume. This can easily be checked by repeating the experiment using a stable scattering molecule in the same solvent and at the same temperature.

iii. Sample flowing techniques. Instead of using pulsed lasers, or modulating the c.w. lasers, the sample itself could be "pulsed" by flowing it across a focused c.w. (or pulsed) laser. The variation of time can be accomplished by either changing the sample flow rate (10) or by changing the focus size of the laser used. With a fixed flow and laser focus, intermediates appearing later in time can also be observed (18) by either increasing the laser power or by changing the laser frequency (to get more enhancement) or both.

2. The detection system. In the time dependent experiment, the OMA offers a more accurate method of detection than the photon counting technique. The details of operation, the different types of applications and the usefulness of this detection technique are given in a number of the articles contained in this

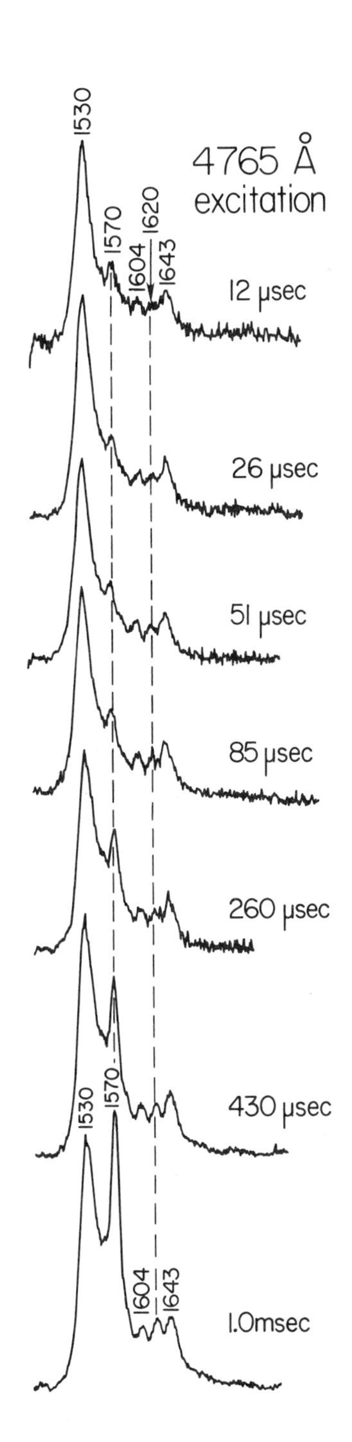

Figure 1. Time-resolved resonance Raman spectra of light adapated bacteriorhodopsin (bR) taken by using a c.w. Ar^+ ion laser modulated with a rotating chopper having one slit of variable width (8, 9). The different times indicated are obtained by varying the slit width and are calculated from the chopping frequency, chopper radius and the slit width. Upon light absorption, bR goes through a number of intermediates appearing at different times (17) and finally the system is recovered (i.e., follows a cyclic scheme, process v, in the text). The total period of the cycle is on the millisecond time scale. The Raman intensity of the bands at 1570 cm^{-1} and at 1620 cm^{-1} increases relative to the band of the unphotolyzed bR at 1530 cm^{-1} as the photolysis pulse width increases. The band at 1570 cm^{-1} is known (19) to be due to the bM_{412} intermediate formed from the bL_{550} intermediate whose lifetime is 40 μsec. By using another Ar^+ laser line (at 5145 Å) and repeating the same experiment (8), the 1620 cm^{-1} band appeared at an earlier time than the 1570 cm^{-1} band suggesting that the two bands belong to two different intermediates, with the 1620 cm^{-1} band probably belonging (8) to the bL_{550} whose absorption maximum is at 550 nm.

volume. We will only discuss here its advantages as they pertain to the time resolved Raman experiment.

By the use of OMA detection, different Raman bands in the spectrum (or a large number of them, depending on the dispersion of the spectrometer used) can be obtained under the same conditions, e.g., the same intensity of photolytic and probe laser sources, the same laser frequencies and the same delay times between the photolytic and the probe lasers. This leaves the observed difference in the different resonance Raman band intensities to result solely from the time dependent behavior of the concentration of the different species resulting from the photolysis of the system being studied. Spectrometers with photon counting detection systems are required to scan the frequency domain to record the Raman spectrum. During the scan, laser power, laser frequency, delay time, pulse-duration or sample flow rate can change and thus can result in making the observed relative Raman band intensities not solely dependent on the time behavior of the photochemical system studied. The OMA is further well suited for subtracting the Raman spectra obtained at low photolysis laser power from that at high power in order to obtain the Raman spectrum of the photolysis products at a certain time delay and with a certain probe laser enhancement (see Fig. 2). The subtraction technique can also be used to get a difference spectrum of short and long delay times (13). Additionally, with a cooled vidicon, the intensified SIT with its integration capability can detect a Raman spectrum with excellent signal-to-noise in a much shorter time than any of the present photon counting methods. The OMA detection with its triggering capability can be extremely useful in the time resolved experiments when using the two pulsed lasers technique. The OMA can be turned off during the photolysis pulse and can then be turned on together with the probe pulse at any specified delay time longer than 50 nsec (the time resolution limit on the existing PARC pulser).

Acknowledgment

The author wishes to thank Dr. James Terner and Dr. Alan Campion whose collaboration on the research in this field has made it both educational and very fruitful. Some of the ideas presented in this paper have come about because of our mutual interaction. I also wish to thank them for giving me permission to use the spectra shown in Figs. 1 and 2, taken from their Ph.D. theses completed here with me at UCLA. The financial support of the Department of Energy, Office of Basic Energy Sciences, is also gratefully acknowledged.

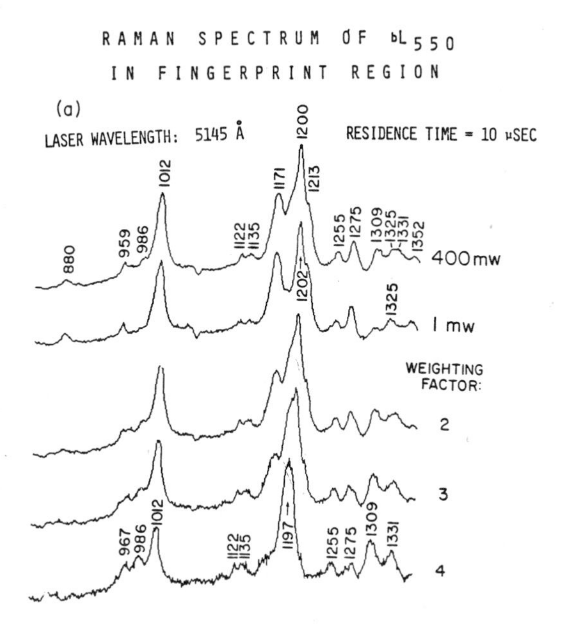

Figure 2. The results of the time resolved resonance Raman spectra of bacteriorhodopsin obtained by using the sample flow technique with one c.w. laser focused in such a volume that the sample residence time is in the 10 μsec range. At 1 mw (second spectrum from top) little or no photolysis of bacteriorhodopsin has taken place. At laser power of 400 mw (top spectrum), a great deal of photolysis has taken place. In the 10 μsec scale, both the bK_{590} and bL_{550} transients should be present together with the unphotolyzed sample. Using a laser at 5145 Å makes the enhancement of the Raman spectrum of the bK_{590} (with a maximum at 590 nm) small compared to that for the bL_{550} (with a maximum at 550 nm). bL_{550} is thus expected to be the only transient that would show Raman scattering together with the unphotolyzed sample. With this in mind, one can obtain (13, 18) the spectrum of bL_{550} (bottom spectrum) by subtracting appropriate amounts of the low power (unphotolyzed) spectrum from the high power spectrum (containing the spectra of the unphotolyzed bR and the bL_{550} intermediate).

Abstract

Various possible time resolved techniques are discussed which enable one to measure the vibrational spectra (and what they entail of structural information) of the distinct transient intermediates formed in different photochemical decomposition schemes and at different times (in the sec-picosec range). The techniques make use of: 1) the difference in the time development behavior of the different intermediates, 2) the difference in the absorption maxima and thus the difference in the resonance Raman enhancements for the different intermediates, and 3) the laser power. The techniques use one or two lasers for the photolytic and probe sources as well as an optical multichannel analyzer as a detector. Some of the results are shown for the intermediates in the photosynthetic cycle of bacteriorhodopsin.

Literature Cited

1. Busch, G. E. and Rentzepis, P. M., Science (1976) 194, 276.

2. Holten, Dewey and Windsor, M. W., Ann. Rev. Biophys. Bioeng. (1978) 7, 189.

3. Bridoux, M., C. R. Acad. Sc. Fr. (1964) 258, 5620; Bridoux, M., Chapput, A., Crunelle, M. and Delhaye, M., Adv. in Raman Spectr., ed. by J. P. Mathieu (1973) pp. 65-69; Delhaye, M., Proceedings of the Fifth International Conference on Raman Spectroscopy, ed. by Schmid et al. (1976) pp. 747-752; Bridoux, M., Deffontaine, A. and Reiss, C., C.R. Acad. Sc. (1976) 282, 771; Bridoux, M. and Delhaye, M., in "Advances in Infrared and Raman Spectroscopy," Vol. 2, eds. R. J. H. Clark and R. E. Hester (Heyden, 1976) p. 140.

4a. Pagsberg, P., Wilbrandt, R., Hansen, K. B. and Weisberg, K. V., Chem. Phys. Lett. (1976) 30, 538.

4b. Lyons, K. B., Carter, H. L. and Fluery, P. A., 3rd Inter-National Conference on Light Scattering in Solids, July 1975, eds. M. Balkanski, R. C. C. Leite and S. P. S. Porto (Flammarion, Paris) pp. 244-248.

5. Yaney, P. P., J. Opt. Soc. Am. (1972) 62, 1297; Van Duyne, R. P., Jeanmaire, D. L. and Shriver, D. F., Anal. Chem. (1974) 46, 213; Lyttle, F. E. and Kelsey, M. S., Anal. Chem. (1974) 46, 855; Nicol, M., Wiget, J. and Wu, C. K., Proceedings of the Fifth International Conference on Raman Spectroscopy, ed. by Schmid et al. (1976) pp. 504-505.

6. Woodruff, W. H. and Atkinson, G. H. Anal. Chem. (1976) 48, 186.

7. Campion, Alan, Terner, James and El-Sayed, M. A., Nature (1977) 265, 659.

8. Campion, Alan, El-Sayed, M. A. and Terner, James, Biophys. J. (1977) 20, 369.

9. Campion, Alan, El-Sayed, M. A. and Terner, James, Proc. Soc. Photo-Opt. Instru. Eng. (1977) 113, 128.

10. Marcus, M. A. and Lewis, A., Science (1977) 195, 1328.

11. Terner, James, Campion, Alan and El-Sayed, M. A., Proc. Natl. Acad. Sci. USA (1977) 74, 5212.

12. Woodruff, William H. and Farquharson, Stuart, Science (1978) 201, 831.

13. Terner, James, Ph.D. dissertation, UCLA, 1978.

14. Johnson, Bruce B. and Peticolas, Warner L., Ann. Rev. Phys. Chem. (1976) 27, 465.

15a. Spiro, Thomas G., Accts. Chem. Res. (1974) 7, 339.

15b. Spiro, Thomas G. and Stein, Paul, Ann. Rev. Phys. Chem. (1977) 28, 501.

16. For a recent article, see: Advances in Subpicosecond Spectroscopic Techniques, C. V. Shank and E. P. Ippen, in Advances in Laser Chemistry," A. H. Zewail, ed., Springer Series in Chemical Physics (Springer, Berlin, Heidelberg, New York, 1978) pp. 145-148.

17. Lozier, R. H., Bogomolni, R. A. and Stoeckenius, W., Biophys. J. (1976) 15, 955; Kung, M. C., De Vault, D., Hess, B. and Oesterhelt, D., Biophys. J. (1975) 15, 907; Kaufmann, K. J., Rentzepis, P. M., Stoeckenius, W. and Lewis, A., Biochem. Biophys. Res. Commun. (1976) 68, 1109.

18. Terner, James, Hsieh, Chung-Lu and El-Sayed, M. A., Biophys. J., in press.

19. Mendelsohn, R., Verma, A. L. and Bernstein, H. J., Can. J. Biochem. (1974) 52, 774.

RECEIVED December 22, 1978.

11

An Apparatus for Obtaining Accurate Transient Absorption Spectra on the Picosecond Time Scale

R. BRUCE WEISMAN and BENJAMIN I. GREENE

Laboratory for Research on the Structure of Matter, Department of Chemistry, University of Pennsylvania, Philadelphia, PA 19104

Steady state absorption spectra of chemical and biological systems have traditionally yielded a wealth of information essential to many types of research. Within the last decade, as time resolved studies have pushed into the picosecond regime, a powerful probe of the ultrafast dynamical behavior of systems has correspondingly proved to be their transient absorption properties. The bulk of these picosecond transient absorption experiments have measured kinetics at a single probe wavelength following optical excitation of the sample. Yet it is increasingly clear that such single wavelength data cannot be properly interpreted without a great deal of auxiliary knowledge concerning the identities and spectra of the states of all components in the system (1). Since such information is obviously rarely available, one must instead attempt to obtain the maximum amount of spectral information from the sample at each time interval — that is, a full transient absorption spectrum — in order to unravel dynamical pathways.

The barriers to this approach have been technical in nature. Mode-locked Nd:glass lasers remain a common light source for picosecond spectroscopic studies, but they suffer from poor reproducibility and very low repetition rates. These features combine to make wavelength scanning techniques unsuitable with such lasers. The alternative approach is to employ multichannel optical detection and thereby obtain full spectral coverage with each laser shot. It is also necessary to eliminate the effects of shot-to-shot variations of the laser output.

In this paper we report the construction and use of a device which meets these goals. It is a double-beam transient absorption spectrometer based on a low repetition rate mode-locked

0-8412-0504-3/79/47-102-227$05.00/0

Nd:glass laser. The two crucial features of this apparatus are an optical configuration designed specifically to optimize the spectrometric range and accuracy, and an advanced two dimensional optical multichannel analyzer system which acquires and processes two full spectral data tracks for each laser shot. In the following sections we present details of the system's design followed by examples of its high accuracy and wide utility in scientific applications.

DESCRIPTION OF THE APPARATUS

The time resolution of our apparatus results from the use of picosecond-scale optical pulses generated by a mode-locked Nd:glass laser system. The oscillator stage of this system consists of an Owens-Illinois ED-2 Brewster angled rod, a 7 meter radius total reflector, an aperture to restrict the transverse mode structure to TEM_{oo}, a type I KDP second harmonic generator for stabilization[2], and a flat output coupler in contact with a flowing dye cell for the Eastman 9860 passive mode-locking solution. Proper mode-locking is obtained only within a narrow range of alignment and operating parameters. The oscillator then produces a low amplitude train of approximately 70 pulses spaced by 5ns and having 8 ps characteristic width, 1.06 μm wavelength, and fundamental Gaussian transverse intensity distribution. We use an electronically driven Pockels cell placed between crossed polarizing prisms to extract one of these pulses from early in the train for use in the experiments. The extracted pulse is then amplified to an energy of 30 mJ in two double-passed amplifier rods. It next passes through two nonlinear KDP crystals which generate the second harmonic, at 530 nm, and the third harmonic, at 353 nm, with high efficiency. The laser system is fired at 100 s intervals.

We are interested in measuring the transient absorption spectra of samples at various times after their sudden excitation to higher electronic states. For this purpose a conventional two pulse excite-and-probe configuration is employed, in which interpulse jitter is negligible because the same single amplified laser pulse is the source for both of those used in the measurement. Figure 1 schematically depicts our optical configuration. A dichroic beamsplitter reflects the ultraviolet third harmonic pulse, used for excitation, while transmitting the first and second harmonics. Filters are placed in the excitation beam to eliminate visible light leakage and to attenuate the ultraviolet beam to an appropriate energy, which corresponds typically to

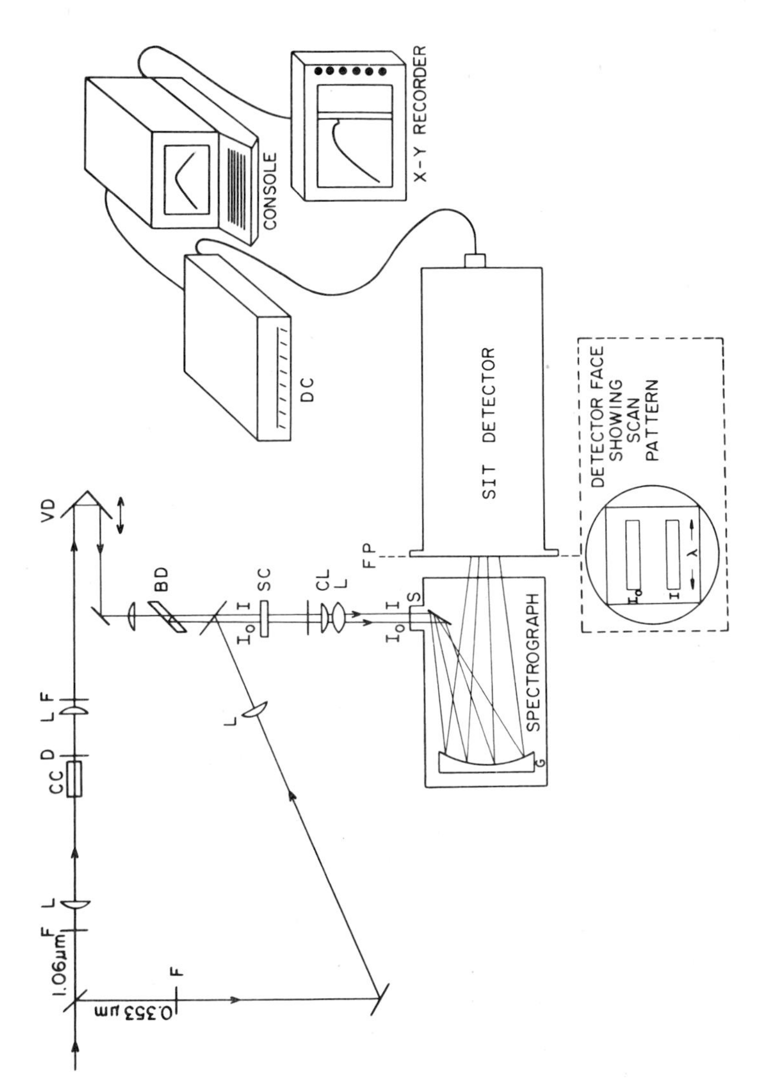

Figure 1. Schematic diagram of the apparatus. The laser system which produces a 1.06 μm ultrashort pulse and its 353 nm third harmonic is not shown. F denotes filter; L, lens; CC, continuum generation cell; D, diffusing plate; CL, cylindrical lens; S, spectrograph slit; G, concave grating; FP, focal plane; DC, detector controller. I_0 *and I label the continuum beams passing through unexcited and excited sample volumes.*

250 μJ at the sample. After the third harmonic has been filtered it passes through a fixed optical delay line and a lens which focuses it into the 1 mm pathlength sample cell through a 320μm diameter aperture in contact with the cell's front window.

The probe beam for our work is a broadband picosecond-duration continuum from which we measure induced absorptions. As found by Alfano and Shapiro[3], such a continuum may be generated by focusing a powerful laser pulse into a suitable liquid medium. We take the 1.06 μm first harmonic transmitted through the dichroic beam splitter, filter it to remove second harmonic light, and focus it into a 5 cm cell of phosphoric acid. The emerging continuum light is spatially filtered by transmission through ground glass scatter plates and separated from residual 1.06 μm light with an infrared absorbing color filter. After recollimation it proceeds through a reflective delay line which can be adjusted to provide for probe pulse arrival times of approximately -100 ps to +700 ps relative to the excitation pulse.

Because the picosecond continuum is generated through a highly nonlinear process, its detailed spatial, spectral, and intensity characteristics vary from shot to shot more severely than do the laser pulses used to generate it. In order to achieve a high degree of reliability in our spectral measurements, it is therefore necessary to obtain double beam spectra in which the data are corrected for continuum fluctuations for every shot. This is accomplished by splitting the continuum into two parallel beams displaced from one another by several millimeters. Both are focused into the sample cell through a dichroic mirror used to collinearly recombine the ultraviolet excitation pulse with the main continuum beam. In the sample, then, that continuum beam passes through the excited volume while the replica continuum beam traverses an unexcited region. A comparison of the two resulting spectral intensity distributions allows a determination of the desired induced absorbance spectrum.

To acquire this information, the two displaced continuum beams are imaged with a cylindrical and a spherical lens onto different positions along the length of the entrance slit of a low dispersion spectrograph (Instruments SA, model UFS-200). The two resulting parallel dispersed spectra are fully separated from each other at the focal plane, where they are detected by the model 1254 SIT detector head of an EG + G Princeton Applied Research Corporation optical multichannel analyzer system. In conjunction with a model 1216 detector controller and model 1215 console, this detector is programmed with a two dimensional scan pattern consisting of two parallel 500-channel tracks with perpendicular widths and positions adjusted to include only the locations of the dispersed continuum beams. Each channel corresponds to a spectral width of 0.6 nm. The spectral resolution is approximately 6 nm (determined by the slitwidth of the spectrograph) and the range, 300 nm.

For each laser shot, the two raw spectra are digitally stored in the memory of the console and processed channel-by-channel in the following programmed sequence. First, the contribution of dark current and flashlamp background light is subtracted from both tracks. The resulting net I_0 spectrum is then divided by the net I spectrum and the logarithm of the ratio spectrum calculated. This result is held for future use. On the next laser shot, the ultraviolet excitation beam is blocked but the data are acquired and processed exactly as described above. Then the difference in the two logarithmic spectra is computed, thereby giving the full double-beam transient absorbance spectrum at the time delay corresponding to the setting of the variable delay line. To improve the signal-to-noise ratio and accuracy of the spectrum, this data collection cycle is repeated several times and the resulting spectra are normalized to the relative excitation energies and then averaged together. The Savitzky-Golay smoothing routine supplied in the OMA software provides some additional noise reduction. Alternation of excited and unexcited data is important in eliminating errors caused by slow optical alignment drifts. Another key factor in achieving reliable results is the careful monitoring of laser pulse-trains, with rejection of all data from shots in which the pulse-trains fail to meet stringent quality criteria.

An important test of a transient spectrometer's accuracy, stability, and noise level is provided by a baseline spectrum. This is an averaged spectrum obtained in exactly the same way as actual data, except that the ultraviolet excitation beam is kept blocked when it would otherwise be open. The lowest trace shown in Figure 2 is a typical 5-cycle baseline spectrum for our system. Systematic deviation from zero is less than 0.01 absorbance units throughout, and the r.m.s. noise level varies from 0.03 near the edges to 0.007 near the center of the spectrum. These noise variations are inversely related to the detected single beam intensity spectrum, which drops on the blue side because of the continuum distribution and the transmissive properties of our beam combiner, and on the red side because of the photocathode response of the SIT detector head. A high degree of intensity linearity in the OMA is necessary for our

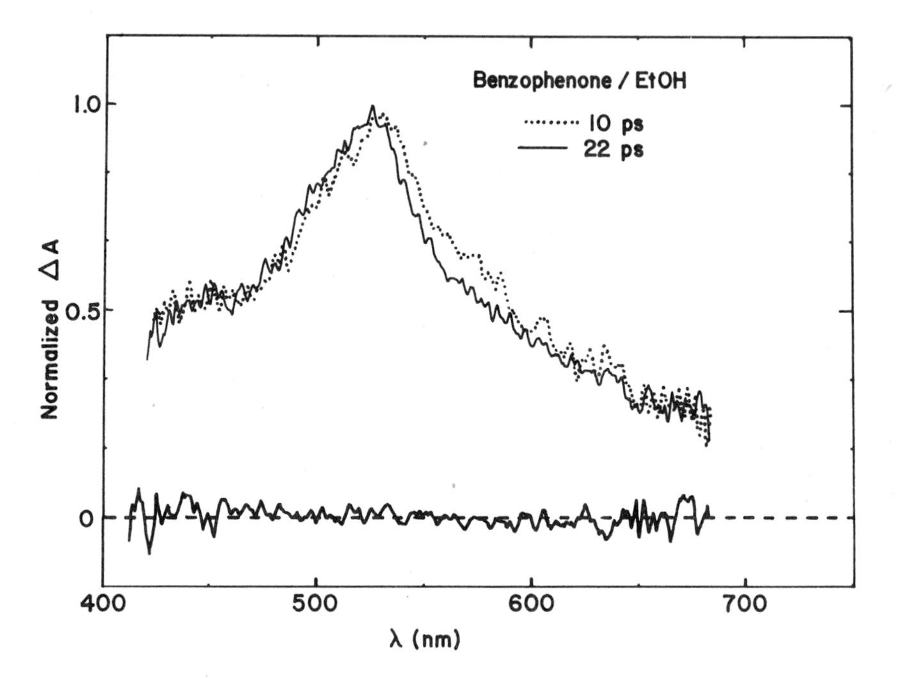

Figure 2. Transient absorbance and baseline spectra for benzophenone in ethanol solution. The lowest trace is a baseline obtained with the 353 nm excitation pulse blocked. The dotted line spectrum was taken 10 ps after sample excitation; the solid line spectrum was taken at a delay of 22 ps. These two transient spectra are drawn normalized to the same peak height to facilitate bandshape comparisons.

application. This is assured by using multiple readout scans to suppress target lag effects and by avoiding light levels large enough to cause local detector saturation. With these precautions even large variations in the single beam spectra are found to normalize accurately. Our techniques are of course suitable for the study of induced transmission (bleaching) as well as induced absorption effects.

For large transient signals it is necessary to consider possible distortions of the observed spectra that result from beam geometrical effects. These spectral distortions are caused by spatially non-uniform concentrations of the excited species across the probed aperture, reflecting the transverse intensity distribution of the excitation beam. The effect tends to reduce the apparent relative size of induced absorption peaks and to magnify induced transmission peaks. When lasers with multimode transverse structures are used in transient absorption spectroscopy, it is impossible to predict the extent of spectrometric errors caused by the beams' extreme and irreproducible spatial intensity variations. By contrast, our system employs an excitation beam with a smooth Gaussian intensity profile of known size and a collinear probing beam which is essentially uniform across the sample aperture. We have numerically solved the equation that predicts the degree to which the resulting radial distribution of excited states causes spectrometric nonlinearities in the observed spectra and have found that the distortions are not significant for peak induced absorbances of ca. 0.5 or less in our experimental configuration.[4] Normally our spectral peaks fall within this limit.

Another possible source of spectrometric error in strong induced absorptions is leakage of light from one beam into the other or between wavelength regions within one beam. By blocking either of the continuum paths with an opaque object at the sample cell, we find less than 1% leakage into the other beam. Scatter within a track is also low because of the holographic grating of our spectrograph. Thus these effects introduce negligible errors into our results.

The time resolution of the system is determined primarily by the convolution of the excitation and probing pulsewidths. This parameter was found to be approximately 10 ps by a determination of the apparent growth kinetics of a promptly rising excited singlet absorption, a measurement which also specified the delay line setting for which the two pulses are synchronized. Because of group velocity dispersion in transmissive optics, various frequency components of the probing continuum will suffer differing delays and thus have different arrival times at the sample position. This effect is known as "chirp" and for our configuration delays the blue edge from the red edge by about 6 ps. The spectral distortion caused by chirp is greatest when the transient spectrum changes rapidly, as often happens near t = 0. Although we have not corrected for this distortion, we do try to minimize its severity by avoiding very early delay settings for spectra. Of course, the apparatus may be used for single wavelength kinetic studies with no such restriction.

APPLICATIONS

To illustrate the quality of data obtained with this apparatus, we present in Figure 2 transient spectra of benzophenone in ethanol solution measured at two different delay times following excitation at 353 nm. The dotted line represents the spectrum obtained at 10 ps delay while the solid line shows the spectrum at 22 ps normalized to the same peak height. It is clear that the benzophenone spectrum narrows slightly and shifts to the blue over this time interval, an effect which is highly significant in relation to the nature of excited state relaxation processes in this molecular system. Yet the spectral changes involved are subtle and would surely have remained undetected if not for the high level of accuracy afforded by this apparatus. There are also other cases for which this quantitative improvement in the quality of picosecond transient data has led to qualitatively different scientific conclusions. Some of these will be presented, along with a detailed interpretation of the above benzophenone results, in a future publication.[4]

In summary, we have combined state of the art optical multichannel analyzer techniques with well established low repetition rate picosecond laser technology to construct an instrument capable of measuring transient spectra with unprecedented reliability. It is, in its present form, a powerful tool for the investigation of ultrafast processes in biological, chemical, and physical systems. We foresee straightforward extension of the technique to the use of fourth harmonic excitation (at 265 nm) and also a future capability to study gaseous as well as condensed phase samples over a more extended spectral range.

ACKNOWLEDGEMENTS

We wish to thank Prof. Robin Hochstrasser, in whose laboratory this work was performed, for advice and support. Funding was provided by a grant by the National Science Foundation (CHE76-84428) and in part by the MRL Program under Grant No. DMR76-80994.

LITERATURE CITED

1. Greene, B. I., Hochstrasser, R. M., and Weisman, R. B., in Picosecond Phenomena, Shank, C. V., Ippen, E. P., Shapiro, S. L., Eds., Springer-Verlag, Berlin, 1978.
2. Weisman, R. B. and Rice, S. A., Spectroscopy Lett. (1975) 8, 329.
3. Alfano, R. R. and Shapiro, S. L., Phys. Rev. Lett. (1970) 24, 584.
4. Greene, B. I., Hochstrasser, R. M. and Weisman, R. B., J. Chem. Phys., in press.

RECEIVED January 10, 1979.

UNCONVENTIONAL APPLICATIONS

Spectroscopy with the Evanescent Wave in the Visible Region of the Spectrum

GERHARD J. MÜLLER

Zentralinstitut für Biomedizinische Technik; Universität Erlangen Nürnberg; D 8520 Erlangen, Turnstr. 5; West-Germany

This article shows how the evanescent wave can be used with advantage for spectroscopic purposes in the field of biomedical engineering. Three types of spectroscopy can be done with the evanescent wave in the UV-VIS range of the spectrum: (a) attenuated total reflection (ATR) spectroscopy, which is well known in the infrared; (b) the excitation of Raman scattering with the evanescent wave; and (c) the excitation of fluorescence with the evanescent wave. The first two types will be discussed in this article; the third is discussed for example by Hirschfeld (1) and more recently by Watkins and Robertson (2). But before going into details a historical review may be of some interest.

Historical Review

Total internal reflection (TIR) at the interface of an optically dense medium to an optically rare one has been of continuous interest over the years. Closely related to this phenomenon is the existence of an evanescent wave in the second (rare) medium, a fact first mentioned and even proved by Newton (3). More than 150 years later Mach and co-workers (4) used TIR to demonstrate the existence of anomalous dispersion. They reported a method for projecting the dispersion curve $n = n(\lambda)$ directly. To the authors knowledge this is the first time that TIR was used for spectroscopic purposes.

After that the behaviour of the evanescent field rather than possible applications was of primary interest. In 1902 Hall (5) succeeded in photographing the evanescent wave and soon afterwards fluorescence (6) and scattering (7) excited by such waves were observed. In 1910 Schaefer and Gross (8) measured quantitatively the exponential decay of the amplitude of the field with microwaves.

A first rather comprehensive theoretical treatment of TIR, based on Maxwell's theory, was published by Schaefer (9) in 1932. In this treatment a displacement of the incoming and the totally reflected ray, as shown in Figure 1, was predicted. But it was

0-8412-0504-3/79/47-102-239$06.00/0

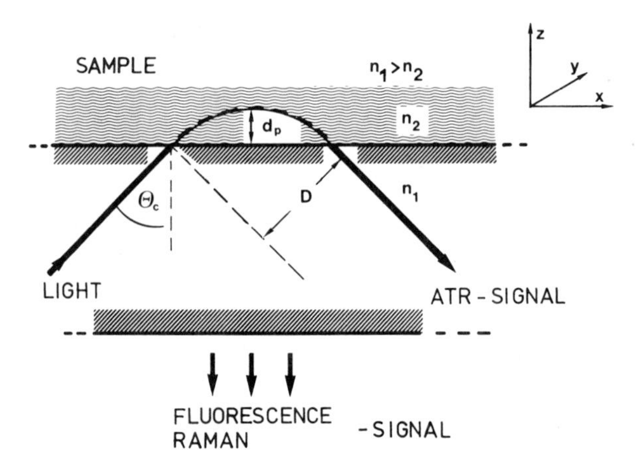

Figure 1. Total internal reflection (TIR). $n_{1,2}$: refractive index; θ_c: critical angle, for TIR the angle of incidence must be larger than θ_c; d_p: penetration; depth; D: Goos-Hänchen shift.

not until 1947 that Goos and Hänchen (10) could report on an experimental proof of that displacement D, which is now known as Goos-Hänchen shift. And it took another 15 years before TIR was again used as a spectroscopic tool. It was rediscovered more or less at the same time by Fahrenfort (11,12) and Harrick (13,14, 15), preferentially for the infrared region of the spectrum.

In 1964 Hansen (16) reported, for the first time, on an application of this technique in the visible region, i.e. the determination of the refractive index n and the absorbance k of Eosin B solutions. A further attempt of applying TIR spectroscopy in the UV-VIS region was published by Hirschfeld in 1966 (17). And it was in 1967 that a detailed review and description of the state of the art of internal reflection spectroscopy was given in a short form by Hirschfeld and Wilks (18) and more comprehensively in the well known book of Harrick (19). In the following years up till now there were many papers on this topic, but with very few exceptions (which will be mentioned later) all of them deal with applications in the infrared region.

This historical review cannot be completed without mention of some of the many theoretical papers, which are recommended to the interested reader for a deeper insight into the physical process of TIR and the behaviour of the evanescent wave (20 - 25).

Total Internal Reflection

Since there are various comprehensive papers and monographs on the physical properties of TIR, this section is restricted to a brief summary of the most important equations and facts.

As seen in the literature cited, in TIR the incoming light forms a standing wave pattern at the interface within the dense medium, whereas in the rare medium the amplitude of the electric field falls off exponentially with the distance from the phase boundary according to

$$\vec{E} = \vec{E}_0 \cdot \exp\left[\frac{-z}{d_p}\right] \tag{1}$$

The depth of penetration d_p (compare Figure 1) which is defined by the distance within which $\vec{E}$ decreases to 1/e, is given by

$$d_p = \frac{\lambda}{n_1 2\pi(\sin^2\theta - (n_2/n_1)^2)^{1/2}}; \quad \theta > \theta_c \tag{2}$$

According to Hirschfeld (26) there is a definite relationship between the penetration depth d_p and the Goos-Hänchen shift D, which is reduced near to the critical angle Θ_c to

$$d_p/D = 1/\cos\theta \quad (3)$$

If the rare medium exhibits absorption, the penetrating wave becomes attenuated. In the case of transmittance measurements at weak absorption the law of Lambert-Beer is valid in a linear approximation also

$$T = \frac{I}{I_0} = e^{-\alpha d} \cong 1 - \alpha d \quad (4)$$

Similarly for the reflectance R can be written

$$R \cong 1 - \alpha d_e \quad (5)$$

where d_e is the "effective layer thickness". That means d_e is that layer thickness that would be needed in transmittance measurements to obtain the same extinction as a single reflection at the boundary to a semi-infinite optically rare medium. Thus d_e can be calculated according to the equation

$$d_e = \frac{(n_2/n_1) E_0^2 d_p}{2\cos\theta} \quad (6)$$

where the denominator corresponds to the finite aperture of the illuminating beam. The behaviour of the electric field is shown in Figure 2 according to theory (20). It should be pointed out that generally the evanescent field has a longitudinal component also, and from Figure 2 it is evident that the field amplitude depends on the polarization of the incident light. Hence the effective layer thickness d_e is different for the incident beam being polarized parallel or perpendicular to the plane of incidence. Therefore, it is general practice to work with polarized light preferentially. For the two directions of polarization of the incident wave the effective thickness $d_{e\perp}$ and $d_{e||}$ are given by

$$\frac{d_{e\perp}}{\lambda} = \frac{(n_2/n_1)\cos\theta}{n_1 \pi (1-(n_2/n_1)^2)(\sin^2\theta - (n_2/n_1)^2)^{1/2}}$$

$$(7)$$

$$\frac{d_{e||}}{\lambda} = \frac{(n_2/n_1)\cos\theta(2\sin^2\theta - (n_2/n_1)^2)}{n_1 \pi (1-(n_2/n_1)^2)[(1+(n_2/n_1)^2)\sin^2\theta - (n_2/n_1)^2](\sin^2\theta - (n_2/n_1)^2)^{1/2}}$$

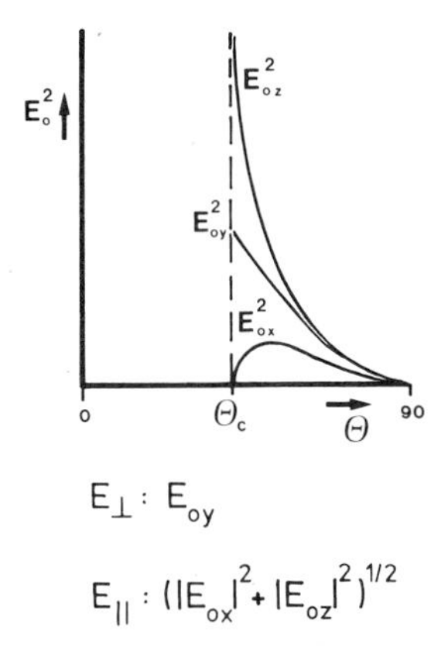

Figure 2. Qualitative behavior of the field strength of the evanescent wave as a function of the angle of incidence ($n_1 = 1.51$; $n_2 = 1.0$). Contrary to the behavior of the electromagnetic field of "normal" light the evanescent field comprises a longitudinal component, too. $E_\perp$ *and* $E_{\|}$ *respectively indicate the direction of polarization of the incident light.*

Equations (2) and (7) are plotted in Figure 3 to indicate the angular dependence.

Considering the mutual relationships of the different parameters in equations (6) and (7) respectively, the effective layer thickness d_e, which is a measure for the "interaction strength" of the evanescent wave with the rare medium, could be increased by increasing the refractive index of the dense material and/or by choosing an angle of incidence close to the critical angle Θ_c.

ATR-Spectroscopy in the Visible Region

As already mentioned, ATR-spectroscopy is a familiar technique in the infrared and has a broad variety of applications. In clinical analysis the samples of interest (e.g. body fluids such as blood, urine, saliva etc.) should remain in their natural composition, i.e., almost always in aqueous solution. Therefore, because of the strong absorption of water in that region, analysis in the infrared is more or less impossible. Thus it is of considerable interest to study the applicability of ATR-techniques in the visible region (27,28).

First there arises the question of high index materials, but contrary to earlier work (17) today there are available some glasses, e.g., SF6 and SF59 from Schott (see Figure 4), which have a sufficiently high refractive index and have adequate resistivity against commonly used solvents. However, as can be seen also from Figure 4, these materials have a relatively high dispersion, i.e., $dn/d\lambda$. Therefore the angle of incidence must be large enough so that at shorter wavelenghts the critical angle will not be included within the finite divergence of the illuminating beam. For in this case the observed spectrum changes dramatically, as shown in Figure 5. This behaviour is well understood and explained in detail in Ref. 19.

There is still another disadvantage normally associated with the use of ATR-techniques for biological samples in the visible. That is the strong adsorption of biomolecules on the surface of the reflection element; this causes adsorption contamination between two successive samples. This problem, however, could be solved (patents pending) by using disposable slides of the same material in optical contact with the reflection element or by using a liquid interface, as shown in Figure 6. For example, $[C_{10}H_7I]$ could be used as a high index liquid, the dispersion of which is also indicated in Figure 4.

When strong adsorption of one or more of the constituents of the sample results in quantitative errors in the determination of the concentration of the various components, a non-polar coating of the disposable slides must be provided.

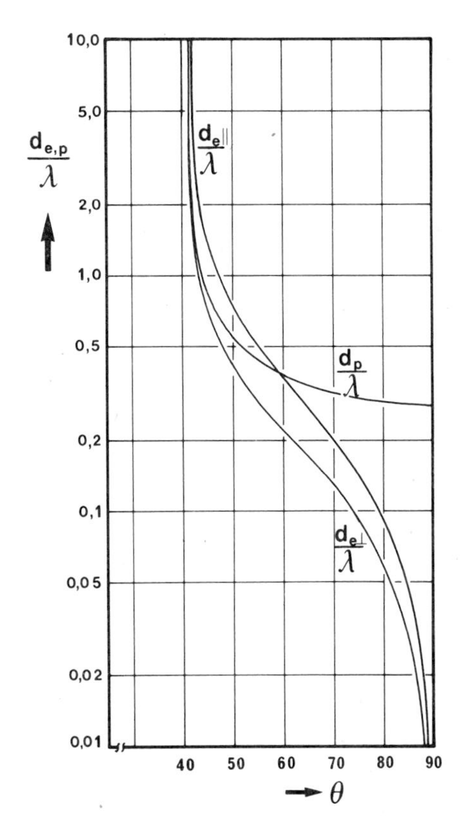

Figure 3. Angular dependence of the "effective layer thickness" (d_e) and the "penetration depth" (d_p) for parallel and perpendicular polarization of the incident light (λ: vacuum wavelength of the light; $n_1 = 1.51$; $n_2 = 1.0$).

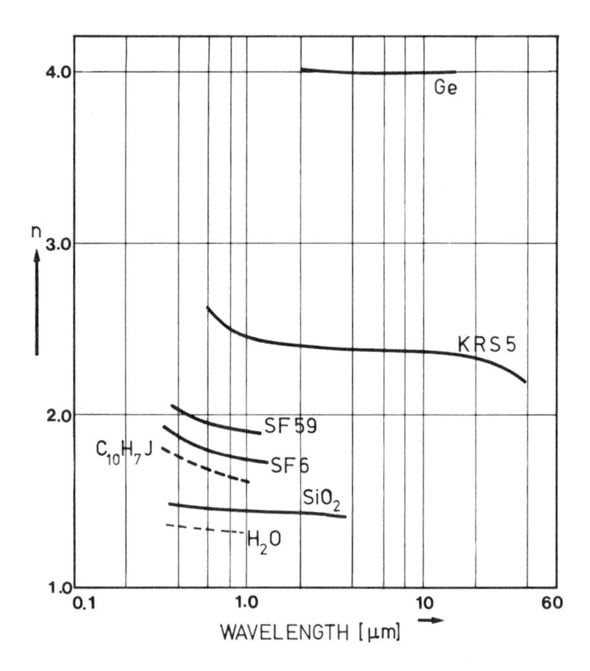

Figure 4. Refractive index as a function of the wavelength for various materials. In the infrared, Germanium and KRS–5 are used preferentially because of their small dispersion in that region. For a comparison also the behaviour of quartz and water is indicated.

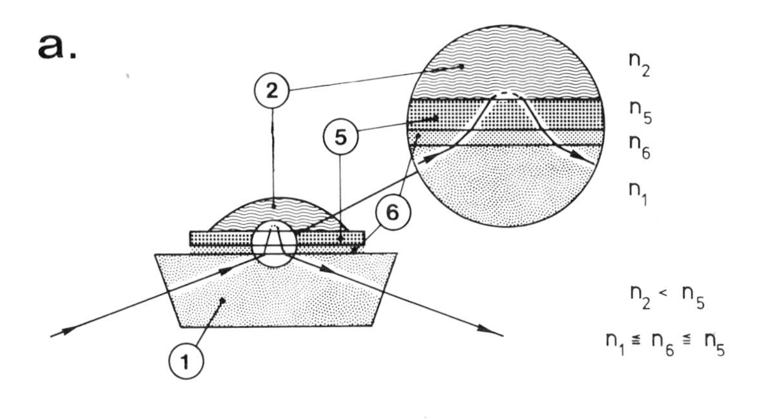

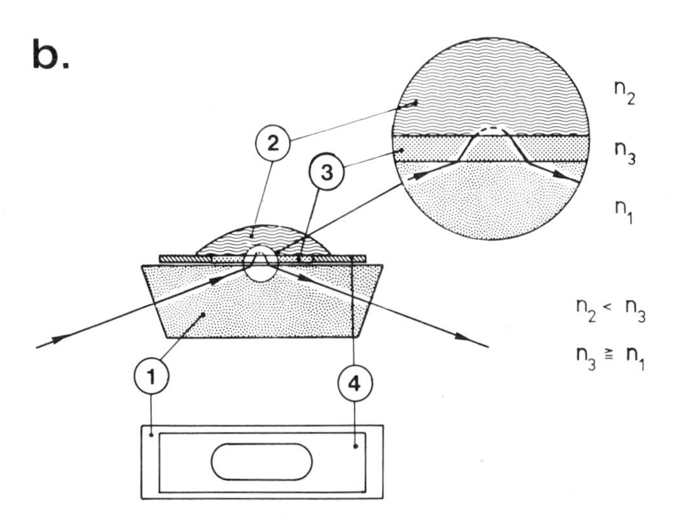

Figure 5. ATR spectra of Eosin B in aqueous solution for three different concentrations and two angles of incidence, one of which is slightly larger than the critical angle. In that case the spectrum represents an "image" of the behaviour of the refractive index (19)*. These spectra are direct recordings, obtained with the OMA II system* (see *Figure 8*).

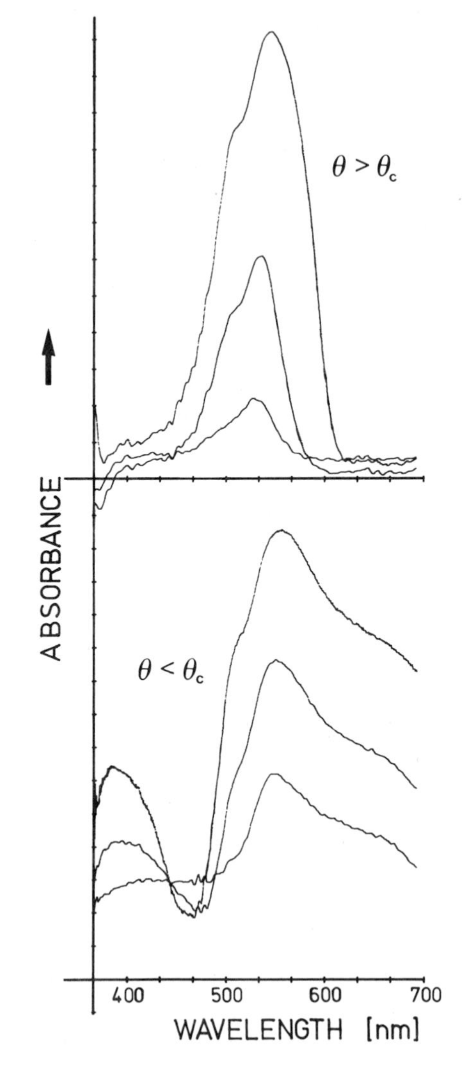

Figure 6. Experimental outfit to obtain a reproducible surface of the reflection element (1). There are two possible solutions, which are especially suited for biological samples (2): (a) disposable slide (5) of high index material in optical contact with the reflection element (1). The optical contact is achieved by means of a liquid (6). (b) coating with a high index liquid (3). The coating is formed by means of a thin foil (4) with an appropriate aperture.

ATR-Experiments

The reflection elements could have geometries similar to those used in the infrared; Figure 7 gives some typical examples. In Figure 8 the entire set-up is shown. The light source is a high pressure xenon arc lamp, which is carefully focussed on a small diaphragm and then collimated by an achromatic lens (L_2) to produce a light beam of small divergency. This light beam is then polarized by means of a polarizer P. The light then travels partially through a horizontal slit and, after being deflected by a mirror M_1, enters the reflection element, where it is totally reflected as previously described. Then it is again deflected by a mirror M_2 back onto the optical axis. This still horizontal "sheet" of light is turned upright by means of an image rotator (a simple Dove prism) and is then focussed onto the entrance slit of a grating polychromator.

Depending on the absorptivity of the sample, multiple reflection elements (Figure 7) may be necessary, rather than the single reflection as described here.

The spectral region of interest is then detected and processed by means of an optical multichannel analyzer (EG&G-PARC; model 1215, OMA). The OMA detector SIT (silicon intensified target), EG&G-PARC model 1254 has been used. It is operated by the detector controller, EG&G-PARC, model 1216, which performs the signal digitization as well. The acquired spectra are displayed in real time on a TV display and on the OMA console. The data storage and processing are also performed by that console which has a 28K of 16 bit core memory and a floppy disk for permanent storage.

The spectra were recorded and processed as follows. In each experiment the background was recorded and stored, then subtracted from both the I and I_o spectra, with and without sample in contact with the reflection element, correspondingly. The two spectra were then compared with each other (I/I_o) to eliminate the nonuniform structures of the lamp and the reflection element (a normalization procedure). Figure 9 shows some spectra obtained in this way.

Perspectives of ATR-Spectroscopy in the Visible Region

In the study of biological samples in their natural composition all spectra of the various constituents are superimposed on one another. Therefore it is difficult to analyze such "natural" spectra, especially if one considers the fact that the spectra of the molecules of interest have little structural information in the UV-Visible region.

In clinical analysis, however, all the possible constituents of a given sample, i.e., a body fluid, are known. What one is seeking is merely the change in the relative concentrations of

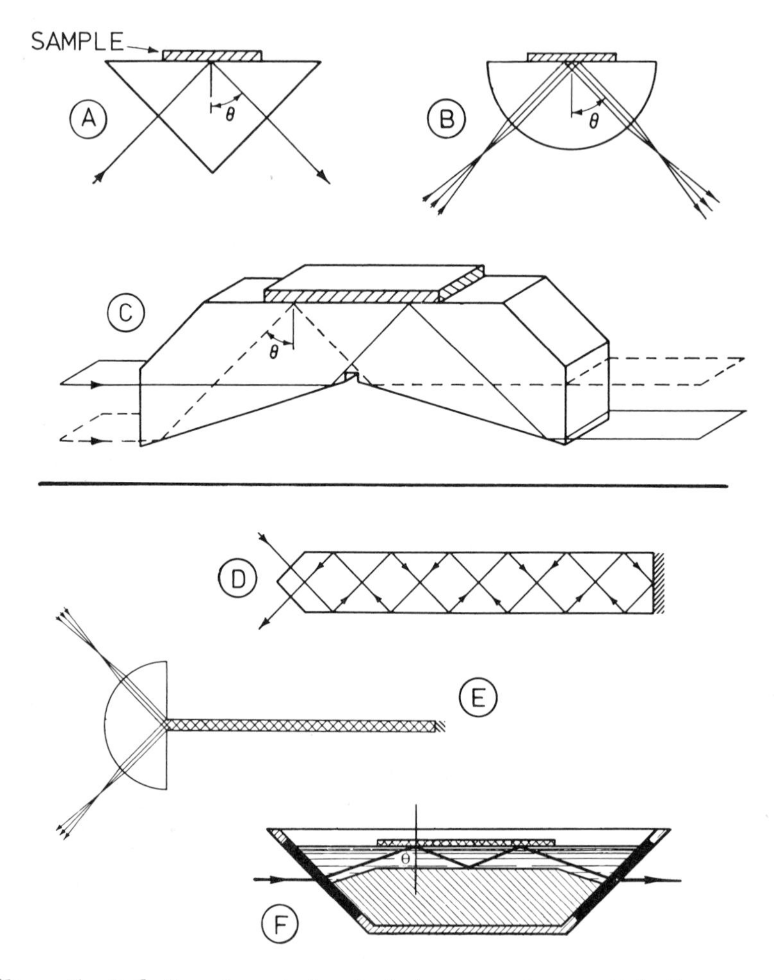

Figure 7. Reflection elements for single (upper part) or multiple (lower part) internal reflection. (A), (D): fixed angle, (B), (E): variable angle, (C): achromatic prism (19), (F): liquid prism for improved optical contact.

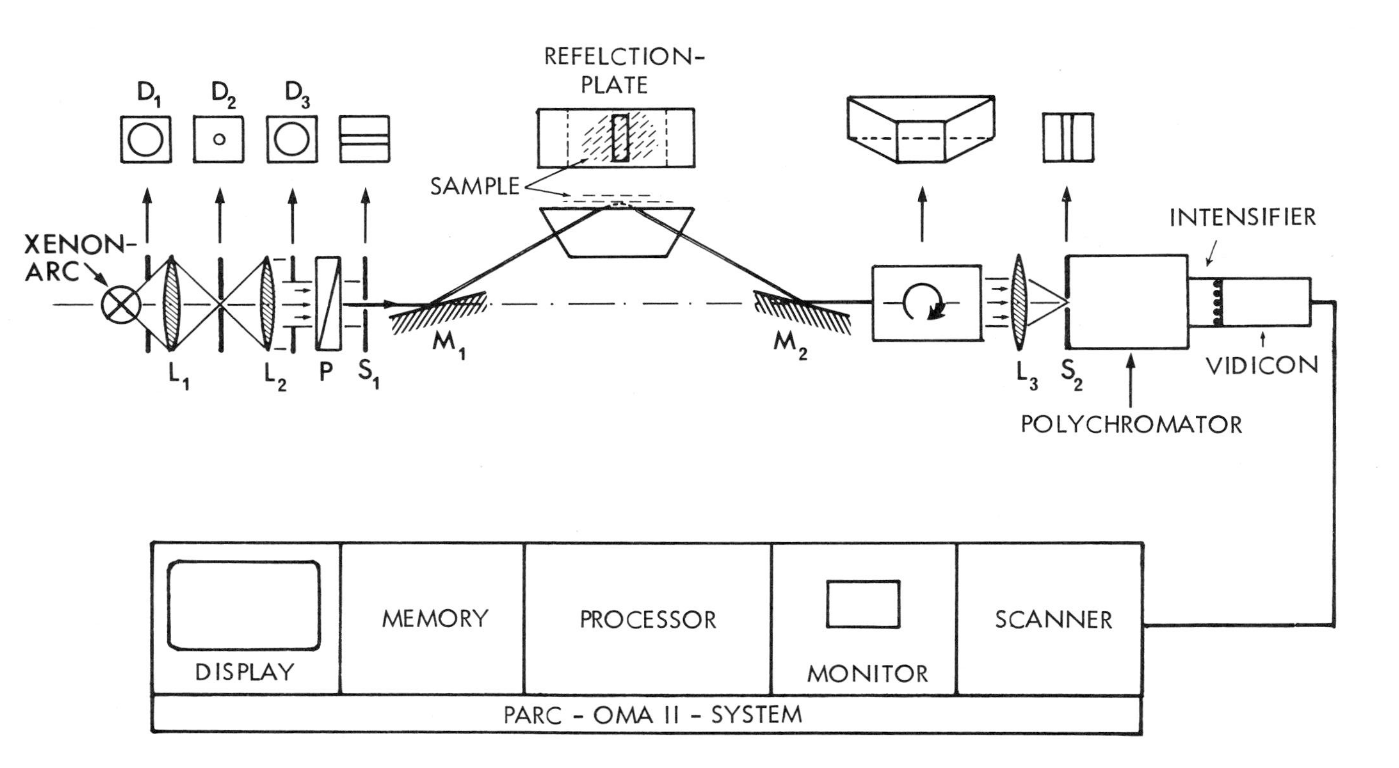

Figure 8. Experimental set-up for ATR spectroscopy by means of an optical multichannel analyzer. $L_{1\text{-}3}$: *lens,* $M_{1,2}$: *mirror, P: polarizer,* $D_{1\text{-}3}$: *diaphragm,* $S_{1,2}$: *slit. For further details see text.*

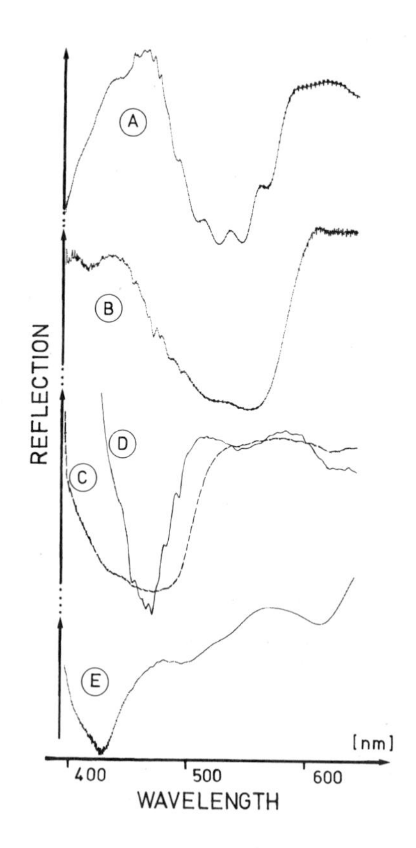

Figure 9. ATR spectra. (A) $KMnO_4$; (B) Cobalamin; (C) Bilirubin; (D) Biliverdin; (E) Haeminacetate.

the various components. Therefore, it is possible to build up a libary of the spectra of the pure constituents and store it on the floppy disk. Now the spectrum of the mixture must be measured with sufficient data points (wavelength resolution elements) taken at the same spectral position as the individual spectra in the library. Each data point then gives an equation with the concentration of the various constituents as variables. In this way an overdetermined set of equations could be formed which can be solved to produce the relative concentration of each individual constituent in the sample (29).

Another and rather tricky approach for analyzing such spectra is described in detail by Wodick and Lübbers (29a).It should be pointed out, however, that in general both methods require the applicability of Beer's law, which is usually absent in ATR (29b). However, if the changes in the relative concentrations are sufficiently small, the relationship between absorptivity and concentration could be linearly approximated. Thus, within this linear range these methods can be used.

Combined with this kind of evaluation the ATR-spectroscopy might be of great importance to clinical analysis. The main advantages of this technique over more conventional techniques for highly absorbing samples (e.g., blood) are the following:

(a) sample preparation is drastically simplified;

(b) very small amounts of the samples are necessary (microsampling);

(c) in comparison with infrared techniques, there is no interference caused by the absorption of water.

For samples of weaker absorbance the use of fiber optics might be required to achieve a sufficiently high number of reflections. Also, using a fiber optics catheter may permit in vivo measurements.

Raman Scattering Excited by the Evanescent Wave

As previously mentioned, the evanescent wave could interact with the optically rare medium not only by being absorbed but also by being scattered either elastically (Rayleigh Scattering) or inelastically (Raman Scattering). Because it is not within the scope of this paper to review the complete history and theory of Raman scattering, further information is indicated in Ref. 30, 31, and 32.

A first attempt to observe a Raman signal excited by the evanescent wave was made in 1973 by Ikeshoji and co-workers (33), but because their signal level was as low as 10 photons per second they could prove only the existence of a Raman signal.

Closely related to the technique described here are the experiments of Takenaka and Nakanaga (33a) using resonance Raman scattering and the excitation of Raman scattering in thin films by means of waveguide effects or resonance enhancement of the electric field, which occurs when the thin film is used as an optical cavity. Within the last few years this work was carried out with great success by Dupeyrat and co-workers (34,35).

Raman scattering with the evanescent wave is of special interest in biochemical laboratories for several reasons (36):

(a) because many of the biological samples are highly absorbent, when conventional scattering geometries are used most of the unscattered light is absorbed and thus damage to the sample may result; whereas the penetration depth of the evanescent wave is very small, and hazardous radiation is totally trapped in the reflection element;

(b) very small amounts of the samples are sufficient;

(c) almost no special processing of the samples is necessary.

Raman Spectroscopy with the Evanescent Wave - Experiments

The main prerequisite to observing a Raman signal excited with the evanescent wave is the use of a high power laser. In the experiments described here the blue line (488 nm) of a cw Argon - Ion laser with a power output of approx. 1.3 watts was used preferentially.

Figure 10 shows the experimental set-up. The sample was placed as a droplet on the upper surface of a double-pass reflection plate made of either fused silica or super dense flint glass (SF6). An image of the solid-liquid interface is formed on the entrance slit of a small grating polychromator, while the elastically scattered Rayleigh light is blocked by an additional coloured glass filter with a cut-off wavelength at 515 nm. The whole spectrum is then detected and processed by the OMA II system. The signal level was on the order of 10^4 photons per second.

Figure 11 gives some spectra of biological samples, which were obtained by evanescent waves, with an angle of incidence close to the critical angle. These rather low resolution spectra are presented merely to demonstrate the potential applicability of the technique.

With the applicability of this method now proved, it was worthwhile to look at the dependence of the spectra on the penetration depth. Figure 12 shows the change of the spectrum of ethanol on quartz caused by tuning the angle of incidence from approx. 80° through the critical angle to a subcritical one, i.e., the laser beam is entering the optical rare material.

Of particular interest is the spectrum at the bottom of Figure 12. In this case the penetration depth is computed to be on the order of approx. 50 nm. Furthermore, considering that the field strength at the interface drops off exponentially, one could expect a possible adsorption effect. Figure 13 speculates on how the alcohol molecules should be arranged on the quartz surface. Unfortunately, however, the spectrum of the reflection plate was predominant here and the possible occurance of new bands - caused by adsorption forces - could therefore not be detected.

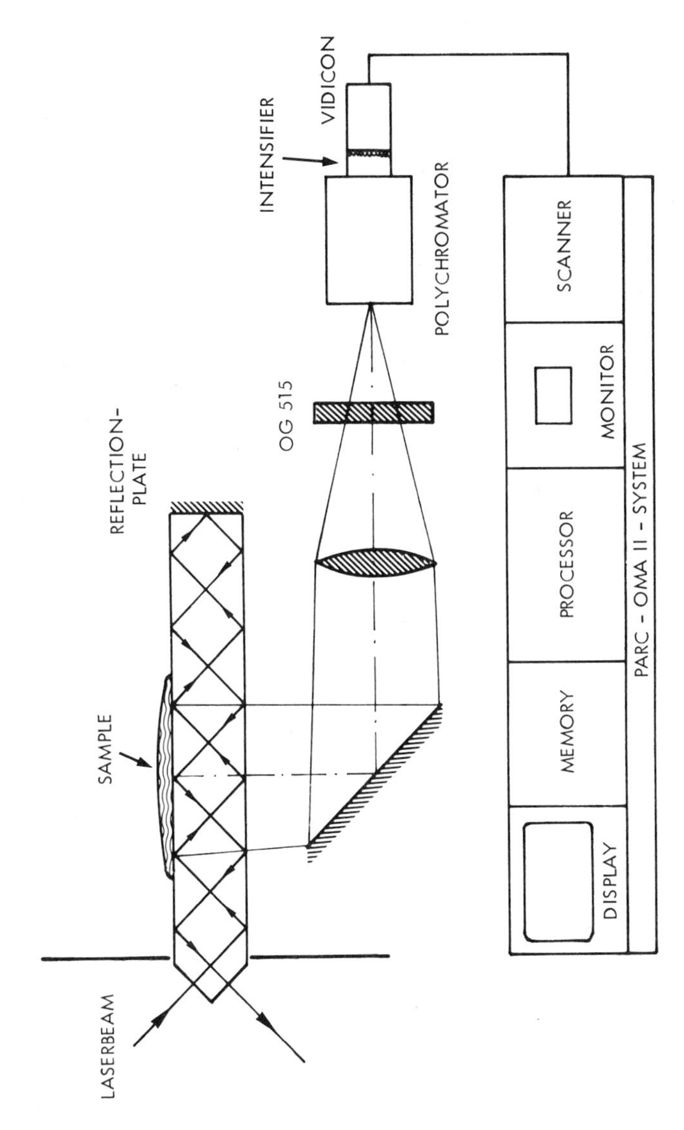

Figure 10. Experimental set-up for Raman spectroscopy with the evanescent wave. For excitation, an argon ion laser was used (λ: 488 nm, output power 1.5 W cw). The material of the reflection plate is fused silica or super dense flint glass. Monochromator: Ebert mount Jarrell–Ash 30 cm focal length; diffraction gratings 150 or 600 g/mm.

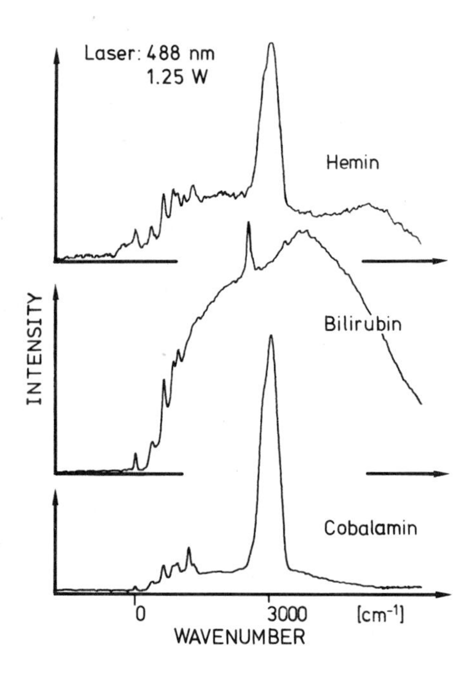

Figure 11. Raman spectra of biomolecules excited by the evanescent wave. (Spectra of the quartz plate and the various solvents not subtracted).

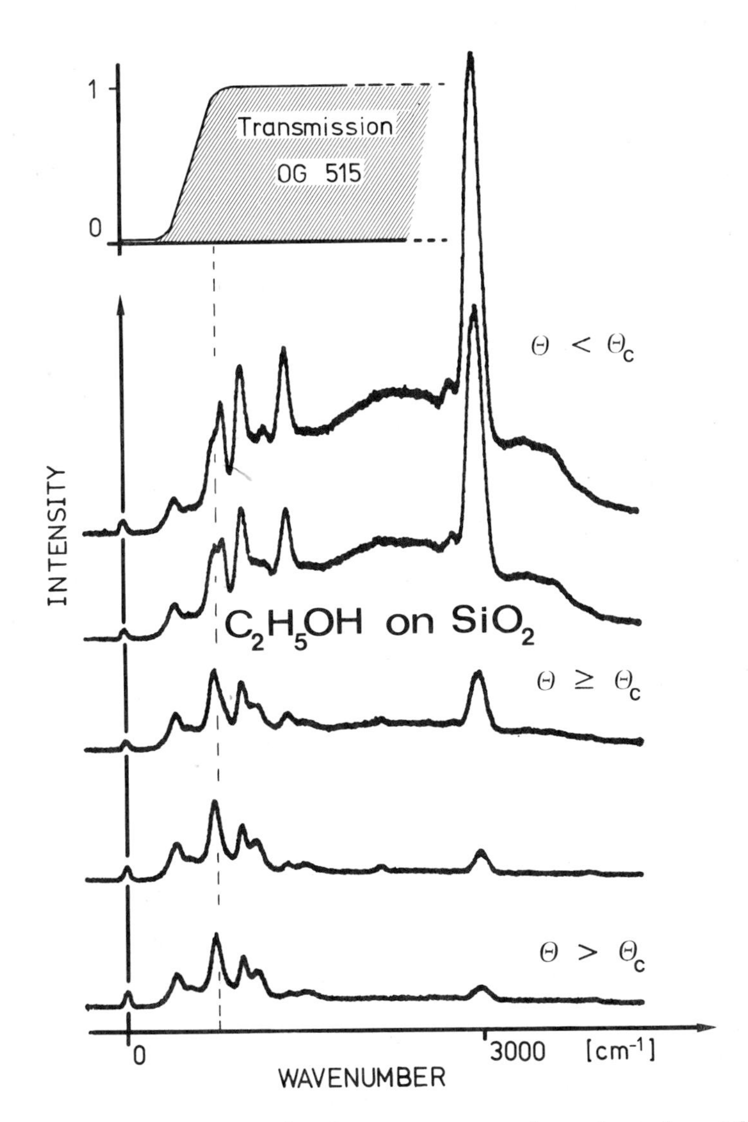

Figure 12. Raman spectra of ethanol on quartz measured at various values of the angles of incidence and thus, various penetration depths. In addition the transmittance spectrum of the glass filter (OG515) is shown (causing the distortion of the spectrum to the left of the cut-off wavelength).

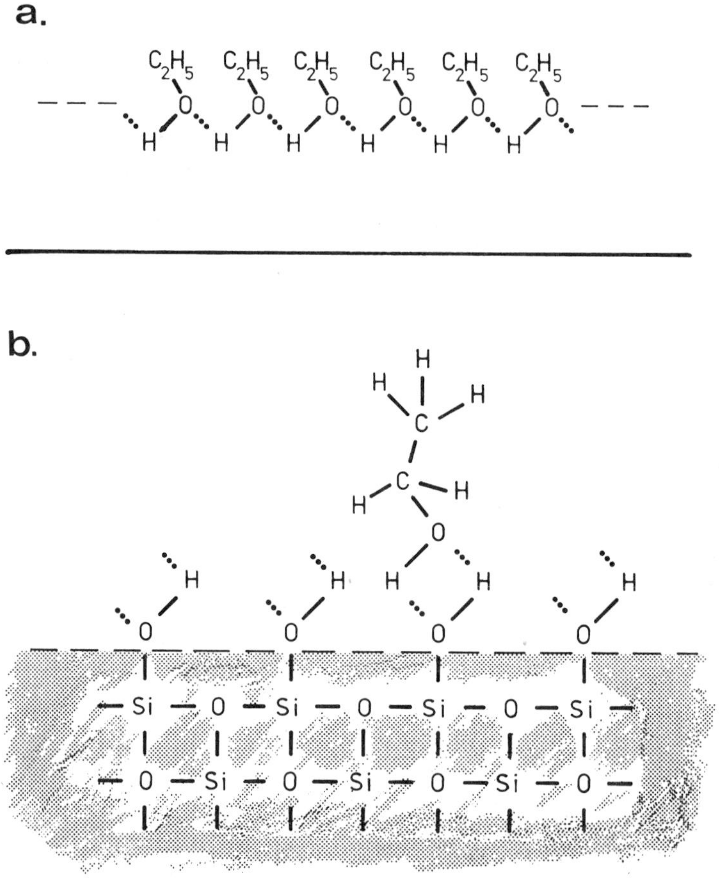

a.

C_2H_5 C_2H_5 C_2H_5 C_2H_5 C_2H_5 C_2H_5

O O O O O O

H H H H H H

b.

H

H C H

C

H C H

O

H H H H H

O O O O

Si — O — Si — O — Si — O — Si

O — Si — O — Si — O — Si — O

Figure 13. (a) schematic drawing of the aggregation of the ethanol molecules in the liquid phase, which is caused by H-bonding (normally the chains are twisted). (b) principle sketch of the adsorption mechanism of ethanol to the silanol groups on the surface of a quartz plate, which is also caused by H-bonding. (For clarity, only one molecule is drawn.)

But with the computing capabilities of the OMA II system this problem was overcome. First the "fingerprint" region of the spectrum was recorded with sufficiently high resolution, both with and without ethanol on the surface of the reflection element. Then the background was subtracted from both spectra, and afterwards the pure quartz spectrum was also subtracted. The results of this procedure, for two different angles of incidence, are given in Figure 14. A significant change can be seen in the region of the [-C-OH] stretching vibration. This is what should be expected from Figure 13.

Perspectives of Raman Spectroscopy with the Evanescent Wave

Further investigations using this method will be of considerable interest, not only because of the practical advantages mentioned above, but also because it now becomes possible to study surface reactions, e.g., catalysis, adsorption phenomena and enzymatic reactions. This is especially so with respect to the modern evaporation techniques and the possibilities of chemical conditioning of the surfaces of almost any material. Extremely thin films and monomolecular layers are sufficiently transparent to maintain an evanescent field in the optically rare medium.

Thus this technique is especially suited to studying enzymatic reactions with considerable advantage. Until now the procedure for determining the active centrum of an enzyme was rather complex because enzymatic reactions are performed only in aqueous solutions and at very low concentrations. Thus, IR-spectroscopy and normal Raman techniques failed. Also, experiments to study enzymatic reactions in the crystalline phase will not succeed, for the native conformation of the enzymes in solution is a prerequisite for optimal reactivity. The usual technique, therefore, is a stepwise modification of the functional groups of either the enzyme or its substratum and the measurement of their kinetic behaviour. This very laborious procedure then provides some information concerning the active centrum.

By means of Raman scattering with the evanescent wave these difficulties can be overcome. The surface of the reflection element can be coated with the enzyme either by adsorption or by chemical linking (without conformational change), thus effecting a higher concentration of the reactants within the region of the evanescent field. By adding the substratum to the solution placed on the reflection element, one can detect the change in the position of the vibrational bands of the functional groups of the enzyme and the substratum. This then directly yields the location of the active centrum and also information on the functional groups of the substratum.

ATR-Raman studies in enzymes may require resonance Raman, since the substratum (and more specifically, its binding region) is only a very small fraction of the total molecule, all of which

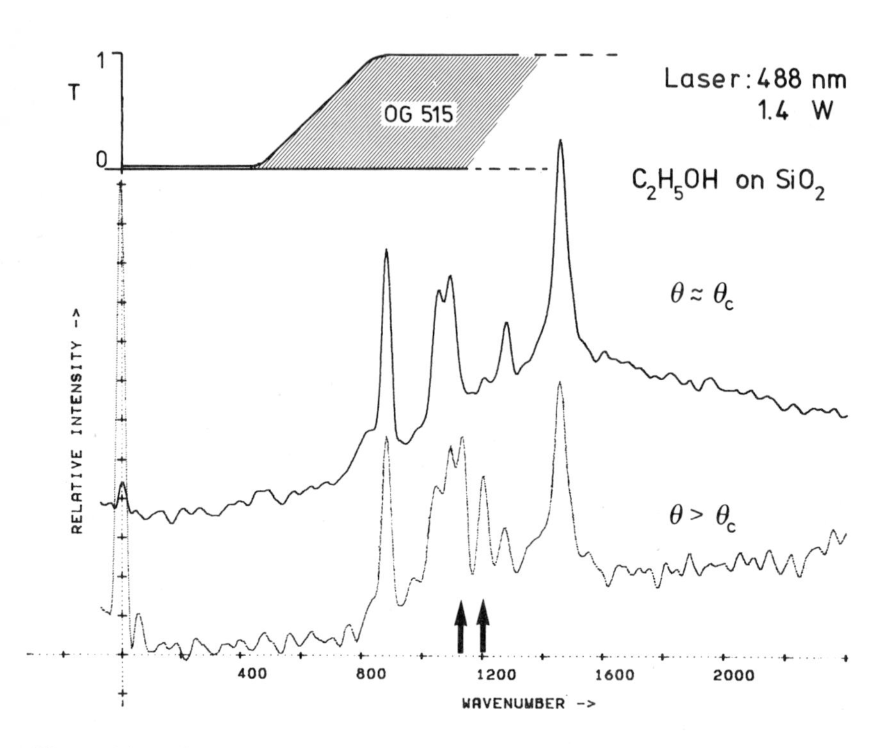

Figure 14. Influence of adsorption on the Raman spectrum of ethanol. The penetration depth for the upper spectrum is on the order of 500 nm whereas in the lower spectrum it is only about 50 nm. Therefore, the Raman intensity is proportionally decreased. This is shown by the intensity ratio of the two Rayleigh lines, since the Raman spectrum is normalized to the 882 cm^{-1} band.

is Raman active. For these investigations the OMA system mentioned above is well suited not only because of its large multiplex advantage but also because of the ease of data handling and computational flexibility.

With a considerable increase in the number of reflections (only three were used in the experiments mentioned above) and an increase in laser power the signal to noise ratio could perhaps be improved enough to allow monitoring of the enzyme kinetics by means of time-resolved spectroscopy.

Conclusion

As shown, the use of the evanescent wave in the UV-VIS region of the spectrum might well develope into a new tool for the biochemical laboratory. This is true for the ATR-techniques as well as for the new type of Raman spectroscopy, although the latter will probably be somewhat more attractive.

These results, though rather qualitative, have been presented here in order to stimulate further work by other groups, especially in the case of Raman scattering with the evanescent wave.

Acknowledgements

The author would like to thank Prof. Dr. M. Schaldach for his steady support. Furthermore, the kind efforts of Prof. R. Dupeyrat and Dr. T. Hirschfeld in supplying the information requested are gratefully acknowledged. Thanks go to Dr. Albrecht for his help in the experiments on Raman spectroscopy, and to Dr. Brauner for his helpful discussions on the chemistry of surfaces. Last, but not least the author would like to express his gratitude to Prof. R. Winkler for reading the manuscript.

Literature Cited

1. Hirschfeld, T. US Patent N°: 3,604,927 (1971).
2. Watkins, R.W.; Robertson, C.R. J.Biomed.Mater.Res. (1971) 11, 915.
3. Newton, I. "Optics", New York: Dover Publications, 1952.
4. Mach, E.; Arbes, J. Wied. Ann. (1866) 27, 436.
5. Hall, E. Phys. Rev. (1913) 15, 73.
6. Selenyi, P. Compt. Rend. (1913) 157, 1408.
7. Fröhlich, P. Ann. Phys. (1920) 63, 900.
8. Schaefer, Cl.; Gross, G. Ann. Phys. (1910) 32, 648.
9. Schaefer, Cl. "Einführung in die Theoretische Physik"Bd.III, 1; Berlin: de Gruyter, 1932.
10. Goos, F.; Hänchen, H. Ann. Phys. (1947) 1, 333.

11. Fahrenfort, J. Spectrochim. Acta (1961) 17, 698.
12. Fahrenfort, J.; Visser, W.M. Spectrochim. Acta (1962) 18, 1103.
13. Harrick, N.J. J. Phys. Chem. (1960) 64, 1110.
14. Harrick, N.J. Phys. Rev. (1962) 125, 1165.
15. Harrick, N.J. Ann. N.Y. Acad. Sci. (1963) 101, 928.
16. Hansen, W.N. Spectrochim. Acta (1965) 21, 815.
17. Hirschfeld, T. Can. Spectry. (1966) 11, 102.
18. Hirschfeld, T.; Wilks, P.A. Jr. Applied Spectroscopy Reviews (1967) 1, 99.
19. Harrick, N.J. "Internal Reflection Spectroscopy" New York: Wiley, 1967.
20. Hansen, W.N. Journal Opt. Soc. Am. (1968) 58, 380.
21. Lotsch, H.K.V. Optik (1970) 32, 116, 189; (1971) 32, 299,553.
22. Tamir, T. Nouv. Rev. Optique (1975) 6, 273.
23. Snyder, A.W. Appl. Phys. (1974) 4, 273.
24. Felsen, L.B. Journal Opt. Soc. Am. (1976) 66, 751.
25. Mahan, A.I.; Bitterli, G.V. Applied Optics (1978) 17, 509.
26. Hirschfeld, T. Applied Spectroscopy (1977) 31, 243.
27. Nöller, H.G. Biomed. Technik (1977) 22E, 389.
28. Albrecht, H.; Müller, G.; Schaldach, M. Biomed. Technik (1978) 23E, 98.
29. Zurmühl, R. "Praktische Mathematik" (4.Aufl.); Berlin: Springer, 1963.
29a. Wodick, R.; Lübbers, W.D. "Photometrische Methoden in der Biologie" in "Angewandte Physik u. Biophysik in Medizin u. Biologie", H. Wolter ed. Wiesbaden: Akademische Verlagsgesellschaft, 1976.
29b. Hirschfeld, T. Applied Spectroscopy (1967) 21, 335.
30. Brandmüller, J.; Moser, H. "Einführung in die Ramanspektroskopie"; Darmstadt: Steinkopf, 1962.
31. Szymanski, H.A. "Raman Spectroscopy" Vol. I+II; New York: Plenum Press, 1967
32. Mathieu, J.P. "Advances in Raman Spectroscopy I"; London: Heyden, 1973.
33. Ikeshoji, T.; Ono, Y.; Mizuno, T. Applied Optics (1973) 12, 2236.
33a. Takenaka, T.; Naganaga, T. J. Phys. Chem. (1976) 80, 475.
34. Dupeyrat, R. et.al. Japan. J. appl. Phys. (1975) 14, 93.
35. Dupeyrat, R. et. al. Optics Communications (1974) 11, 66,70; (1977) 20, 443; (1977) 21, 162.
36. Albrecht, H.; Müller, G.; Schaldach, M. "Proc. VI. Intern. Conf. on Raman Spectroscopy" Vol.2; Schmid E.D. ed. London: Heyden, 1978, 524.

RECEIVED January 17, 1979.

A High Resolution Grating Microspectrofluorometer with Topographic Option for Studies in Living Cells[1]

J. G. HIRSCHBERG[2], A. W. WOUTERS[2], E. KOHN[3], C. KOHEN[3], B. THORELL[4], B. EISENBERG[5], J. M. SALMON[6], and H. S. PLOEM[7]

Papanicolaou Cancer Research Institute, 1155 N.W. 14th St., POB 016188, Miami, FL 33101

A multichannel microfluorometer allows the measurement of fluorescence spectra from living cells and the topographic study of transient coenzyme (NAD(P)H, flavoproteins) fluorescence (oxido-reduction) changes, triggered by intracellular microinjection of metabolites. The method is limited by the number, F_λ, of fluorescence photons at λ. F_λ itself is a function of the fluorescence efficiency at λ, the cell area, spectral resolution $\Delta\lambda$, time within which each resolution element $\Delta\lambda$ is measured and the collected solid angle. Maximum spectral and temporal resolution is obtained via vertical illumination with high NA objectives, using combined dichroic and barrier filters, a field lens, a two-dimensional slit in the image plane, and turrets providing a topographic option with choice of magnification and a spectral option with choice of dispersion. The spectral approach allows the resolution of natural cell fluorescence and its dynamic changes (i.e. in bound, free NAD(P)H, flavoproteins) in different metabolic conditions. The fluorescence of carcinogens is analyzed in correlation with spontaneous metabolization or possible appearance of new metabolites. Using the topographic approach, metabolic rate laws are determined in cell compartments, and intercellular transfer of metabolites and the metabolic cooperation of living cells are investigated. Thus methods are provided for *in situ* monitoring of metabolic activity.

Introduction

The spectral and topographic analysis of fluorescence associated with biologically active compounds (1-11) is of great interest in the study of cell metabolism (12,13,14) and cell-to-cell interactions (15,16,17). The dynamics of intracellular metabolism (18,19,20,21) are better unraveled if transient shifts from steady state are triggered via microinjections of metabolites, which requires instrumental arrangements allowing micromanipulatory techniques (22,23,24).

[1] For authors' current addresses see page 289.

0-8412-0504-3/79/47-102-263$06.75/0

When interest is focused on individual cell parts (25, 26) the number of fluorescence photons limits the precision of the measurements. A series of computations based on observation of NAD(P)H fluorescence spectra recorded from single living cells, using an Ultropak (objective with ring condenser) and prism-microspectrofluorometer (27), has established the basis for a grating-microspectrofluorometer centered on a Leitz-Diavert inverted microscope and Ploemopak illuminator, providing maximum spectral, temporal and topographic resolution.

The need for such an instrument is based on the following findings:

1) It is desirable to enhance the accuracy of the method developed for the resolution of intracellular coenzyme fluorescence spectra into their components (free vs. bound reduced pyridine nucleotides (7,8,9,10,11, 28-34), flavoproteins (35,36, 37,38). This resolution may be important to understand and evaluate different metabolic steady states, drug effects, pathological conditions or divergence between cell types and their transformed variants.

2) The spectra recorded from cells treated with fluorescent carcinogens (e.g. hydrocarbons) suggest carcinogen metabolization (39-43). The detection of spectral shifts of the order of a few nm associated with metabolites, possible interactions or other phenomena such as electron tunneling (44,45) requires high resolution in the recording of spectra. There may be associated changes in coenzyme spectra and there are indications that the sequence of changes in carcinogen-treated cells (46,47,48) may vary depending upon other treatment of the cells (starvation, glucose, microinjection of glucose-6-P leading to transients).

3) An improved signal-to-noise ratio in the topographic analysis of coenzyme fluorescence transients will mean enhanced accuracy in the determination of metabolic rate laws (18,19,20, 21, 26) from transient kinetics.

4) Since intracellular metabolic phenomena are seemingly accompanied by cell-to-cell interactions (15,17) the above will mean more accurate evaluations of these in terms of intercellular transfer of metabolites and concerted metabolic activity within cell clusters.

Other similar instruments (49-54) have been developed but:

1) Either they have been used mainly for high quantum yield exogenous fluorochromes rather than natural cell fluorochromes (NAD(P)H), or

2) They were extensively used to study NAD(P)H changes, as in the case of the Ultropak prism-microspectrofluorometer (27) but did not optimize cell areas observed, time increment and spectral resolution.

Therefore, it was found necessary to develop an instrument providing maximum sensitivity in order to make measurements with the highest precision and temporal resolution, especially of the following parameters:

1) Spectral shifts associated with intracellular changes in molecule structure or binding.
2) Rise and decay kinetics of metabolically-induced transients,
3) Intercellular transfer kinetics.
Such an instrument will be described here.

Principle of the Instrument

The apparatus consists of a microscopic optical system, a grating mirror combination (Fig. 1A, 1B) for spectral and topographic measurement, and an optical multichannel analyzer (OMA) equipped with a silicon intensified tube (SIT) as a photon detector (55).

A. Microscopic optical systems of the Diavert. The instrument (Fig. 1) is based on the Leitz "Diavert" inverted microscope with vertical illumination using high NA objectives (Fig. 1C and D, d) with large collecting power, designed for rapid changes of excitation wavelengths. Several excitation blocks (Ploemopak) (Fig. 1C and D, e) with different dichromatic and interference filters (Fig. 1C and D, e1, e2, e3) are available to facilitate observation of different wavelengths. In the present design 366 nm excitation from a 100-watt mercury high pressure arc lamp (Fig. 1C and D, M) is used for blue fluorescing NAD(P)H and carcinogenic hydrocarbons (benzpyrene).

The Ploemopak illuminator block (Fig. 1C and D, e,) for NAD(P)H excitation comprises: 2 mm thick special UG11 filter prepared by Leitz (Fig. 1C and D, e2,e3) + BP 365 interference filter (Zeiss) with very low transmittance above 390 nm for excitation, (Fig. 1C and D, e4) and a TK 380 as the dichromatic beam splitter (Fig. 1C and D, e1). The illuminator block for hydrocarbon (benzpyrene) fluorescence excitation comprises: 2 mm UG 1 + BP 365 nm interference filter from Zeiss for excitation, a neutral beam splitter instead of the dichromatic beam splitter, and no barrier filter.

A Balzers dichromatic beam splitter (Fig. 1C and D, i) replacing the standard reflecting prism in the base of the Diavert reflects the red portion of the spectrum into the normal path of light (towards the ocular) for visualization of cell and micro-instruments. The rest of the spectrum which includes natural cell fluorescence and carcinogen fluorescence is sent downwards towards the detector, through an aperture provided in the base plate (Fig. 1C and D, j).

The visualization provided by transmitted red light illumination (Fig. 1C and D, T) can be improved by using phase optics with a halogen 50-watt lamp, a Leitz-Phaco II ring, a Leitz-91 phase condenser and a 40x immersion objective with a built-in phase ring. In this case the 1.30-1.40 N.A. objectives are replaced by the Leitz 1.00 N.A. immersion objective (56), but

A.

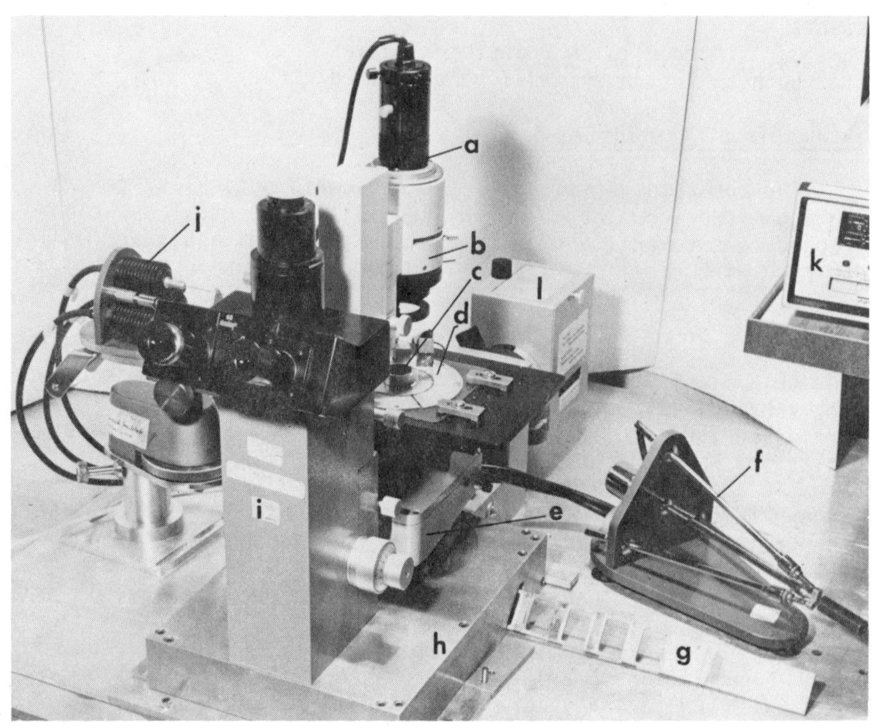

Figure 1. Microspectrofluorometer

A. Microscopic and optical arrangement with components for fluorescence excitation and cell visualization, micromanipulatory assembly. All components above the microscope base plate are seen.

- *a.* *White light source. Tungsten lamp.*
- *b.* *Condenser lens within housing*
- *c.* *Microcuvette with glass-grown cells attached to the bottom and stainless steel ring shaped to allow introduction of micro-instruments*
- *d.* *Heated stage*
- *e.* *Ploemopak with illuminator filter blocks (four options)*
- *f.* *Handle of Cailloux micromanipulator*
- *g.* *Filter–mirror slide with different options of dichromatic beam splitters and mirror (to allow versatility in simultaneous or near simultaneous fluorescence detection, cell visualization, fluorescence visualization or fluorescence photography)*
- *h.* *New base for Diavert microscope allowing insertion of g*
- *i.* *Leitz-Diavert inverted microscope*
- *j.* *Cailloux pneumatic micromanipulator*
- *k.* *OMA Model 1205 Console (PAR)*
- *l.* *Mercury Arc-Ultraviolet light source (for 3656 excitation)*

B.

Figure 1. Microspectrofluorometer

B. Intermediate optical arrangement for optional topographic or spectral operation. Components under the microscope base plate are seen.

- *m.* *Microscope baseplate*
- *n.* *Variable x-y slit*
- *o.* *90° Prism housing*
- *p.* *Filter sector (for different filter options)*
- *q.* *Control for filter sector*
- *r.* *Mode turret*
- *s.* *Housing for 381 mm lens*
- *t.* *Mirror*
- *u.* *Grating–mirror turret*
- *v.* *Base of OMA detector*
- *w.* *Micropositioners for three-dimensional control allowing alignment of SIT target with pinpoint accuracy*
- *x.* *Mounting for OMA*
- *y.* *Shutter control cable*

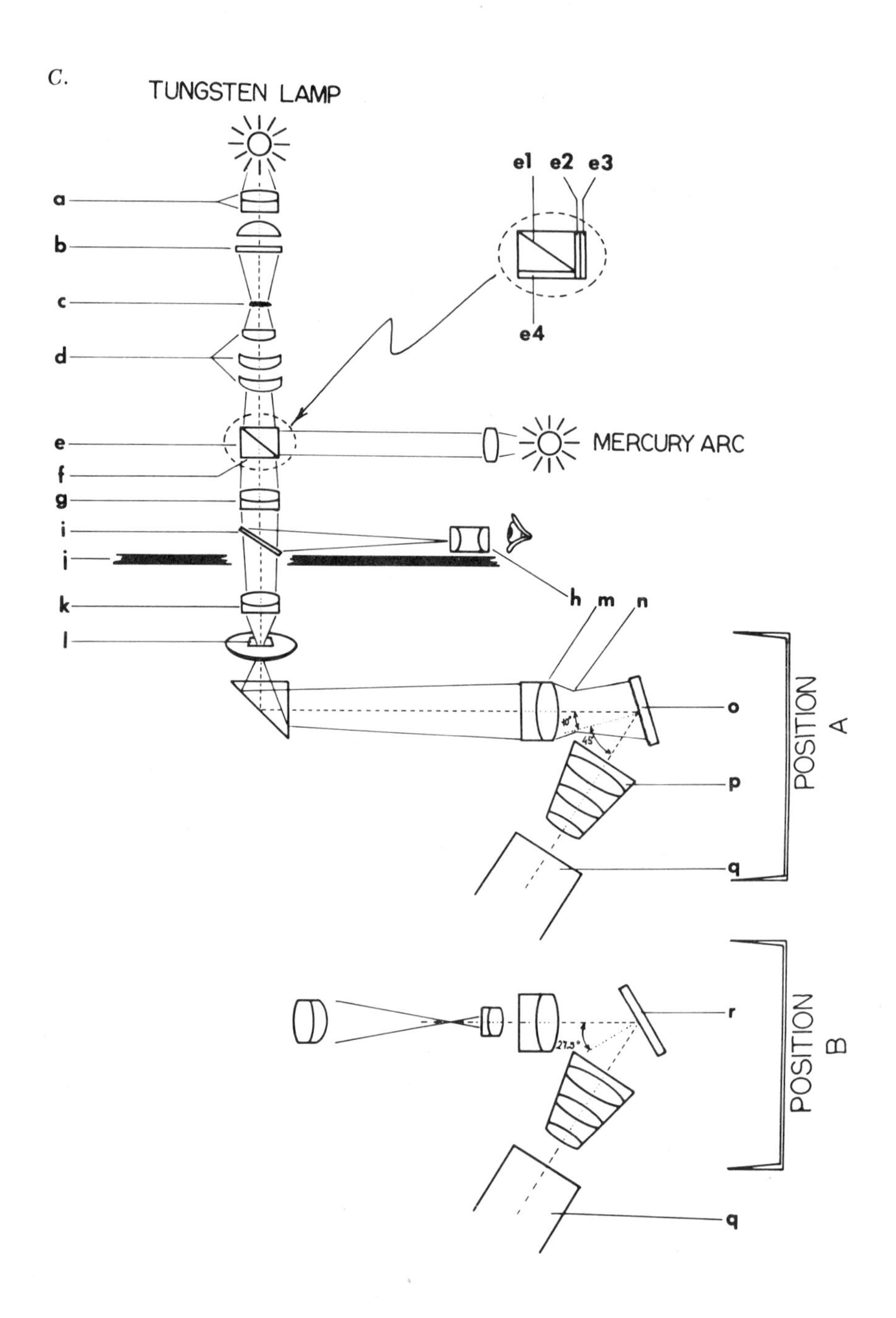
C.
TUNGSTEN LAMP
a
b
c
d
e
f
g
i
j
k
l
e1
e2
e3
e4
MERCURY ARC
h
m
n
o
p
q
POSITION A
r
q
POSITION B

Figure 1. Microspectrofluorometer

C. Schematic representation of microspectrofluorometer with topographic option for studies in single living cells.

- *a.* *Condenser lenses in front of tungsten lamp (T)*
- *b.* *red filter RG2 (Schott)*
- *c.* *Microscopic object, i.e. a living cell*
- *d.* *Leitz objective for Diavert, e.g. 63× oil*
- *e.*
  - *e1: TK380 dichromatic beam splitter reflecting 366 nm excitation from mercury arc (M) and transmitting NAD(P)H fluorescence or the emission of exogenous fluorochromes (carcinogens, probes)*
  - *e2 and e3: special UGII filter prepared by Leitz, plus BP365 interference filter (Zeiss) with very low transmittance above 390 nm for excitation*
  - *e4: optional barrier filter.*
- *f.* *Ploemopak illuminator block*
- *g.* *Lens providing a near 1:1 magnification*
- *h.* *Ocular and observer*
- *i.* *Beam splitter or mirror in slide with different options to allow cell or fluorescence visualization simultaneously with fluorescence detection, or fluorescence photography in place of detection*
- *j.* *Base plate with aperture to connect the base of Diavert microscope to remaining components of optical design*
- *k.* *Field lens (Fl = 95 mm) collecting the light from the objective to produce an image of the objective pupil near the reflection grating used for spectral dispersion*
- *l.* *Slit located in the microscope image plane and variable along x,y coordinates to regulate spectral resolution or cell region viewed by detector channels for topographic studies*
- *m.* *381 mm lens at focal distance from slit*
- *n.* *Image of the objective near the reflection grating or mirror*
- *o.* *Reflection grating (e.g. 300, 600, 900 grooves/mm options)*
- *p.* *Dallmeyer Ultrac camera lens F0.98, focal length 25 mm*
- *q.* *OMA*
- *r.* *Mirror*

Position A. Topographic option
Position B. Spectral option

For further details see Figures 1D,E,F.

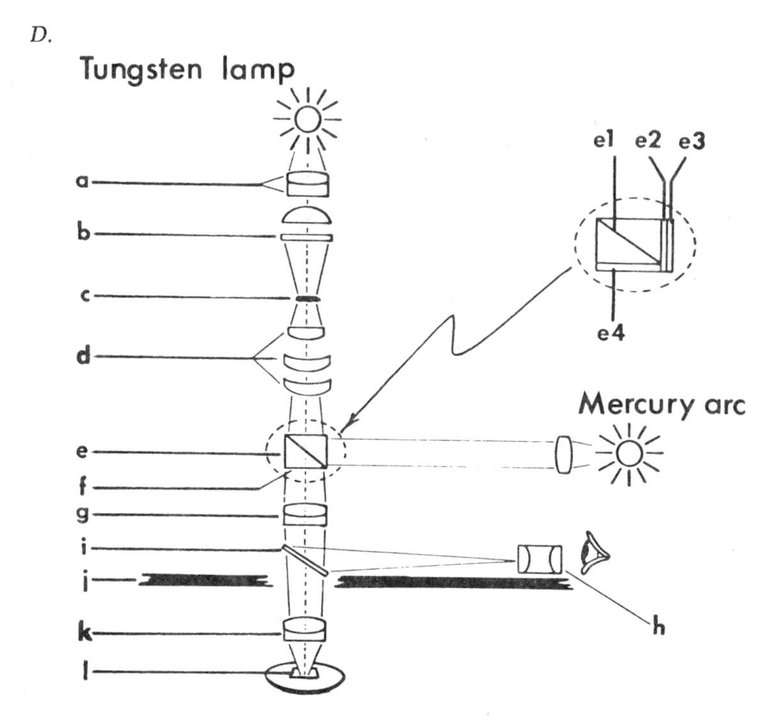

Figure 1. Microspectrofluorometer

D. Microscopic optical arrangement centered around the Leitz-Diavert inverted microscope

a to l like in Figure 1A.

The tungsten lamp from above is used for visuialization of cell and micro-instrument with red light.

Excitation wavelengths emitted by a mercury arc are filtered through e2 and e3, and reflected towards the cells by dichromatic mirror e1 fluorescence emission is filtered through optional e4 filter.

The red light for cell–instrument visualization is reflected towards the ocular by dichromatic mirror 1, which transmits towards slit 1 the fluorescence emission.

The visualization of cells is made by using phase optics with a halogen 50-watt lamp, a Leitz Phaco II ring, 91-phase condenser and 40× immersion objective with built-in phase ring.

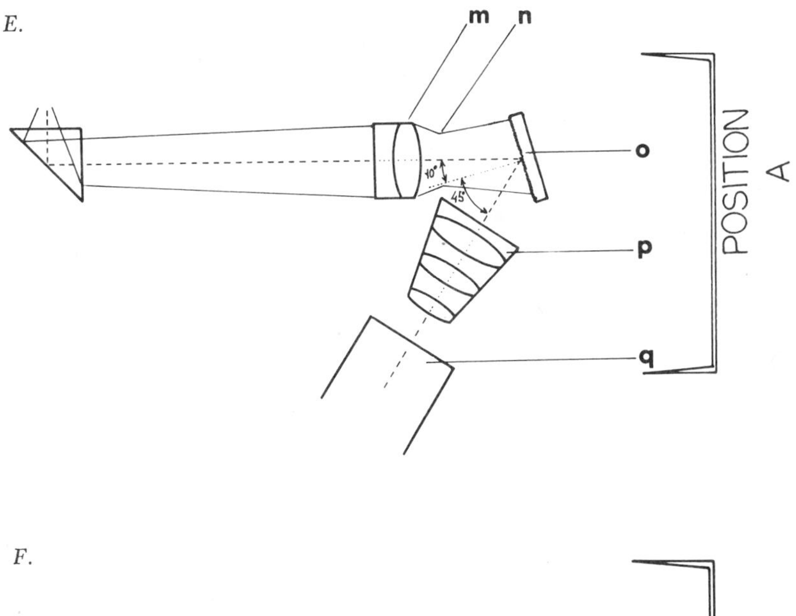

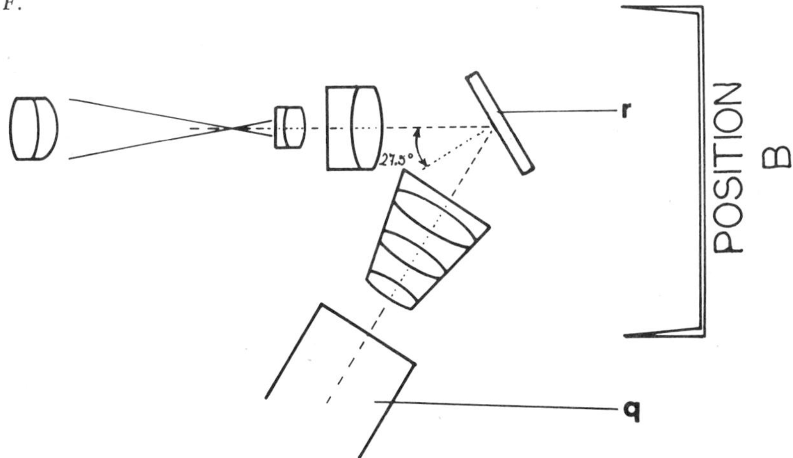

Figure 1. Microspectrofluorometer

E. Spectral option: m,n,o,p,q like in Figure 1A.
The alignment is: mode turret with no magnification option—f1 381 mm lens—any of three gratings—Ultrac camera lens—OMA.
The total angle of deviation is 55°.

F. Topographic option with 10× magnification.
The magnification is: mode turret—f1 381 mm lens—mirror r—Ultrac camera lens—OMA.

visualization of intracellular detail is improved and if the fluorescence signal is not too weak, the loss in intensity due to the lower N.A. becomes acceptable.

B. Considerations to be applied in the design.

1. Theoretical calculations on the attainable precision of the instrument. Straightforward consideration of photon gathering indicates that the maximum obtainable number of photons F_λ at wavelength λ is given by:

$$F_\lambda = 2\pi K_\lambda \ ab \, \Delta\lambda \ T \ (1 - \cos \arcsin \frac{NA}{n}) \quad (1)$$

where:

K_λ is a proportionality constant expressing the fluorescence intensity at the wavelength λ.

a,b are the rectangular dimensions of the cell region under observation (μm).

$\Delta\lambda$ is the spectral resolution (smallest resolvable variation of wavelength (nm)).

T is the time each wavelength is observed during one scan (msec).

NA, n: the microscope objective has a numerical aperture NA in a medium with index of refraction n.

Since NA = n sin Θ_0, the half angle of the collected cone $\Theta_0 = \arcsin \frac{NA}{n}$ and the collected solid angle is 2π (1-cos Θ_0) steradians.

A series of computations based on observation of NAD(P)H fluorescence in single living cells under strong 366 nm excitation suggests that the order of magnitude of the fluorescence intensity constant K_λ in the maximum of the fluorescence band at 470 nm is:

$$K_\lambda = 1.2 \times 10^{-2} \text{ emitted photons } \mu m^{-2} \text{ msec}^{-1} \text{ nm}^{-1} \text{ str}^{-1}$$

These considerations were fundamental in the design of the microspectrofluorometer and allowed, on a purely theoretical basis, the estimation of the expected signal-to-noise ratio (SNR).

Taking into account the different efficiences of the instrument, the signal to noise ratio at wavelength λ is given by:

$$SNR_\lambda = \sqrt{n_{D\lambda}} \cdot \sqrt{n_{Q\lambda} \ \tau_\lambda \ F_\lambda} \quad (2)$$

where $n_{Q\lambda}$ = quantum efficiency of the detector at wavelength λ, $n_{D\lambda}$ is a factor to account for the degradation of SNR due to spurious signal $S_{D\lambda}$ under dark condition. For consistency it is written as an efficiency (under the square root sign) and is equal to $\frac{S_\lambda}{S_\lambda + S_{D\lambda}}$, since the real noise is

$\sqrt{S_\lambda + S_{D\lambda}}$ instead of the theoretical $\sqrt{S_\lambda}$.

τ_λ = transmission of instrument, including the effects of absorption, reflection losses and blaze efficiency, and

F_λ is the maximum number of photons available, as described above.

When the signal under dark condition is subtracted from the reading the measured signal $S_\lambda = n_{Q\lambda}\, \tau_\lambda\, F_\lambda$.

In the design of the present instrument $n_{Q\lambda}$ and $n_{D\lambda}$ were already defined by the choice of the detector, an OMA, P.A.R. Corp., the same as in the Ultropak microspectrofluorometer and τ_λ is of the order of unity and limited by available optical parts.

As compared to the Ultropak design, large improvements were attainable in terms of F_λ:

a) via an increased NA from 0.85 to 1.30 to 1.40 or at least 1.00. A change of NA from 0.85 to 1.15, for example, gives a gain of 2 in signal,

b) by adjusting ab and $\Delta\lambda$ to the particular biological problem studied and then ensuring that no available photons are wasted by geometrical factors,

c) since fluorescence excitation is provided via the same objective as fluorescence collection, F_λ can be higher than for the Ultropak ring condenser using high NA objectives, but there are biological limitations (46) with respect to the highest excitation energy to which the cell may be exposed. When the excitation energy is increased beyond a certain level, fluorescence fading due to irreversible photochemical alteration becomes noticeable. Such fading, as expressed by ln (I_{Ft}/I_{Ft_0}), proceeds as a linear function of time.

(I_{Ft} = fluorescence at time t, I_{Ft_0} = fluorescence at time t_0)

The tolerance of different fluorochromes to excitation energy is quite different. Thus, the same excitation intensities under which the natural cell fluorescence due to pyridine nucleotides will remain stable for about 20-30 minutes are enough to produce nearly total disappearance of the emission due to intracellularly accumulated polycyclic aromatic hydrocarbons or heterocycles. Furthermore the accumulation of radiation products (e.g. free radicals) can affect various enzymatic reactions of the cell. Fading and radiation damage may be however minimized by restricting the exposure time of the cell to high energy radiation.

d) the use of objectives with very high NA for collecting the fluorescence signal ensures that the maximum number of photons is collected compared to the number of photons used for the excitation of the cell.

2. Principles defining the overall magnification and the resolution of the optical multichannel analyser (OMA). Detailed considerations of the design concern the required spectral or topographical resolution in terms of the corresponding spectral or topographic resolution element per detector channel. Each channel element has a 25 μm width (57). The proper imaging on the channels therefore requires evaluation of the overall magnification. At the base of the Diavert, a field lens (fl: 95 mm), Fig. 1C and D, k, collects the light from the objective and places a 2/3 reduced image on a slit (Fig. 1B, n, Fig. 1C and 1D, l) which is variable in two dimensions.

Thus using a 63x objective, (Fig. 1C and D, d) the magnification at the Diavert image plane will be 42.

In the spectral option, a demagnification of about 1/15 is obtained in the intermediate optics using a fixed optical system.

Thus, the overall magnification in the spectral option is 3.

On this basis 15 μm of the cell is imaged on ∿ 50 μm or two channels of the detector (Fig. 1C and 1E, g). At the slit level in the primary image plane of the microscope, 15 μm of the cell is magnified to 630 μm, which corresponds to the slit opening for an adequate spectral resolution. In this case some redundancy of channels occurs in detecting resolution elements, i.e. each resolution element is imaged upon two channels. This is really necessary because faster lenses to produce convergence of each resolution element on single channels cannot easily be obtained and may moreover result in loss of photons in the fiber optic face plate of the detector, since the fibers are limited in their field of acceptance.

Greater convergence would moreover exaggerate another problem. While each detector channel is 25 μ wide, it is 2.5 mm long. Thus if a cell of dimensions 15 x 30 μm is imaged on the channels, since b = 30 μm, using an overall magnification of 3 it will cover only 1/25th of the channel length. Since saturation by high light intensity is a function of photons/unit area, if the light is concentrated, saturation and consequent lack of linearity in the channel response may occur at lower levels than if the light were spread over the whole channel length. This may be corrected by use of a cylindrical lens placed directly in front of the detector. Such an arrangement has been considered for future use, but it is not yet included in present design.

Using a magnification equal to the spectral option, for the topographic display a 30 μm cell will be imaged on 4 detector channels. In this case since a 30 μm cell corresponds to 1260 μm in the image plane and the maximum opening of the slit is 10 mm, an array of about 8 cells can be imaged on 32 detector channels.

3. Light levels and size of cells. Once the calculations of F_λ and S_λ, $\Delta\lambda$ and the required dispersion of spectral or topographic resolution elements on the detector channels were

made, it was possible to proceed to the actual details of the design, such as the choice of lenses and intermediate optics on the basis of the following principles:

a) To attain a spectral resolution $\Delta\lambda$ = 1 nm with F_λ = at least 100 photons/32 msec scan, it is necessary to collect on the slit in the image plane the light from a 15 x 30 μ cell region. Since the magnification at the slit is about 42x, the actual slit breadth is about 0.6 mm which is mechanically convenient to obtain.

b) The desired spectral resolution depends on this slit width as well as on the grating spacing (300, 600, 900, 1200, 1800 grooves/mm).

c) With the topographic display one can use either the same intermediate optics as the spectral option or other lenses with greater magnification which may be added for more detailed topographic analysis, using the rotating turret.

4. Need for micromanipulatory procedure. The metabolic studies require the observation of dynamic changes triggered by microinjection of metabolites. The usefulness of both spectral and topographic operation is critically dependent upon the ability to micromanipulate (microinject) living cells, in order to measure changes in injected cells and their neighbors.

Therefore the microscopic arrangement must take into account the need for the introduction of micromanipulatory instruments (Fig. 1A, f and j) into the microscopic object field. This has already been achieved in the standard Diavert microscope with vertical illumination for fluorescence studies. The top of the microscope stage is free for manipulatory procedures and the cell temperature may be regulated by a heated stage. The phase arrangement used for better visualization of intracellular detail with the 40x immersion objective has a long enough working distance (6 cm), see Fig. 1A, to be compatible with the manipulatory requirements.

C. General principles in the choice of optical components

1. Gratings. The design is adapted for spectral operation with different gratings (Fig. 1A, u and 1C, 1E, o), e.g. 1200 grooves/mm Bausch and Lomb grating for high resolution spectra, 600 grooves for lesser resolution, and also 300-900 and 1800 grooves, if desired, using a rotating turret mounting.

For work with single living cells, the 600 groove grating has been found satisfactory, yielding NAD(P)H or carcinogen spectra of sufficiently high resolution (in the nm range) at a signal-to-noise ratio of 10-15 to 1 per single scan which is improved by n for n accumulations (58).

In the case of topographic operation, a mirror replaces the grating, again using the rotating turret.

2. Beam splitters. Two types of beam splitters are incorporated in the system:

a) Beam splitter, Fig. 1C and D, e (Leitz TK series of dichromatic beam splitters) in the illuminator block (Fig. 1A,e) to reflect excitation wavelength towards the objective and transmit fluorescence wavelengths towards the detector.

b) Beam splitter for cell visualization (Fig. 1, i) as described in Section II. a.

A slide (Fig. 1A,g) with different beam splitter or mirror options (Fig. 1C and D, i) can be placed at the base of the Diavert, e.g.

- with Lingby or Balzers dichromatic mirrors reflecting all of the red and 50% of the blue-yellow fluorescence to visualize fluorescence changes simultaneously with photoelectric measurements.
- dichromatic mirrors with cutoffs at different wavelength regions.
- mirror to allow fluorescence photography or cinematography.

3. Required lenses. The field lens (fl = 95 mm), Fig. 1C and D, k, see Section II, b. 2., collecting all the light from the objective produces an image of the objective pupil near the reflection grating used for spectral dispersion or the mirror substituted for topographic operation. This ensures that all the available photons reach the effective area of the grating or mirror.

The same fixed optical system can be used for the spectral and topographic option, to provide the required dispersion on the OMA channels. The demagnification of 1/15 mentioned in a preceding section is obtained by a 381 lens (Fig. 1B, S, 1C and 1E, m) at its focal distance from the slit together with a Dallmeyer Ultrac camera lens, F/0.98 of focal length 25 mm (Fig. 1C, 1E, p) in the beam of light diffracted from the grating or reflected from the mirror, 1/15.

D. Overall construction principle. Once the requirements of cell area (ab) to be viewed, the spectral resolution $\Delta\lambda$ and the dispersion on the detector channels are established and the general principles on the choice of optical elements are defined, it is possible to implement the overall construction design (Fig. 1).

1) The fluorescence radiation transmitted through the Balzers dichromatic mirror (Fig. 1B, i) is collimated by a field lens (Fig. 1C and D, k) (Section II, b. 2.).

2) A two-dimensional slit (Fig. 1B, n, 1C and D, l) limiting the cell region(s) or cells viewed is placed in the new microscope primary image plane.

3) Between the slit and the detector the intermediate optics comprise the following components:

a) Reflecting prism to change the optical axis from vertical to horizontal (Fig. 1B,o).

b) A filter sector. A three-position filter sector (Fig. 1A,p) allows a choice of glass filters, neutral density filters or others, to block residual red light or excitation wavelengths in fluorescence measurements, and to restrict measured intensities in calibrations with spectral lines.

c) A mode turret (Fig. 1B,r) with either no magnification or different magnification options (Turret A). The mode turret provides three positions, the first with no magnification (spectral operation), the second with magnification provided by an afocal system of lenses (10x for more detailed topographic operation), and a third empty option where subsequently another afocal system may be installed for another larger or smaller magnification in the topographic mode, as needed.

d) Mirror-grating turret (Turret B) (Fig. 1B,u). Three gratings (Fig. 1C and E,p) and a mirror (Fig. 1B,t, 1C and F, r) are provided.

e) Around turret B the fixed optical system of two lenses, Fig. 1C and E, m and p (See Section II, c. 2), is placed.

4) The detector front, Fig. 1C and E, is positioned in the image plane of the Ultrac camera lens and perpendicular to the central beam diffracted by the grating.

For spectral operation the alignment will be:
Turret A: No magnification (empty option) - fl 381 - any of three gratings (e.g. 600, 900 or 1200 grooves/mm - Ultrac camera lens f/0.90 fl 25 - detector.

For topographic operation the alignment will be:
Turret A: No magnification or 10x magnification - fl 381 - mirror - Ultrac objective - detector.

Design Details

A. Adjustments:

1. Mounting of OMA. The position of the OMA (55) Fig. 1B,V, Fig. 1C and E,P, is determined by the total angle of deviation of the central part of the spectrum, defined by the gratings. The total angle of deviation is fixed in the design at 55°. The central wavelength is given by the grating equation:

$$m\lambda = d(\sin i + \sin \Theta)$$

where m = order in which grating is used (0, 1st, 2nd, etc)
d = spacing between lines
i = angle between incoming beam to the grating and normal to the grating
Θ = angle between diffracted beam and normal.

For instance for λ = 445 nm for a grating of 1200 lines/mm in first order, with i = 10°, Θ = 45°.

For 600 lines/nm i = 18°.9, Θ = 36.1.

The OMA is mounted perpendicular to the central diffracted beam, with the analyzer front in the image plane of the Ultrac lens. In the mirror option, the mirror is positioned so that the light is reflected at the same angle as the diffracted light from the grating: Θ = i = 27.5°.

The detector region in the OMA front is a rectangle comprising 500 channels (55, 57) each 25 μm wide and 5 mm long. To correct automatically for the dark signal half of each channel (background) is maintained in the dark. Therefore the image has to be precisely on the signal half of each channel, and pinpoint accuracy in position is obtained by positioning the detector by means of a tridimensional micropositioner.(Fig. 1B,W). Since the detector has 500 channels, in the topographic mode the object of interest is centered as closely as possible to channel 250.

2: Adjustment of gratings and mirrors. The grating and mirror have adjustments allowing lateral and angular movement which help initially in the optimization of imaging on the channels. However once optimal conditions are set, these adjustments are ordinarily not touched.

B. Controls. Controls outside the chamber are provided for two-dimensional adjustment of the slit opening, selection of filters on the wheel, positioning of turrets A and B and a shutter for the protection of the detector between measurements.

Electrical Design and Data Processing. Whether in topographic or spectral mode each scan is completed in 32 msec. However up to 9 delays may be introduced in a real time scan, thus prolonging the scan time to multiples of 32 msec, e.g. 64, 96, 128, 164 ... For detection of very low light signals, it will be required to extend the number of delays, i.e. the period of "on target" signal integration. In such case the dark noise may be minimized by cooling the OMA.

The digital output can be transmitted to a Hewlett Packard digital printer. A 1205-060 interface makes possible real time or memory mode recording on a rapid option Kennedy magnetic tape recorder for subsequent readout in a Univac computer or a minicomputer.

In real time up to 8000 bytes/sec are produced.

Performance

A. Fluorescence spectra

1. Real Time Operation. Fluorescence spectra or topographic scans of fluorescence can be recorded on magnetic tape every

64 msec or during longer scan times if longer delays are used. Resolution in the 1-2 nm range is attained and NAD(P)H fluorescence spectra are recorded from the living cell with a S/N ratio of 10:1.

2. Signal accumulation. In case the phenomenon observed (e.g. recorded spectra) is of such duration that the attainment of maximal temporal resolution is not critical "ensemble averaging" is preferable, as achieved by integration of n scans (e.g. n = 100). Two digital memories are provided capable of storing one complete spectrum each, e.g. a memory A for signal and B for background. Thus, fluorescence spectra can be recorded in the A-B mode after entering background in B.

3. Calibration methods. Wavelength calibration is achieved with spectral lamps, e.g. mercury (Fig. 2) or helium. The separation of mercury lines 2 nm apart is readily achievable. Calibration in intensity (relative) is done using an incandescent source of known temperature.

4. Linearity of the output signal vs. input. When the light intensity, i.e. number of photons in the input signal, is increased, the output remains linear until saturation is reached, which is attained at about 800 counts per scan per channel (1 count ∿ 2 photons). This can be observed in experimental conditions when a high quantum yield fluorochrome (e.g. a carcinogenic hydrocarbon) is gradually concentrated in a living cell. The limit of 800 counts holds when incoming light is more or less distributed throughout the channel. However (as stated in Section II, B.2.) if light is concentrated over a smaller region of the channel, it can be expected that the limit will be encountered before 800 counts, but in practice, at the cellular level one is rarely confronted with such levels of fluorescence.

Among expected future applications one should contemplate the use of a pulsed laser as a light source which will require multiple readouts when using a single pulse. This is due to the fact that the Vidicon surface of the SIT tube has a "lag"; thus not all the signal is read off the target in a single readout. Single light pulses, particularly at low light levels, must be read at least 10 consecutive times to ensure detector linearity.

B. Topographic mode. In the topographic mode, up to 8 adjacent cells, each 30 μm wide can be imaged on detector channels (see II, b. 2). In the no magnification position, a portion of the cell, corresponding to a rectangle 7.5 x 30 μ will be imaged on one channel. In the 10x magnification position this portion will correspond to a rectangle 0.75 x 30 μ. The topographic performance is analogous to that published for an earlier version of the microspectrofluorometer (see ref. 27) but with considerable improvement in signal-to-noise ratio.

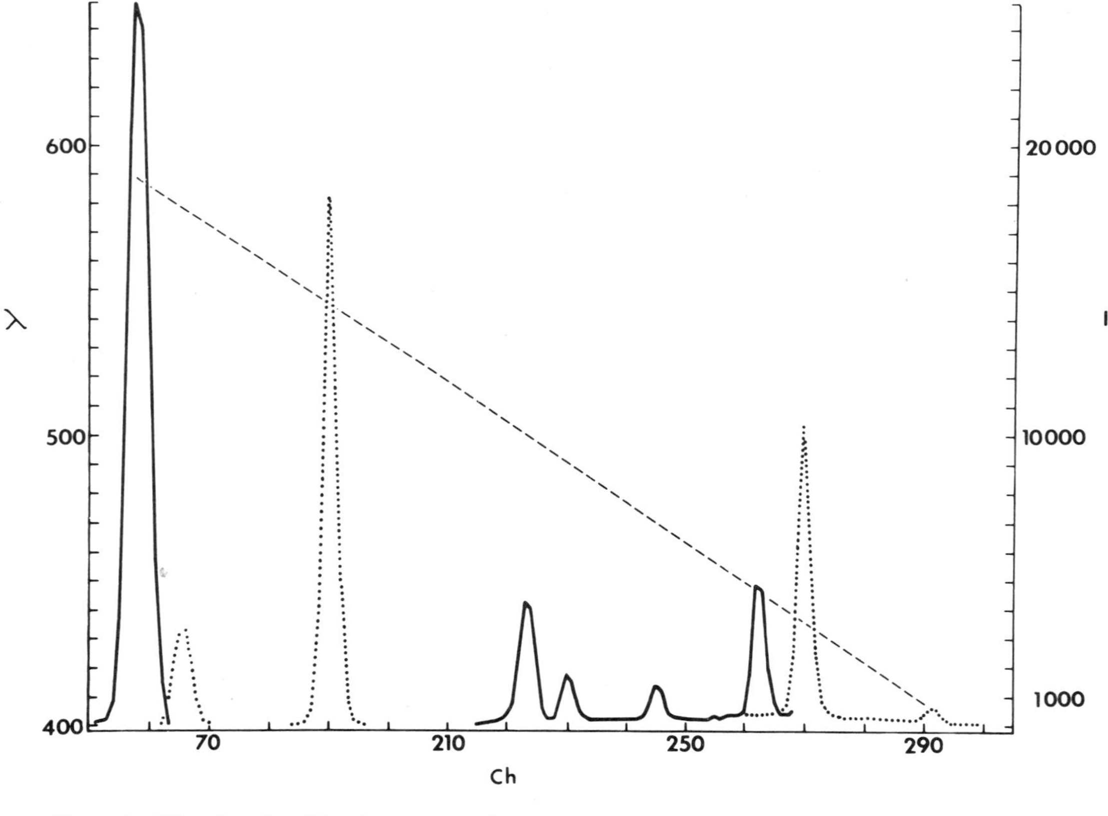

Figure 2. Wavelength calibration curve of the microspectrofluorometer using mercury and helium lines

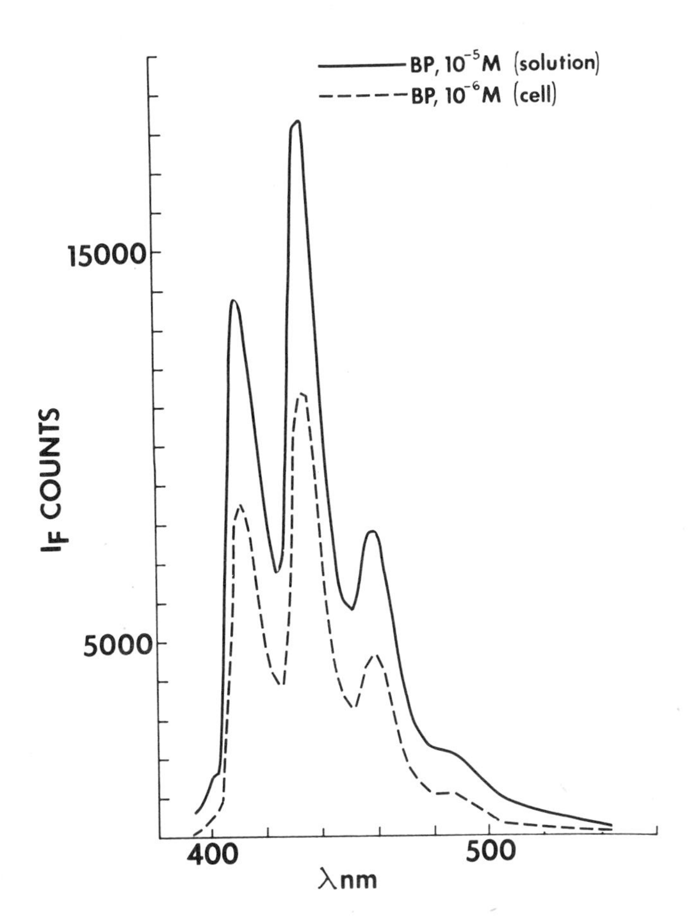

Figure 3. Fluorescence spectrum of benzo(a)pyrene in solution and in the living cell

Operation

Typical procedure. Living cells in culture are placed in a microchamber and incubated in glucose-free or glucose-containing HEPES-buffered medium. Cells are either exposed to different substrates or biologically active compounds, e.g. carcinogens, or they can be microinjected with substrates. Initial fluorescence and fluorescence changes are monitored spectrally or topographically.

In Figure 3 the fluorescence spectra (42) of benzpyrene are compared in solution (10^{-5}M) and following absorption by a living cell after exposure to 10^{-6}M benzpyrene.

100 scans were accumulated. The characteristic three maxima of benzpyrene are seen. The benzpyrene spectrum from ∿ 395 nm to 540 nm is distributed over ∿ 120 channels (see Fig. 2, Calibration Curve). In the living cell there are up to ∿ N=500 counts per scan at the 430 nm maximum, which correspond to a S/N ratio over 20:1.

Conclusion

The measured spectral resolution of the new grating microspectrofluorometer is about 1 nm and preliminary trials show that the luminosity is improved by at least ten-fold as compared to the older Ultropak-prism-microspectrofluorometer. The acquired increased sensitivity is best exploited using objectives and immersion oils of low intrinsic fluorescence.

Optimal conditions are realized for spectral analysis and resolution of natural cell fluorescence as well as carcinogen fluorescence. The further improvements in topographic analysis make possible parallel studies in both modes of operation, determining on one hand fluorochrome distribution with respect to cell organelles or intracellular structure and allowing one on the other hand to follow changes in the molecular structure or binding of the fluorochrome. Since such studies are now possible at a level of resolution and accuracy unattained before, it is hoped that they may help in the search of coenzyme changes, carcinogen metabolites and more precise rate laws of intra- or intercellular interactions. Thus, phenomena of critical significance may be unraveled in the understanding of cell physiology and pathology.

ACKNOWLEDGEMENTS

The authors acknowledge thankfully the help of Mr. G. Ondricek and I. May in preparing drawings and prints. They are also thankful to Mrs. G. Salisbury and Mr. B. Wendelheim for efficient help with typing. This work was supported by American Cancer Society Grant BC - 15E, HEW grants 5 R01 CA 21153-01-02 from the National Cancer Institute and 5 R01 GM 20866-04-05 from the National Institute of General Medical Sciences, Grant 5 R01 AM21330.01, 02 from the National Institute of Arthritis, Metabolism and Digestive Diseases, Grant B78-12X-00630-14C from the Swedish Medical Research Council.

The authors thank Mr. R. Meyer from Leitz for making the specially prepared UG11 filter available.

LITERATURE CITED

1. Theorell, H. and Bonnichsen, R.: Studies on liver alcohol dehydrogenase. I. Equilibria and initial reaction velocities. Acta Chem. Scand., 5: 1105-1126, 1951.

2. Boyer, P.D. and Theorell, H.: The change in reduced diphosphopyridine nucleotide (DPNH) fluorescence upon combination with liver alcohol dehydrogenase (ADH). Acta Chem. Scand., 10: 447-450, 1956.

3. Duysens, L.N.M. and Amesz, J.: Fluorescence spectrophotometry of reduced phosphopyridine nucleotide in intact cells in the near-ultraviolet and visible region. Biochim. Biophys. Acta, 24: 19-26, 1957.

4. Chance, B. and Baltscheffsky, H.: Respiratory enzymes in oxidative phophorylation. VII. Binding of intramitochondrial reduced pyridine nucleotide. J. Biol. Chem., 233: 736-739, 1958.

5. Chance, B. and Thorell, B.: Localization and kinetics of reduced pyridine nucleotide in living cells by microfluorometry. J. Biol. Chem., 234: 3044-3050, 1959.

6. Chance, B., Perry, L., Åkerman, L. and Thorell, B.: Highly sensitive recording microspectrophotometer. Rev. Sci. Instr., 30: 735-741, 1959.

7. Velick, S.F.: Fluorescence spectra and polarization of glyceraldehyde-3-phosphate and lactic dehydrogenase coenzyme complexes. J. Biol. Chem., 233: 1455-1467, 1958.

8. Winer, A.D., Schwert, G.W. and Millar, D.B.S.: Lactic dehydrogenase. VI. Fluorometric measurements of the complex of enzyme and reduced diphosphopyridine nucleotide. J. Biol. Chem., 234: 1149-1154, 1959.

9. Galeotti, T., van Rossum, G.D.V., Mayer, D.H. and Chance, B.: On the fluorescence of NAD(P)H in whole-cell preparations of tumours and normal tissues. Eur. J. Biochem., 17: 485-496, 1970.

10. Scott, T.G., Spencer, R.D., Leonard, N.J. and Weber, G.: Emission properties of NADH. Studies of fluorescence lifetimes and quantum efficiencies of NADH, AcPyADH, and simplified synthetic models. J. Amer. Chem. Soc, 92: 687-695, 1970.

11. Bucher, T., Brauser, B., Conze A., Klein, F., Langguth, O. and Sies, H.: State of oxidation-reduction and state of binding in the cystosolic NADH-system as disclosed by equilibration with extracellular lactate/pyruvate in hemoglobin-free perfused rat liver. Eur. J. Biochem., 27: 301-317, 1972.

12. Kohen, E., Thorell, B., Kohen, C. and Salmon, J.-M.: Studies on metabolic events in localized compartments of the living cell by rapid microspectrofluorometry. In: Advances in Biological and Medical Physics, Vol. 15. J.H. Lawrence, J.W. Gofman and T.L. Hayes (eds.) pp. 271-297. Academic Press, New York and London, 1974.

13. Kohen, E., Kohen, C. and Thorell, B.: Rapid automatic microspectrofluorometric study of intracellular energy metabolism. Exptl. Cell Res., 101: 47-54, 1976.

14. Kohen, E., Kohen, C., Hirschberg, J.G., Wouters, A. and Thorell, B.: Multisite topographic microfluorometry of intracellular and exogenous fluorochromes. Photochem. Photobiol., 27: 259-268, 1978.

15. Loewenstein, W.R. and Kanno, Y.: Studies on an Epithelial (gland) cell junction. I. Modifications of surface permeability. J. Cell. Biol., 22: 565-586, 1964.

16. Kohen, E. and Kohen, C.: Rapid automated multichannel microspectrofluorometry. A new method for studies on the cell-to-cell transfer of molecules. Exptl. Cell Res. 107: 261-268, 1971.

17. Kohen, E. and Kohen, C.: The intercellular transfer of molecules in tissue culture cells: A kinetic study by multichannel microfluorometry. In: The Tenth Miami Winter Symposia, 9-13 January 1978. Differentiation and Development. W. Whelan and J. Schultz (eds.)pp. 411-439. Academic Press, New York, 1978.

18. Chance, B.: The identification of enzyme-substrate compounds. In: Modern Trends in Physiology and Biochemistry (Woods Hall Lecture dedicated to the Memory of Leonor Michaelis). E.S. Guzman Barron (eds.) pp. 25-46. Academic Press, New York, 1952.

19.Atkinson, D.E., Roach, P.J. and Schwedes, J.S.: Metabolite concentrations and concentration ratios in metabolic regulation. Adv. Enzym. Regul., 13: 393-411, 1975.

20. Hess, B.: Organization of glycolysis: Oscillatory and stationary control. In: Symposia of the society for Experimental Biology, No. XXVII. Rate control of Biological Processes. D.D. Davies (ed). pp. 105-131. Cambridge, 1973.

21. Savageau, M.A.: The behaviour of intact biochemical control systems. In: Current Topics in Cellular Regulation. Vol. 6. B.L. Horecker and E.R. Stadtman (eds.). pp. 63-130. Academic Press, New York 1972.

22. Kopac, M.J.: Micromanipulators. Principles of design, operation, and application. In: Physical Techniques in Biological Research. Vol. V. Electrophysiological Methods, Part A. pp. 191-233. Academic Press, New York 1964.

23. Nastuk, W.L.: Membrane potential changes at a single muscle end plate produced by transitory application of acetylcholine with an electrically controlled microjet. Fed. Proc., 12: 102 (abstract 330), 1953.

24. Curtis, D.R.: Microelectrophoresis. In: Physical Techniques in Biological Research. Vol. V. Electrophysiological Methods. Part A. pp. 144-190. Academic Press, New York 1964.

25. Chance, B.: Localization of intracellular and intramitochondrial compartments. Ann. N.Y. Acad. Sci., 108: 322-330, 1963 (Article 1).

26. Kohen, E., Kohen, C., Thorell, B. and Bartick, P.: A topographic analysis of metabolic pathways in single living cells by multisite microfluorometry. Exptl. Cell Res. In press.

27. Kohen, E., Hirschberg, J.G., Kohen, C. Wouters, A.W., Pearson, H., Salmon, J.-M. and Thorell. B.: Multi-channel microspectrofluorometry for topographic and spectral analysis of NAD(P)H fluorescence in single living cells. Biochim. Biophys. Acta. 396: 149-154, 1975.

28. Shifrin, S., Kaplan, N.O. and Ciotti, M.M.: Fluorescence studies of coenzyme binding to beef heart dehydrogenase. J. Biol. Chem., 234: 1555-1562. 1959.

29. Langan, T.: Changes in the fluorescence spectrum of reduced triphosphopyridine nucleotide on binding to isocitric dehydrogenase. Acta Chem. Scand., 14: 936-938, 1970.

30. Salmon, J.M., Kohen, E., Kohen, C., Viallet, P. and Zajdela, F.: A preliminary microspectrofluorometric study of NAD(P)H reduction in dibenzo(a.e) fluoranthene-treated single living cells. Histochemistry, 47: 291-302, 1976.

31. Salmon, J.-M., Kohen, E., Kohen, C. and Viallet, P.: Microspectrofluorometric study of free/bound NAD(P)H ratio in single living cells. Acute and long-term effects. In: Abstracts. VIIth International Congress in Photobiology, Rome, Aug. 29 - Sept. 30, 1976. p. 340.

32. Salmon, J.-M., Kohen, E., Kohen, C. and Viallet, P.: Microspectrofluorometric study of free/bound NAD(P)H ratio in carbazole and methyl carbazole treated cells. In: Abstracts. Fourth Meeting of the European Association for Cancer Research, Lyon, Sept. 13-15, 1977. p. 81.

33. Viallet, P., Kohen, E., Schactschabel, D.O., Marty, A., Salmon, J.M., Kohen, C., Leising, H.B. and Thorell, B. The effect of atebrine and an acridine analog (BCMA) on the coenzyme fluorescence spectra of cultured melanoma and Ehrlich ascites cells (EL2 cells). Histochemistry 57, 189-201. (1978).

34. Salmon, J.-M., Kohen, E., Viallet, P., Kohen, C. and Thorell, B.: Microspectrofluorometric approach to the study of free/bound NAD(P)H ratio as metabolic indicator in various cell types. In preparation.

35. Brester, T.W., De Abreu, R.A., De Kok, A., Visser, J. and Veeger, C.: The Pyruvate Dehydrogenase Complex. From Azotobacter Vinelandii to purification and properties. Eur. J. Biochem., 59: 335-345, 1975.

36. Chance, B. and Schoener, B.: Fluorometric Studies of flavin component of the respiratory chain. In: Flavins and Flavoproteins, B.B.A. Library. Vol. 8. E.C. Slater (ed). pp. 510-518. Elsevier Publishing Co., Amsterdam, London, New York, 1966.

37. Chance, B., Mela, L. and Wong, D.: Flavoproteins of the respiratory chain. In: Flavins and Flavoproteins. 2nd Conference on Flavins and Flavoproteins. K. Yagi (ed.). p. 107-121. University Park Press, Baltimore 1968.

38. Tataryunus, T., Karnaukhov, V.N., Enenko, S.O., Khaspekov, L.G., Shungskaya, V.E.: In: Abstracts, IVth International Biophysics Congress. Vol.3, Oxred States of a Nervous Tissue During Long Term Cultivation. Abstract EXVA4/3. August 7-14, 1972, Moscow.

39. Shires, T.K.: A fluorescence microscopic study of methodologic effects on the intranuclear distribution of benzo-(a)pyrene. Cancer Res., 29: 1277-1289, 1969.

40. Tarbell, D.S., Brooker, E.G., Seifert, P., Vanterpool, A., Claus, C.J. and Conway, W.: Studies on the metabolic products obtained from mouse skin after painting with 3.4-benzpyrene. Cancer Res., 16: 37-47, 1956.

41. Sloane, G.H.I. and Loeser, C.N.: Spectroscopic analysis of carcinogenic hydrocarbons in biologic interaction in vivo and in vitro. Cancer Res., 23: 1555-1565, 1963.

42. Daudel, P., Croisy-Delsey, M., Alonso-Verduras, C., Duquesne, M., Jacquignon, P., Markovitz, P. and Vigny, P.: Etude par fluorescence d acides nucleiques extraits de cellules en culture traitees par le methyl 7 benzanthracene. C.R. Acad. Sci. Paris, 278: 2249-2252, 1974.

43. Salmon, J.-M., Kohen, E., Kohen, C. and Bengtsson, G.: Microspectrofluorometric study of benzo(a)pyrene metabolization in benzo(a)pyrene-grown single living cells. Histochemistry, 42: 85-98, 1974.

44. Mason, R.: Charge transfer processes in biological systems. Dis. Faraday Society, 27:129-133, 1959.

45. Birks, J.B.: Dis. Faraday Society, 27: 243-244, 1959.

46. Kohen, E., Salmon, J.-M., Viallet, P., Kohen, C. and Deumie, M.: The UV fading of hydrocarbon fluorescence and its prevention for observations in single living cells. Histochemistry, 44: 357-361, 1975.

47. Deumie, M., Kohen, E., Viallet, P., Kohen, C.: Rapid microspectrofluorometric studies in EL2 cells following intracellular accumulation of dibenzocarbazoles. Histochemistry, 48: 17-27, 1976.

48. Kohen, E., Kohen, C. and Salmon, J.-M.: New methodological criteria in rapid multichannel microspectrofluorometry. Mikrochimica Acta, 1976 II: 195-210, 1976.

49. Norden, G.: The rate of appearance, metabolism and disappearance of 3.4-benzpyrene in the epithelium of mouse skin after a single application in a volatile solvent. A microfluorescence-spectro-analytical study. Acta Pathol. Microbiol. Scand. Suppl. XCVI. Berlingska Boktryckeriet, Lund, 1953.

50. Rousseau, M. : Spectrophotometrie de fluorescence en microscopie. Bull. Micr. Appl., 7: 92-94, 1957.

51. Olson, R.A.: Rapid scanning microspectrofluorometer. Rev. Sci. Instr., 31: 844-849, 1960.

52. Caspersson, T., Lomakka, G. and Rigler Jr., R.: Registrierender Fluoreszenzmikrospektrograph zur Bestimmung der Primar- und Sekundarfluoreszenz verschiedene Zellsubstanzen. Acta Histochemica, Suppl. 6: 123-126, 1965.

53. West, S.S.: Fluorescence microspectroscopy of mouse leukocytes supravitally stained with acridine orange. Acta Histochemica, Suppl. 6: 135-153, 1965.

54. Rost, F.W.D.: A microspectrofluorometer for measuring spectra of excitation, emission and absorption in cells and tissues. In: Fluorescence Techniques in Cell Biology. A.A. Thaer and M. Sernetz (eds.). pp. 57-63. Springer-Verlag, Berlin, Heidelberg, New York, 1973.

55. Karasek, F.W.: Optical Multichannel Analyzer. Res./Dev., 23: (No.1) 47, 48, 50 (1972).

56. Ploem, J.S.: Reflection-contrast microscopy as a tool for investigation of the attachment of living cells to a glass surface. In: Mononuclear Phagocytes in Immunity, Infection and Pathology. R. van Furth (ed.). pp. 405-421. Blackwell Scientific Publications, Oxford, London, Edinburgh, Melbourne, 1975.

57. Optical Multichannel Analyzer OMA. Operating and Service Manual. Princeton Applied Research Co., Princeton, New Jersey, 1975.

58. Kohen, E., Bengtsson, G., Salmon, J.-M. and Kohen, C.: The investigation of critical parameters in the glycolytic response of single living cells by rapid microspectrofluorometric analysis. Mikrochimica Acta, 1976 I: 249-261, 1976.

[2] Laboratory for Optics and Astrophysics, Department of Physics, University of Miami, Coral Gables, FL 33124.

[3] Also, Affiliate Faculty, Department of Pathology, University of Miami.

[4] Department of Pathology, Karolinska Institute, Stockholm, Sweden.

[5] Deceased.

[6] Laboratoire de Chimie Physique, Centre Universitaire de Perpignan, Avenue de Villeneuve, 66025 Perpignan, France.

[7] Leiden University Medical School, Department of Histochemistry and Cytochemistry, Sylvius Laboratories, P.O. Box 722, Leiden 2405, The Netherlands.

RECEIVED January 31, 1979.

14

Electro-Optical Ion Detectors in Mass Spectrometry Simultaneous Monitoring of All Ions over Wide Mass Ranges

HEINZ G. BOETTGER, C. E. GIFFIN, and D. D. NORRIS

Earth and Space Sciences Division, California Institute of Technology, Jet Propulsion Laboratory, Pasadena, CA 91103

Efficient signal collection has been a major problem in the development of observational instrumentation systems since their beginnings. One of the earliest approaches to this problem involves the utilization of photographic techniques. Light sensitivie emulsions (photographic plates) have been used for recording images at the focal point of a telescope since the middle of the 18th century. Similarly, they have been used for recording the spectra produced by various spectrographs for nearly 75 years. The ion-sensitive photo-plate has been the traditional method for recording mass spectra since Thomson (1) and, particularly, Aston (2) built their first mass spectrographs.

Unfortunately, it is not free of a number of problems, as will be shown below. The efforts made to solve some of the shortcomings attending its general use have been discussed by Ahearn (3) and Honig (4).

In principle, the photographic plate is ideally suited for simultaneously detecting and integrating the signal from all ion species over an extended mass range, limited only by the ion optics of the mass analyzer, with good resolution (typically $>$100 lines/mm). However, its sensitivity is limited, its use awkward, and the conversion of the image to numerical data is time consuming and costly. The limited sensitivity (it takes from 10^3 to 10^4 ions to produce a measurable line) and its associated lack of dynamic range (typically in the order of 30:1) have severely limited the use of photographic plates in routine applications of mass spectrometry. The search for alternate ion detection systems has resulted in the wide-spread use of electrical detection systems. Modern implementation of these devices drastically shortens the time required to collect both quantitative and qualitative analytical results and greatly simplify the associated data reduction problems. Conventional electrical detection devices are based upon sweeping the resolved ion beam

0-8412-0504-3/79/47-102-291$07.00/0

across an image slit which is located at the focal point of the mass resolving system. The detector, usually some form of electron multiplier, is placed behind the slit. In spite of the inherent sensitivity of the electron multiplier, and the popularity of electrical detection systems, there are also a number of serious limitations (5,6). The most significant of these is the loss of sensitivity by 3 to 6 orders of magnitude due to the limited observation time for each ion species (typically 1 ion in 10^3 to 10^5) in a spectrum as well as the sample as a whole (usually less than 1/10 of the sample in the ion source is utilized). Consequently, today's electrical detection methods are no more sensitive for recording complete mass spectra than the traditional photographic methods. Attempts to overcome the loss of sensitivity have resulted in a technique where only a limited number of mass values (generally not more than 4 or 5) are monitored either continuously or cyclicly. However, due to the loss of usually more than 99% of the information content of the spectrum, this approach is restricted to the detection and quantitation of highly purified known substances for the majority of practical analytical problems. Thus, one can conclude that prior to the developments described in this paper, there was no completely satisfactory detection system for mass spectrometers which combined sensitivity of the electron multiplier with the simultaneous collection characteristics of the photographic plate.

Outside the field of mass spectroscopy, the search for a more efficient method for observation of astronomic and spectrographic images had led to the use of a variety of image converters including television systems. The application of these types of devices to the recording of ion images at the focal plane of a mass spectrograph appeared to be a natural extension of this technology. The general feasibility of the approach had been demonstrated by the use of "Ion Image Converters" for the visual inspection of complete mass spectra by von Ardenne (7,8) and, for more efficient ion collections of resolved single ion beams, by Daly (9,10,11) and several other investigators. These devices are all based upon some form of ion electron converter ranging in gain from as little as 5 for a simple CuBe wire mesh or plate to as high as 10^8 for a Chevron type Multi-channel Electron Multiplier Array (MCA). In the Daly type detectors the low gain ion-electron-photon conversion stage is followed by a high gain photomultiplier resulting in total gain of 10^6 - 10^8 permitting counting of single ion events. While the work of earlier investigators proved the overall feasibility of the approach, a number of major problems had to be solved before a detector monitoring a suitable mass range simultaneously could be implemented. Figure 1 shows the schematic representation of the two most frequently encountered ion optical arrangements in commercial magnetically focusing mass spectrometers. For the present, only the case of the Mattauch-Herzog type Double Focusing Mass

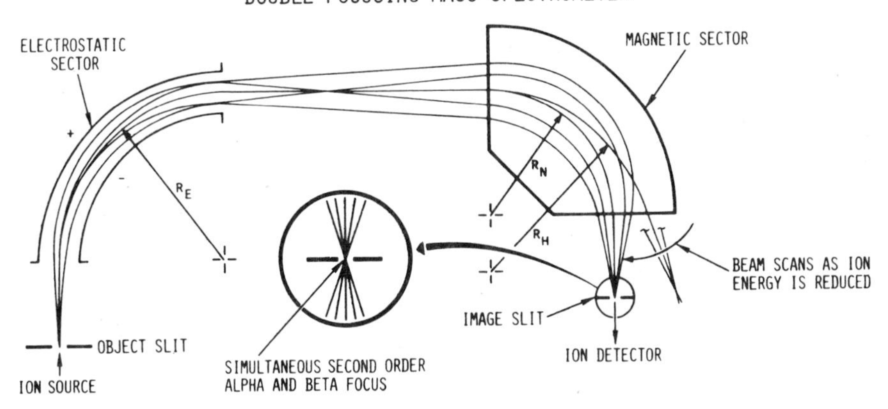

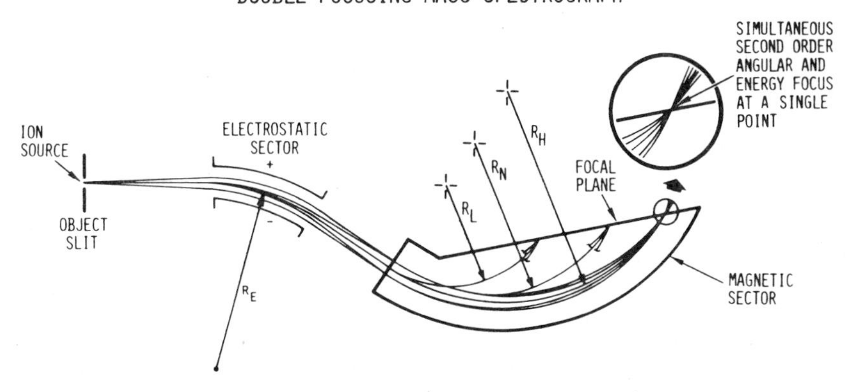

Figure 1. Schematic representation of the ion optical configuration of commercial magnetically focusing mass spectrometers

Spectrometer will be considered. In this geometry the resolved ion beams are focused simultaneously in a plane which can range from 5 cm upwards (e.g., 36 cm for the CEC-21-110 series mass spectrometers). The commercial version of a Robinson (13) modified Mattauch-Herzog mass spectrograph places the focal plane approximately one-half gap width external to the analyzer magnet pole pieces. Figure 2 shows a schematic representation of the Electro-Optical Ion Detector. An ion exiting from the magnetic field penetrates into one of the channels of the micro-channel electron multiplier array (MCA) and, upon collision with its wall, initiates a cascade of secondary electrons. The electrons emerging from the MCA are accelerated and proximity focused onto an aluminized phosphor screen where each electron generates a number of photons. The photons are conducted via fiber optics to the target of a solid state imaging device (camera).

The first of the aforementioned problems concerned the fact that the MCA must operate in the strong transverse magnetic fringe field of the spectrometer. In the case of the 30.5 cm maximum radius Mattauch-Herzog-Robinson geometry mass spectrometer, the fringe field at the focal plane is approximately one-half of the homogenous field in the analyzer magnetic gap. Under typical operating conditions of 10-12 K-Gauss in the gap, the field at the focal plane is 5-6 K-Gauss. A study of the effect of such a field on the operation of the MCA has shown (14) that the the collected output current is virtually unattenuated at all angles with respect to the magnetic field except in the vicinity of an angle of 0°. At 0° the MCA still functions properly, but the electrons emerging from the MCA are unable to reach the collector plate. Thus, it was concluded that indeed the MCA electron multipliers work well in a strong magnetic field and efficient secondary electron collection efficiencies can be achieved by angling the MCA collector plane with respect to the magnetic field vector at an angle $> 10^{o}$.

The next problem concerned the fact that high quality images were obtained only up to approximately 4 K-Gauss in the analyzer magnet. ($\sim$2 K-Gauss fringe field). However, severe distortion and foreshortening of the images took place at high fields. This was presumed to be due to the curvature of the magnetic fringe field. A soft iron magnetic shunt, as shown in Figure 3, was placed above the EOID, which was angled at approximately 20°, to force common field lines to intersect both the active area of the MCA and the phosphored collector plane. The distortion disappeared.

Another problem to be solved, involved the development of an electron multiplier array of sufficient length to cover the entire focal plane. Commercially available MCA's were nowhere near the required dimensions of approximately 1 mm high x 361

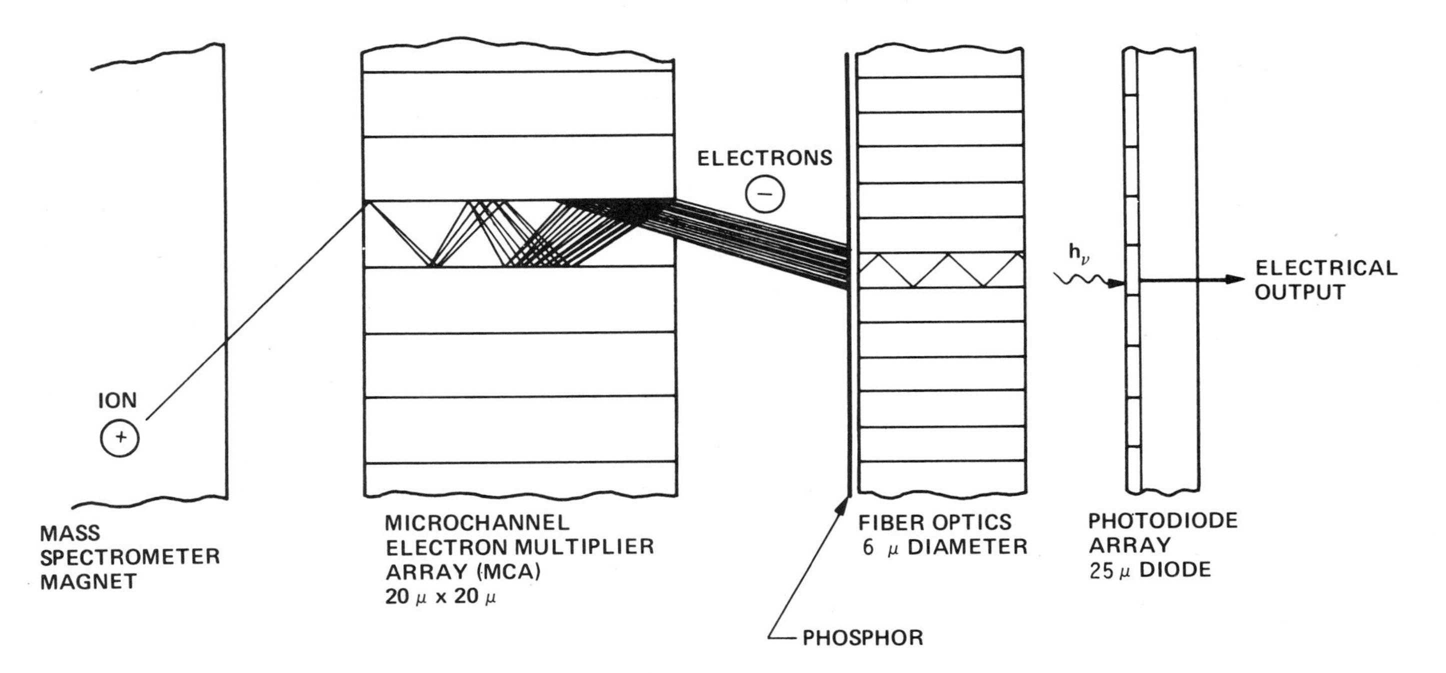

Figure 2. Schematic representation of electro-optical ion detection

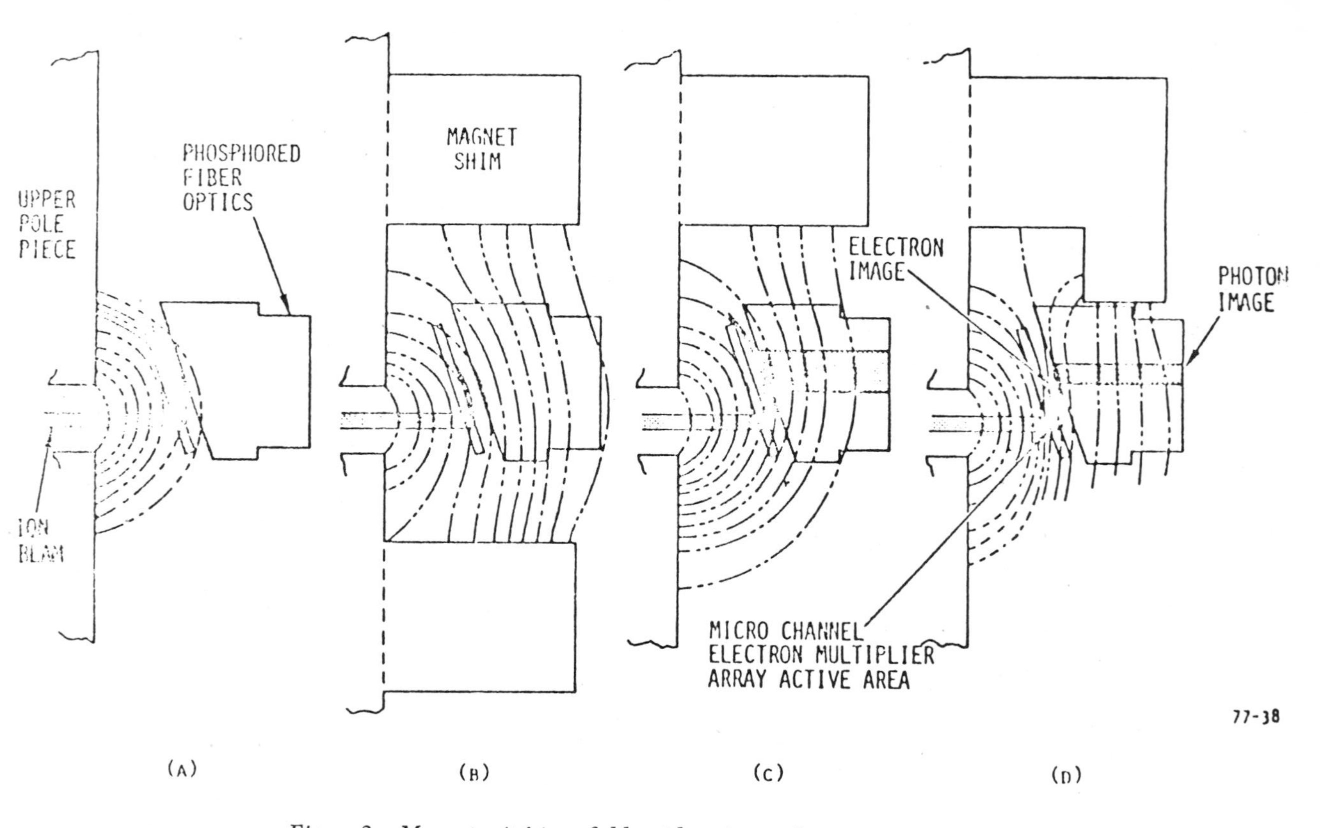

Figure 3. Magnet exit fringe fields with various pole piece terminations

mm long. Existing manufacturing techniques as well as cost factors precluded the production of single arrays of these dimensions. Futhermore, conventional units, using round or polygonal channels could not be used in segment form to generate a long array without losses due to end-effects created by cutting through channels (these fractional channels also tend towards "auto-emission", i.e., secondary electron emission in the absence of incoming ions). The problem was solved, eventually, by means of a novel development (ITT Electro-Optical Products Division) utilizing square electron multiplier channels (16 um on a side placed on 20 um center to center). This configuration allows the active area of the MCA plate to be continuous from end to end with no dead or broken areas at the ends, as shown in Fig. 4. Hence, MCA's 26 mm long can be placed end to end to make up the required length. There are several distinct advantages to this approach. (1) Each MCA is inexpensive on a production basis; (2) MCA's can be selected for gain uniformity; (3) arrays of variable, theoretically unlimited, length can be built up in 26 mm increments; (4) damaged MCA's can be replaced individually; (5) the small MCA's are less fragile than longer ones.

Thus, with the development of the primary detector (conversion from ions electrons to photons) complete, the remaining problem involved the coupling of the detector with a solid state imaging device. Three types of devices were investigated: (1) Vidicon camera system; (2) Photodiode arrays (Reticon); (3) Charge Coupled Devices (CCD's). Based upon considerations of the state-of-the-art at the time, as well as cost, the first generation EOID was implemented with a television type camera (Vidicon), as shown in Fig. 5. This decision required one additional problem to be solved, namely, matching the format of the primary image (1 mm x 361 mm) to that of the vidicon (19 mm x 19 mm). This task was accomplished by means of a fiber-optic image disector (14) which segments the horizontal input fiber-optic face into nineteen 1 mm x 19 mm segments and stacking these segments vertically at the output face, as shown in Fig. 6. Each individual fiber is 15 um in diameter, thus giving 30 line pairs/mm resolution. The dissector has a numerical aperture of ~0.55 and a transmission of ~60%.

The image of the mass spectrum produced at the output end of the dissector was focused onto the target of the Vidicon Camera via relay optics, as illustrated in Fig. 5. The camera used for the conversion from optical data to electronic display of information was a modified version of the camera system used on the Viking spacecraft. It was capable of integrating the light output from the primary detector for up to two seconds. Fig. 7 depicts the image format at the vidicon.

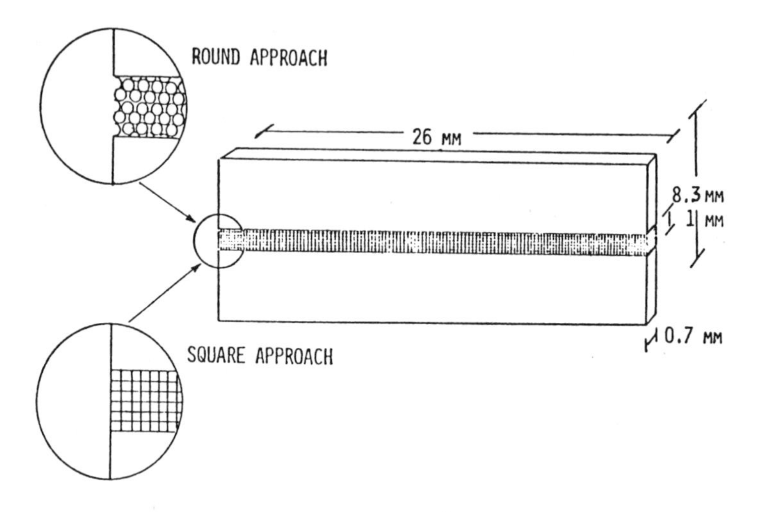

Figure 4. Micro channel electron multiplier plate. Round approach: 14 μm diameter, 17 μm center-to-center. Square Approach: 16.3 μm square, 20 μm center-to-center.

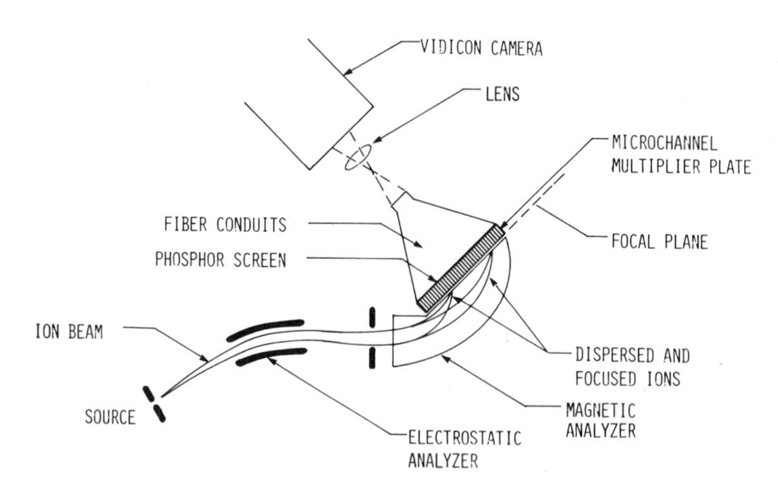

Figure 5. Integrating electro-optical ion detector mass spectrometer with TV read-out

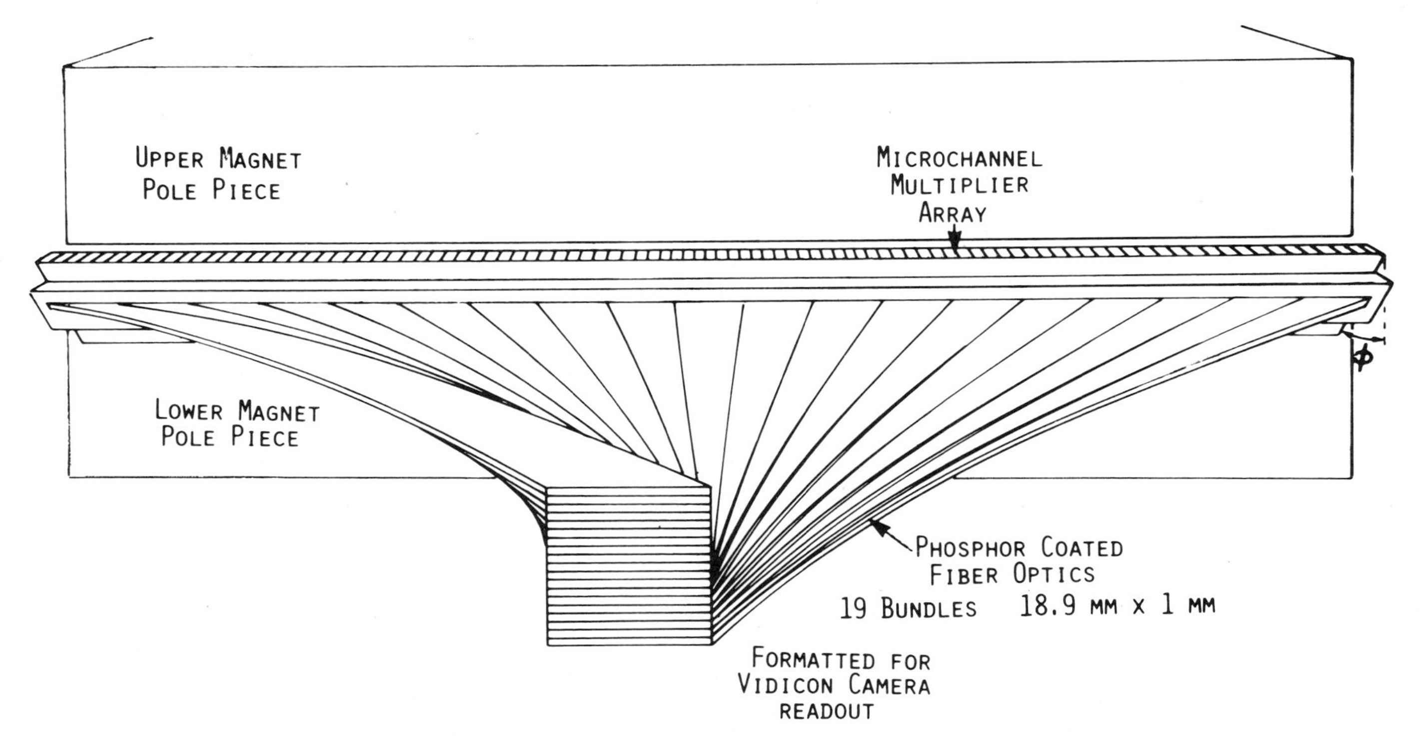

Figure 6. First generation detector with folded fiber optics image converter

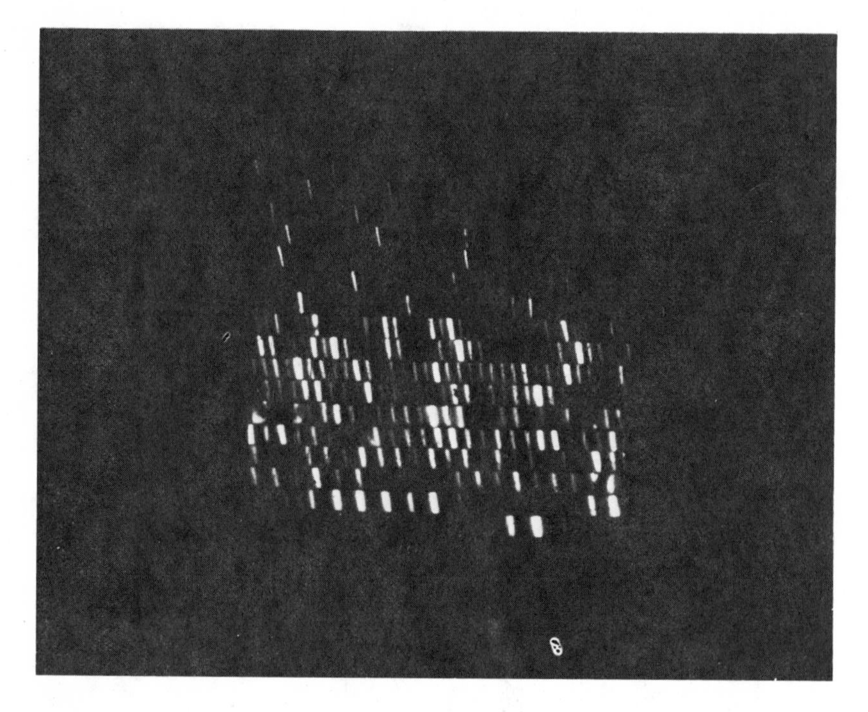

Figure 7. Converted spectral image as seen by the vidicon camera system

The results obtained with this first generation focal plane M.S.-EOID system as well as studies by Beynon and others at Purdue University (15) demonstrated the technical feasibility of such a system. Furthermore, these studies led the way to solutions for the variety of fundamental problems, which were encountered during the development and helped point out the directions towards future changes necessary on the road towards a commercially practical design for use of the concept in routine applications of mass-spectrometry. It became obvious that the vidicon based camera system was not the best approach. Some of the reasons for this are: (1) Loss of sensitivity due to light losses in the dissector and the transfer optics; (2) cost of the image dissector; (3) lower dynamic range and sensitivity, slower read-out rate, etc., of the vidicon compared to alternate devices.

Theoretically, CCD's offered the most attractive features of the remaining choices, photodiodes and CCD's. However, at the time when the decision had to be made, CCD technology was, and still is, too much in flux, for their use in a mass spectrometer system and too high in cost to be a reasonable choice. The cost factor would be amplified even further when one considers the increased requirements on the data acquisition system due to the 60-fold increase in data rate (860,00 vs 14,300*) data points per spectrum. These and other considerations led to the decision to implement the second generation detector with a photodiode (Reticon) based camera. This system is now in operation producing excellent data and will be described in detail in the following section.

In parallel with the development of the EOID for focal plane mass spectrometers of the Mattauch-Herzog type, similar devices were developed for use with conventional sector-type mass spectrometers (15, 16, 17, 18). A schematic representative of this type detector, versus that implemented on a CEC type 21-490 single focusing mass spectrometer, is shown in Fig. 8. The main differences between these two applications of the EOID are a result of the differences in the ion optics of the two types of mass analyzers, as shown in Fig. 1. First, the detector of a sector type instrument resides outside the magnetic fringe field, thus eliminating the need for angling the primary ion sensors. This simplifies the overall detector design greatly. Second, the number of resolved ion beams that is in simultaneous focus is greatly reduced, therefore, only a limited mass range can be displayed simultaneously, typically 10-20% on either side of the central mass which is in optimum focus. However, this range of masses as well as the line shape can be improved through the use of auxiliary lenses (17, 18). Due to the simplicity of the detector design, such systems have been in routine use for several years at JPL and at the FOM Institute in Amsterdam (19).

*14" long focal plane x 1024 photodiodes per inch.

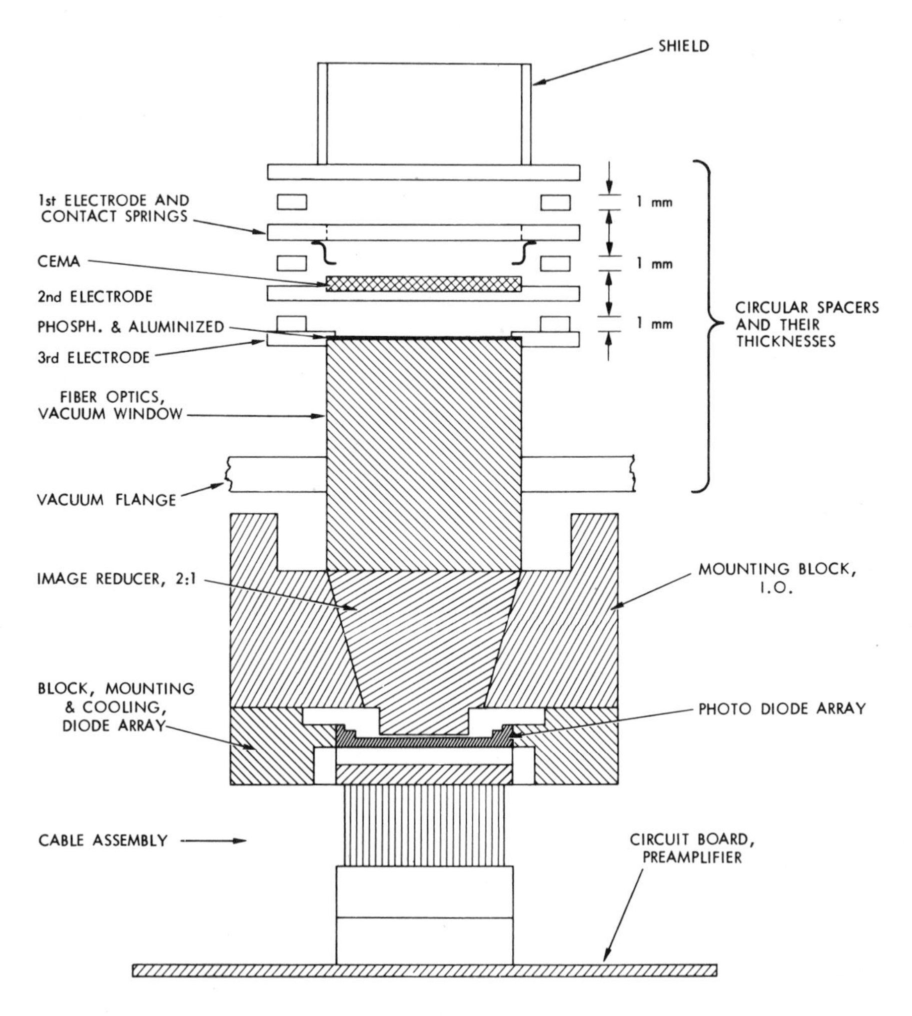

Figure 8. Schematic presentation of an electro-optical ion detector for spector type mass spectrometers

DESCRIPTION OF THE FOCAL PLANE M.S. - EOID - COMPUTER SYSTEM

The mechanical concept of the focal plane MS/EOID can be seen in Fig. 9. The MCA plates are placed at a 20° angle with respect to the magnet pole pieces. Secondary electrons produced by the MCA are accelerated to the phosphor coated fiber optics via the magnetic fringe field lines as noted above. The phosphor coated fiber optics is, in actuality vacuum window whereby the image of the ion beam made visible at the phosphor is transmitted with high efficiency outside the mass spectrometer vacuum. Since the primary ion beams do not strike the angled MCA's at normal incidence, the spectral lines form a set of non-orthoganal (but parallel) images as shown in Figure 10. The "tilt" angle of the spectrum is not 20°, however, due to the effects from the magnetic fringe field gradient.

To quantify the insensity and position of the ion images (as a measure of their abundance and mass, respectively) photodiode arrays (PDA's) were selected as the imaging elements. Table I gives the performance specifications of these devices. An orthoganal format for the array of 25 cm wide 2 mm high sensitive elements was selected so as to develop a generally useful spectroscopic sensor rather than one suited only for this particular MS/EOID application. This, and the consideration that each PDA was physically 1.6" long with an active area of only 1.0" long, meant that an additional fiber optic device was needed to couple the images presented at the vacuum window to the PDA's and in the process rotate them such that they are aligned with PDA picture elements (pixels).

The fiber optic couplers are pictorially explained in Figure 11. These devices are constructed from forty-two 320 x 320 square multi-fiber elements (each fiber being 6 um on a side) and one coupler is used to transmit the images on each 1" long portion of the focal plane to a PDA. The couplers are butted side by side alternately above and below horizontal so as to avoid physical interference between PDA's. This can be seen in Figure 9. In the case of the CEC, 21-110B MS, there are seven detectors above horizontal and seven below. Figure 12 is a photograph of a PDA with the fiber optic coupler attached. Also seen in the photograph is the preamplifier board directly attached to the PDA. This is done for signal-to-noise considerations.

Figure 13 is an overall block diagram of the MS/EOID system being developed under a grant from the National Institute of General Medical Sciences, National Institutes of Health. It is reasonably self explanatory. The shutter control operates from a sampling of the integrated total ion current and acts to prevent saturation of the EOID. The mass shift control allows

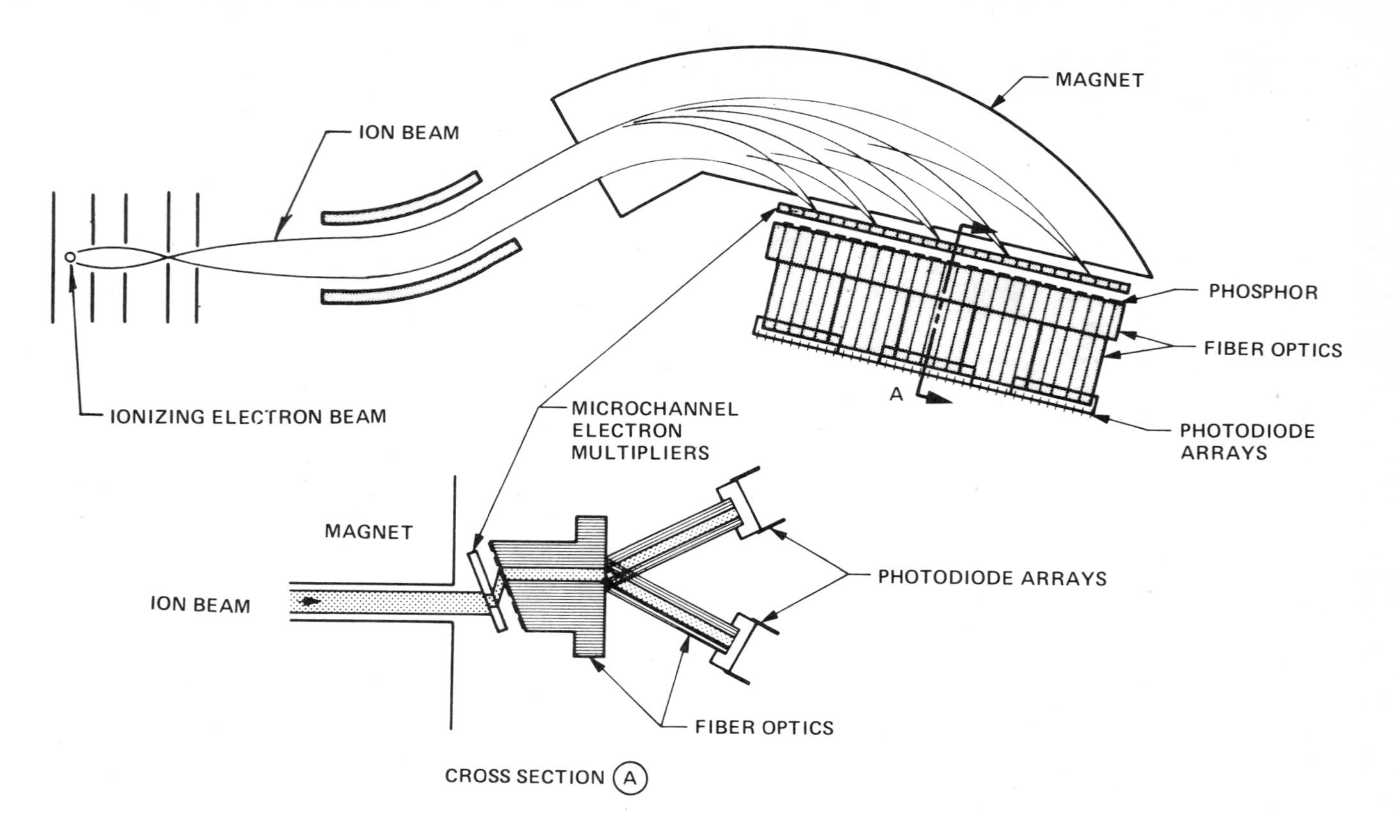

Figure 9. Schematic representation of double focusing of focal plane mass spectrometer/electro-optical ion detector system

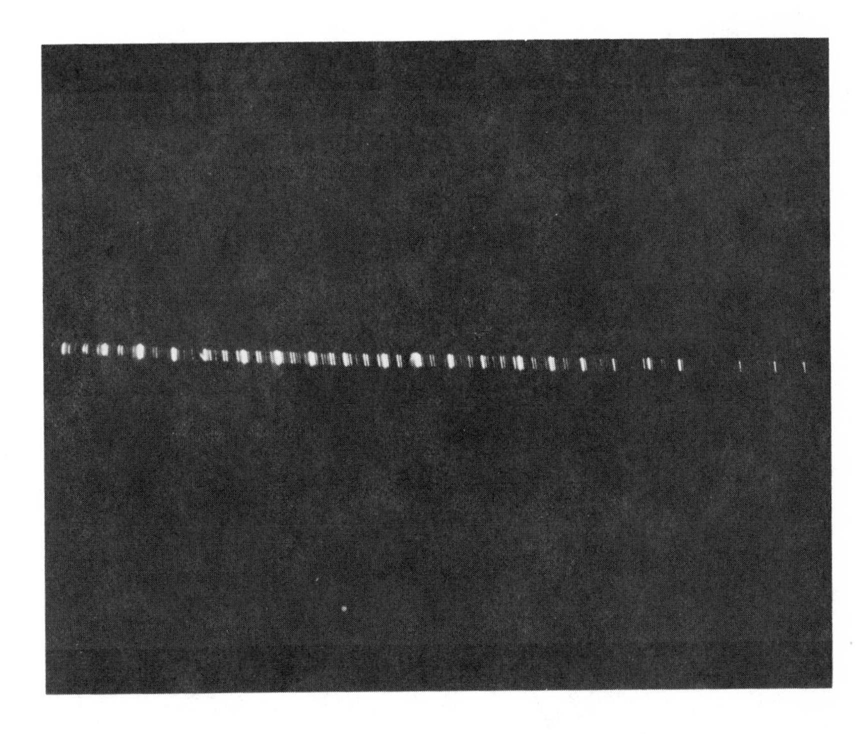

Figure 10. Spectral image as seen by the photo diode array camera

APERTURE WIDTH	2.54 CM
APERTURE HEIGHT	2.5 MM
DIODE WIDTH	25 μM
NUMBER OF DIODES	1024
SATURATION EXPOSURE	5.05 x 10^{-5} μ-WATT-SEC
QUANTUM EFFICIENCY	75% (@ 520 NM)
DYNAMIC RANGE	$\geqslant 1 \times 10^4$

Table 1. Photodiode Array Specifications

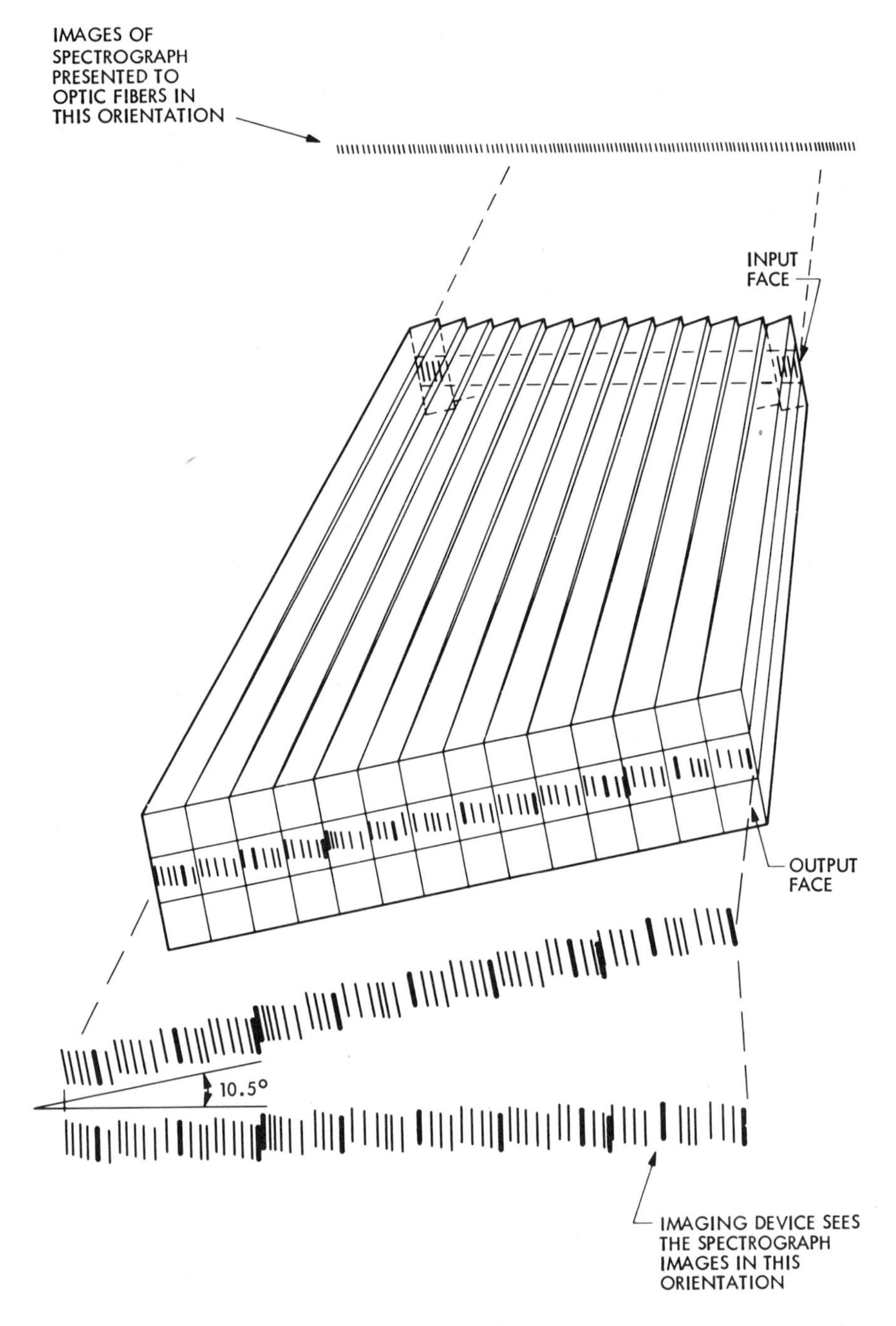

Figure 11. Schematic representation of fiber optic image rotator

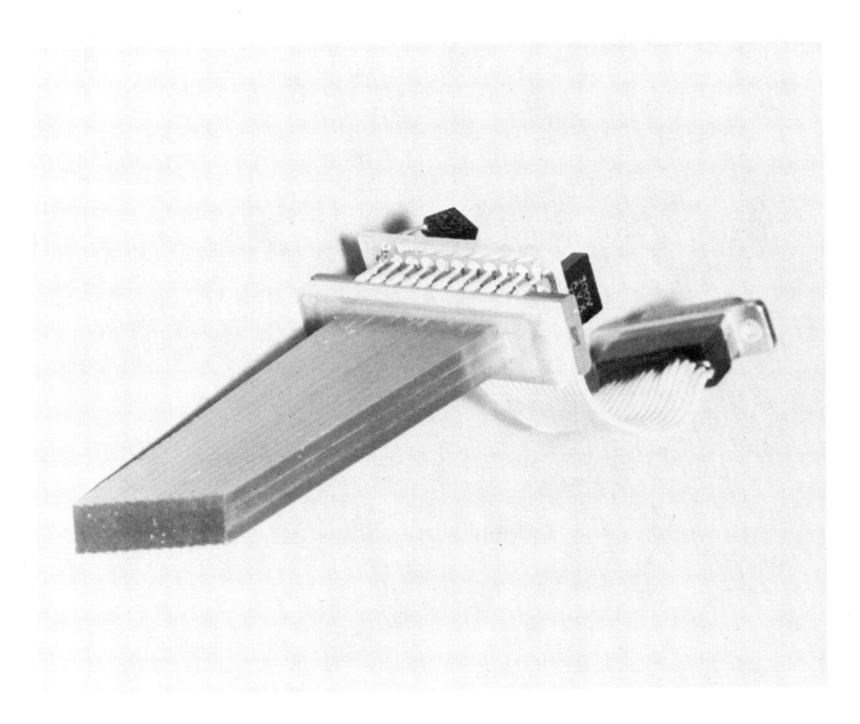

Figure 12. Fiber optic image rotator and photo diode array assembly

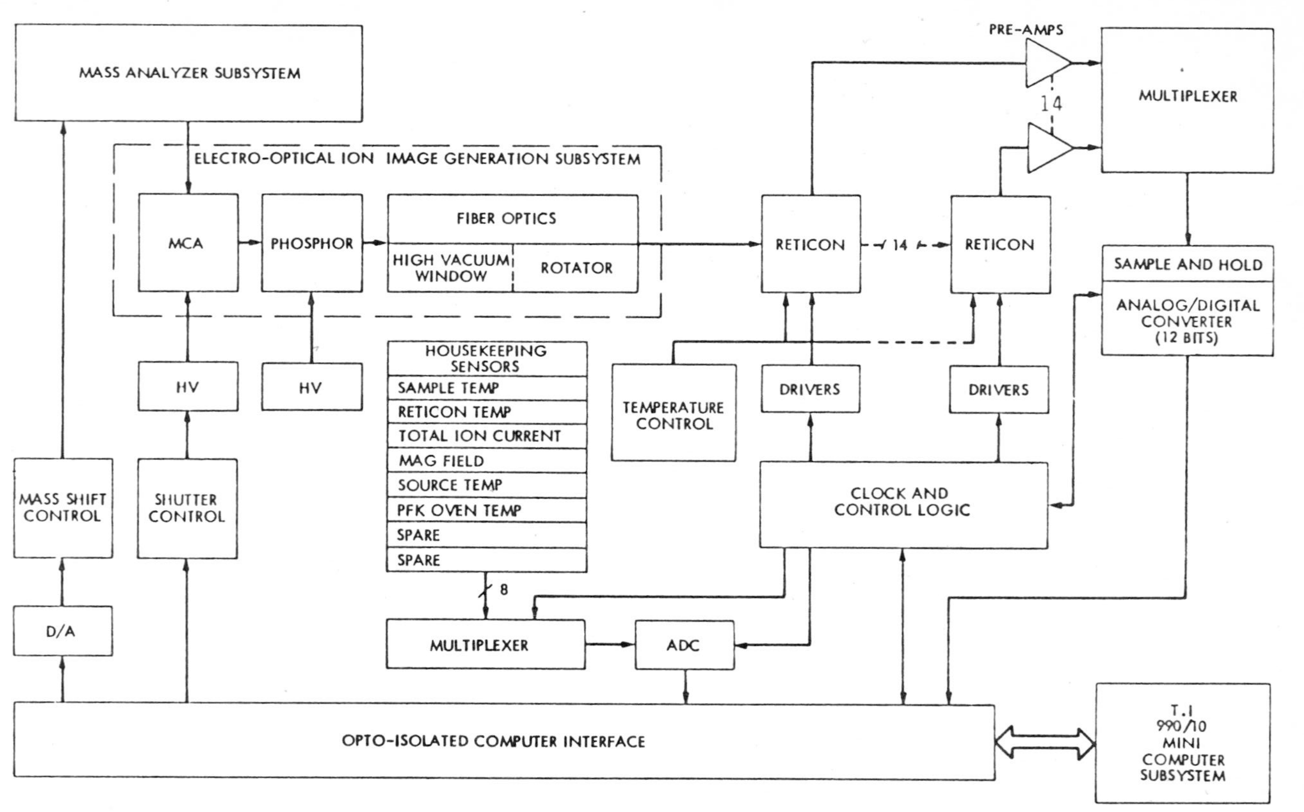

Figure 13. Block diagram of the NIH EOID/MS system

a known spectrum (e.g., perfluorokerosene) to be "slid" along the focal plane by scanning the magnetic field in order to calibrate each one of the 14,336 detector positions on the focal plane.

An opto-isolated interface is used to couple the MS/EOID to a mini-computer where a new complete spectrum can be taken as often as every 50 milliseconds. With real time decalibration "on-the-fly" complete spectra can be processed every 4.5 seconds.

Since the EOID is truly an integrating detector, the collected spectra are insensitive to sample transients as might be experienced, for example, during GCMS analyses using capillary columns. This is because all positions along the focal plane are active simultaneously. The cycle time between spectra is purely a function of diode readout rate and the degree of real-time decalibration desired. The lesser the amount of calibration, the greater the amount of data that must be stored with the advantage of more frequent spectra-taking but with the disadvantage that less spectra can be stored for post-run analysis. On the other hand, sophisticated decalibration on the fly results in fewer data bits per spectrum being stored, but the cycle time is lengthened. Obviously, the particular application will dictate the data handling format.

Figures 14-18 are examples of the computer plots of selected data. These spectra have had dark current and fixed pattern noise subtracted "on-the-fly". (Both of these items are inherent in PDA's, the correction for which represents trivial implementation in terms of software and hardware). In some of the printouts, the individual diode levels can be seen representing 25 um spatial resolution across the focal plane. The ordinate is quantified to only 12 bits while the PDA's themselves have a dynamic range of 14 bits. This was done for expediencey only.

DESCRIPTION OF THE EOID FOR SECTOR TYPE MASS SPECTROMETERS

Figure 8 gives an overall view of the EOID. The overall design is self-explanatory. Briefly, the primary detector, consisting of the channel electron multiplier array (14 mm diam. 17 mm center-to-center channels in a 1" diam. array) and the aluminized phosphor (P-35) coating are mounted upon a 1" diameter x 2" long fiber optic vacuum window. The coating is applied directly to the face of the window. A set of mounting ring-electrodes and ceramic spacers are provided to position the CEMA relative to the phosphor and to furnish the necessary potentials. The window is adjustable longitudinally via a micrometer screw mechanism in order to locate experimentally the optimum plane of focus. The photodiode array (1024 diodes x 24 micro m wide x 2.5 mm high) is provided with a fiber optic

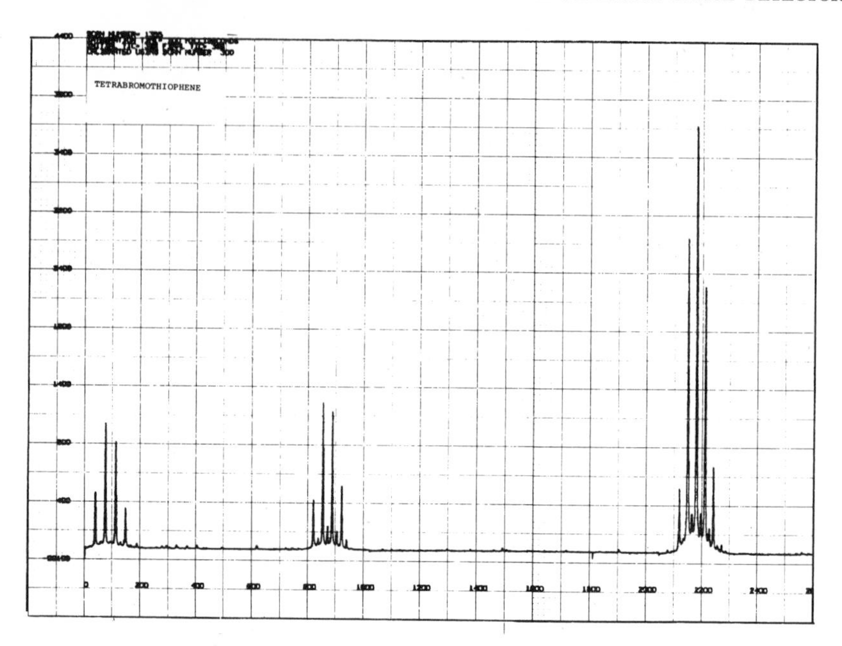

Figure 14. Computer plot of a partial spectrum of Tetrabromothiophede from mass 271 to 420

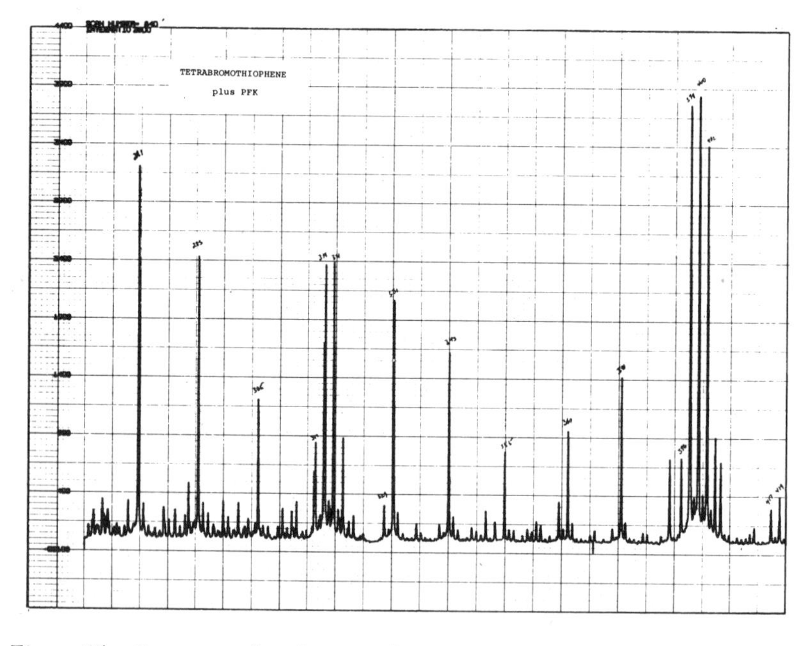

Figure 15. Computer plot of a partial spectrum of Tetrabromothiophene plus Perfluorokerosene from mass 271 to 420

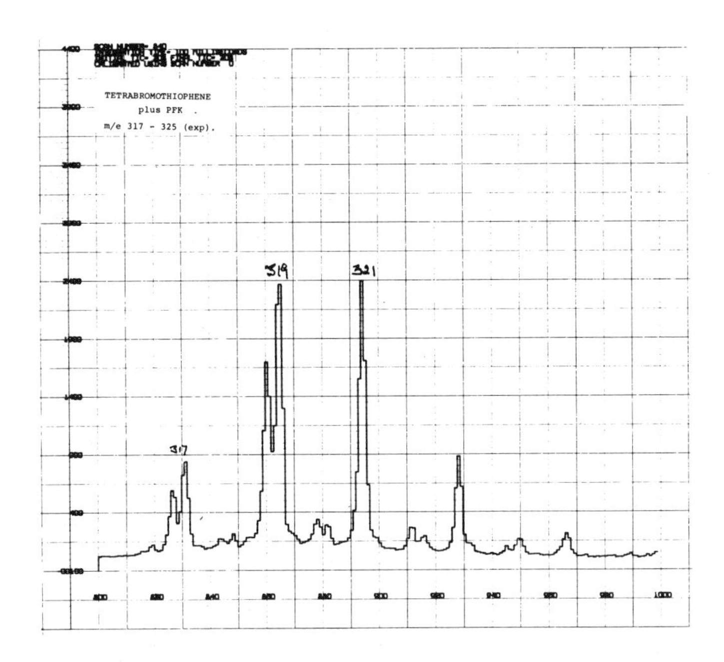

Figure 16. Expanded computer plot of the mass range from 316 to 326, showing partial resolution of the —Br/—F doublets at m/e 317 and 319. The steps on the peaks represent the signal level in individual diodes.

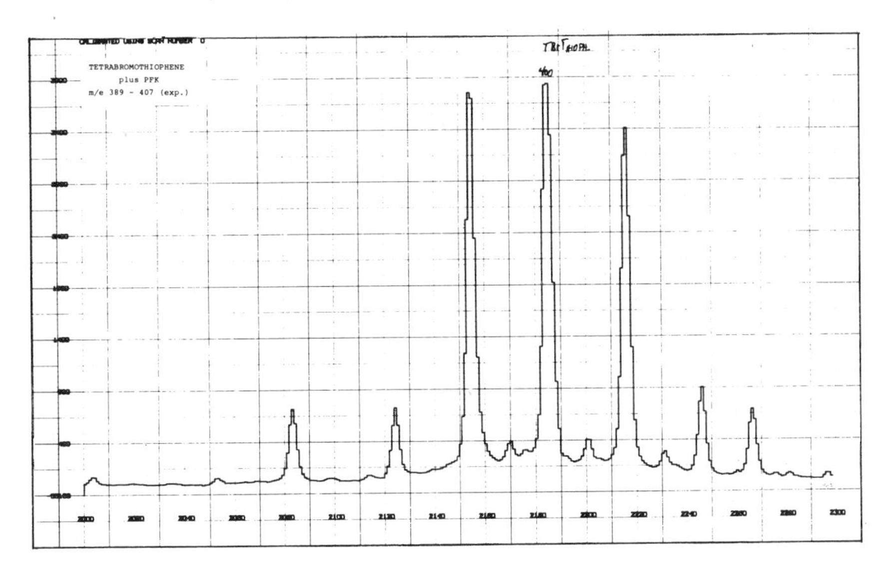

Figure 17. Expanded computer plot of the molecular ion region of Tetrabromothiophene from mass 388 to 407. Peaks at 391, 393, and 405 are caused by PFK. The peak at m/e 400 is slightly saturated.

window which is in direct contact with the 2.5 mm diameter vacuum face plate. The preamplifier and the driver electronics for the PDA are mounted at the detector to keep extraneous noise at a minimum. The entire camera assembly, outside the vacuum, is cooled to -30 to -50° to reduce the dark current and thus increasing the dynamic range of the system, since the maximum usable signal is limited by the saturation current of the device.

RESULTS

Initial tests, as shown in Figures 14-19, demonstrate clearly that the performance goals have been achieved. These goals are shown in Table 2. While Fig. 19, a composite of photographic recording and a photometric scan of the line spectrum at the fiber optic interface, demonstrates the result of these tests. As implemented presently on the CEC 21-110B, the resolving power of the EOID-MS system is greater than 1000 and good spectra are recorded at total ions currents of less than 10^{13} amp using integration times of 100 milliseconds. These results are illustrated in Figures 14 to 18. Figure 14 shows a photograph of the visual image at the fiber-optic window, of a partial PFK spectrum covering the mass range from approximately m/e 500 to 800. Figures 15 and 16 represents the high mass portion of the spectrum of tetrabromo-thiophene (TBT) with and without PFK present as a mass marker, showing clear separation of the TBT/PFK doublet at m/e 317, 319, 320 and 322. This fact is demonstrated more clearly in Figure 17 which shows an expanded display of the mass range from m/e 317 to 325. Figure 18 represents the region of TBT from m/e 393 to 405, demonstrating the proper isotopic distribution of a four-bromine ion. Peaks at 393 and 405 are due to PFK. Finally, Figure 19 shows a partial spectrum of cholesterol plus PFK from m/e 271 to approximately 400. The spectrum represents the integrated ion currents from less than 100 femto-gram of cholesterol deposited on the direct probe of the mass spectrometer.

APPLICATIONS

The eventual application towards which this work is progressing is biomedical mass spectrometry in the form of sophisticated research instruments and, ultimately, a fully automated "Clinical Mass Spectrometer" (22). This instrument will be capable of carrying out sophisticated analyses of physiological fluids and tissue in as routine a fashion in the clinical laboratory as conventional automated wet chemical procedure are employed today. In addition, many other applications of mass spectrometry are expected to benefit from the development of the EOID, e.g., spark source mass spectrometry, of mass spectrometers in spacecraft and on the surface of the planets, etc.

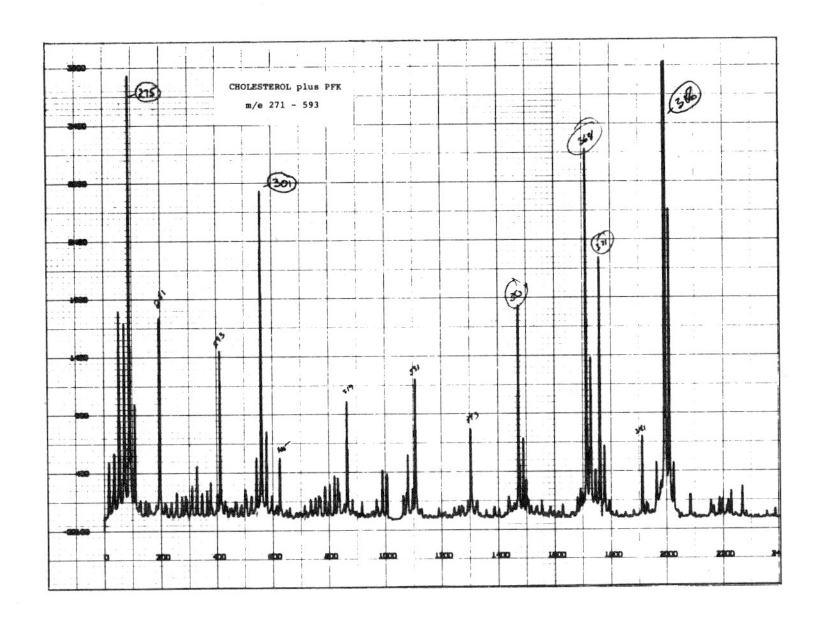

Figure 18. Computer plot of a partial spectrum of a mixture of PFK and approximately 100 femtogram of cholesterol from mass 271 to mass 410 using an integration time of 100 milliseconds. Parent peak at m/e 386 is saturated.

PARAMETER	PHOTO-PLATE CAPABILITY	ELECTRO-OPTICAL SENSING CAPABILITY	
		VIDICON IMAGING	SOLID STATE IMAGING
THRESHOLD OF ION DETECTION	10^3 TO 10^5	10 TO 100	1
DYNAMIC RANGE	< 30:1	>1000:1	10^5
TIME REQUIRED TO OBTAIN SPECTRAL PLOTS	>1 HOUR	<1 MINUTE	<1 SECOND
SPATIAL RESOLUTION AT FOCAL PLANE	<2 μ	20 μ	10 μ

Table 2. Comparison of Photographic and Electro-Optical Ion Detection Methods

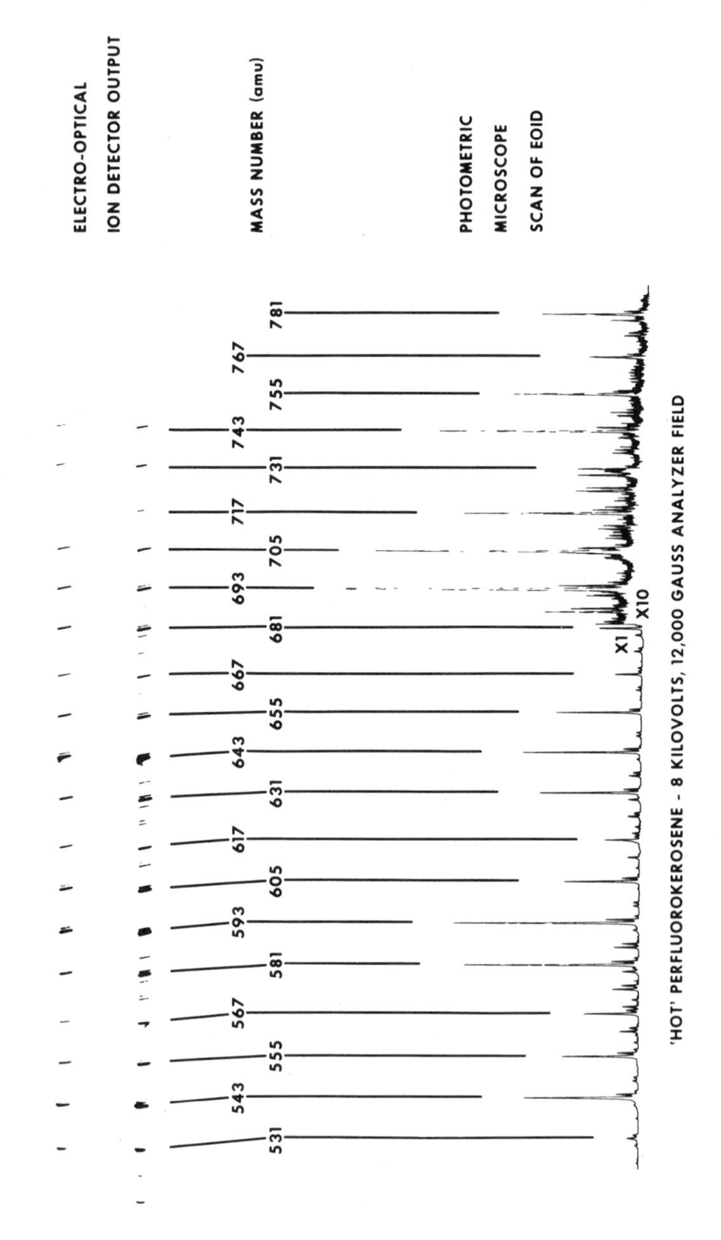

Figure 19. Composite of photographic and scanning photometric microscope recording at the fiber optic interface of a partial spectrum of PFK from approximately mass 525 to mass 786

At present, EOID's have been implemented on several experimental mass spectrometers beyond the ones described above: (1) a miniaturized (4.5" focal plane) Mattauch-Herzog type mass spectrometer with a mass range of 25-500 and resolution 1/500, which has been built (Perkin-Elmer Corp., Pomona, California) for JPL as a prototype for future space and/or clinical applications; and (2) an ultra-miniature (2" focal plane) Mattauch-Herzog type mass spectrometer for outer-space use. Additional uses of the EOID are presently in the planning and/or design stages.

Analytical research applications of mass spectrometers fitted with electro-optical ion detectors are carried out at the present time at JPL and the FOM Institute. These involve" (1) at JPL a 1" EOID on sector type mass spectrometer (CEC type 21-490) in conjunction with an API (armospheric pressure ionization) source for the development of an automated assay procedure for amino acid derivatives produced by a novel Edman type sequenator (23), and (2) at the FOM Institute a 1" EOID on a sector mass spectrometer,fitted with magnetic and electrostatic quadruple "Zoom" lenses, permitting variation of dispersion for focusing a greater number of masses on the 1" detector (24,25).

This instrument has been used extensively over the past several years for studies in the field of pyrolysis mass spectrometry and laser desorption.

Proposed nearterm applications for new Mattauch-Herzog type (14" and 4.5" focal plane) EOID mass spectrometers include their use in field desorption mass spectrometry (FDMS), laser desorption mass spectrometry (LDMS), high performance liquid chromatography mass spectrometry (HPLCMS) and pyrolysis mass spectrometry (PyMS). All of these applications have one feature in common, the measurement of rapidly changing sample profiles at, usually, low concentration levels. Further complications arise in some cases, e.g., PyMS and GC or LCMS, due to the fact that the sample in the mass spectrometry's ion source represents not a single component but a more or less complex mixture. The most difficult example of this type is found in pyrolysis mass spectrometry when a complex sample, e.g., micro-organism, bio-polymer, tissue, etc., is broken down into a multitude of smaller compounds. The reactions leading to these pyrolysis products, while extremely fast, proceed at different rates. As a result, the overall spectrum of the pyrolysate changes rapidly with time. Thus, in order to get meaningful data, which can be correlated with the sample, integration of the ion insensities of interest over the entire sample is required. For reasons outlined previously, conventional integration methods, such as photographic recording or electronic integration of multiple fast scans are either not sensitive enough or too cumbersome or both. The same principles apply to the mass spectrometry of unresolved peaks in chromatographic applications. However, the problem is usually less complicated due to the fact that, typically, unresolved chromatographic peaks seldom contain more than two or three components.

A different, but no less severe problem, is encountered with the analysis of unknown biological substances by field desorption, laser desorption, and/or laser assisted field desorption mass spectrometry. A priori, it is not known at what point in time a component of interest is desorbed. This makes it difficult, if not impossible to time a scan or several scans in such a way that a representative spectrum is obtained. Again the answer to the problem is found by integrating the ion output over the entire sample or repeatedly over portions of the sample profile as it emerges from the ion source.

The foregoing applications represents but a small sampling of all the potential uses of an EOID-MS system. It can be expected that many others will materialize as instruments of this type become more widely available.

CONCLUSIONS

The history, development and implementation of high sensitivity electro-optical ion detector for simultaneous detection of all ions arriving at the focal plane of Mattauch-Herzog-Robinson geometry as well as the adaptation of the same principle to the quasi focal plane sector type mass spectrometers has been discussed. Experiments were performed which proved the feasibility of the detector concept. The critical aspect of the detector design for mass spectrometer geometries, requiring location of the detector inside the fringing magnetic field, involve the rotation of the primary detector (MCA and phosphor) at an angle greater than 10° with respect to the magnetic fringe field vector and shaping of the fringe field in such a way as to properly collimate the equivalent electron beams between the MCA and the phosphor. Electro-optical ion detectors have been built and operated for several focal plane mass spectrographs and sector type mass spectrometers. One of these, a CEC 21-110B, has been implemented with dedicated computer systems for data acquisition and analysis. Results to date have shown that all design parameters have been attained and that, indeed, the EOID-MS system provides a powerful tool for the solution of a wide variety of analytical problems.

ACKNOWLEDGMENTS

The authors wish to thank Prof. W. J. Dreyer and his staff at Caltech for his support of part of this work. We also wish to acknowledge D. Helprey of Caltech and Dr. J. Yinon of the Weizmann Institute of Science (Israel) who materially contributed to the design, construction and initial testing of the sector type EOID-MS, V. Taylor and H. Mohan for their contribution to the mechanical design and fabrication of the detector assemblies, and R. Johansen and his staff for the design implementation of the data system.

This work was funded in part by the National Institute of Health (NIGMS Grant #GM-20850 and Division of Research Resources Grant #RR-00922), by the National Aeronautics and Space Administration under NASA Contract 7-100, and the Caltech Presidents Fund.

BIBLIOGRAPHY

1. J. J. Thomson, Phil. Mag. 21 (1911) 225

2. T. W. Aston, Phil. Mag. 37 (1919) 707

3. A. J. Ahearn, Mass Spectrometric Analysis of Solids, Elsevier, Amsterdam, 1966, Ch.1.

4. R. E. Honig, Rev. Sci. Instrum., 40 (1969) 1364

5. C. R. McKinney and Heinz Boettger, 13th Annual Conference of Mass Spectrom and Allied Topics, 1965, p. 345

6. K. H. Maurer and K. Habfast, 14th Annual Conference on Mass Spectrometry and Allied Topics, 1966, p. 271

7. M. Von Ardenne, Elektronenanlagerungsmassenspectrographie Organischer Substanzen, Springer, Berlin, 1971, pp. 54-56

8. M. Von Ardenne, Tab. Zur. Angew. Physik, Band 1, Springer, Berlin, 1962

9. M. R. Daly, Rev. Sci. Instrum., 31 (1960) 720

10. M. R. Daly, Rev. Sci. Instrum., 31 (1960) 264

11. M. R. Daly, Rev. Sci., Instrum., 34 (1963) 1116

12. M. R. Daly, R. E. Powell and R. G. Ridley, Nucl. Instrum. Methods, 36 (1965) 226

13. C. F. Robinson, Rev. Sci. Instrum., 28 (1957)

14. C. E. Giffin, H. G. Boettger and D. D. Norris, Intern. J. of Mass Spectr. and Ion Physics, 15 (1974) 437

15. J. H. Beynon, D. O. Jones, and R. G. Cooks, Anal. Chem., 47 (1975) 1734

16. D. D. Norris and C. E. Giffin, Proceedings of SPIE, 77 (1976) 103

17. H. G. Boettger, et al., Advances in Mass Spectrometry in Biochemistry and Medicine, Vol. II, (1976) 513

18. J. Yinon and H. G. Boettger, 25th Ann. Conf. on Mass Spectrometry and Allied Topics, Washington, D. C. (1977)

19. H. H. Tuithoff and A. J. H. Boerboom, Int. J. Mass Spectrom Ion Phys. 15 (1974) 105

20. J. H. Tuithoff, A. J. H. Boerboom and H. C. L. Meuzelaar, Inst. J. Mass Spectrom. Ion Phys., 17 (1975) 229

21 H. L. C. Meuzelaar, et al and P. J. Kistemaker, et al., 26th Ann. Conf. on Mass Spectrometry and Allied Topics, St. Louis, Missouri (1978)

22. H. G. Boettger, et al., U. S. Patent No. 4,084,090 (11 April 1978)

23. J. Yinon and H. G. Boettger, 25th Ann. Conf. on Mass Spectrometry and Allied Topics, Washington, D. C. (1977)

24. H. H. Tuithoff and A. J. H. Boerboom, Int. J. Mass Spectrom. Ion Phys., 18 (1976) 111-115

25. H. H. Tuithoff and A. J. H. Boerboom, Int. J. Mass Spectrom. Ion Phys. 15 (1974) 105

RECEIVED January 8, 1979.

15

Use of the OMA for Analyzing Light Intensity Gradients from the Absorption Optical System of the Ultracentrifuge

DARREL L. ROCKHOLT and E. GLEN RICHARDS

Pre-Clinical Science Unit, Veterans Administration Medical Center and Department of Biochemistry, University of Texas Health Science Center, Dallas, TX 75216

In this symposium on Image Detectors in Chemistry there have been described a number of physical techniques that have been greatly aided by the use of the Optical Multichannel Analyzer (OMA) for the recording of light intensity patterns. We have used the OMA with the absorption optical system of the ultracentrifuge (1,2). Obtaining data from any desired cell in a multicell spinning rotor requires a Silicon Intensified Target (SIT) vidicon camera tube operating in the pulsed mode; this detector system is not described elsewhere in this symposium.

Described in this paper are three aspects of our work dealing with the verification of the performance of the system that may aid other users of the OMA: 1) the measurement of the deterioration of the image caused by pulsing the SIT vidicon and how to eliminate the deterioration, 2) the measurement of pincushion distortion, and 3) the use of a triangular mask in a spinning rotor to simulate an optical density wedge.

Background Information

Historical. The ultracentrifuge was developed in the late 1920's by Svedberg and co-workers for the purpose of generating high centrifugal fields to study the sedimentation behavior of macromolecules in solution, thereby providing information as to their size and shape (3,4). The first commercial instrument was constructed by a company that later became the Spinco Division of Beckman Instruments, Inc. (Palo Alto, CA). In spite of the development of other commercial ultracentrifuges, most of the instruments currently in use are versions of the original design updated with improved components as they became available.

Rotor and Cells. In the ultracentrifuge a rotor spins about a vertical axis at speeds ranging from about 600 to 68,000 rpm. A variety of rotors can be used, holding 2, 4 or 6 cells. The cells, 1 in. in diameter, are assembled from a pair of transparent windows, quartz or sapphire, in holders placed on both sides

Published 1979 American Chemical Society

of a hollowed centerpiece. The parts are assembled in a cylindrical barrel with a bottom lip, and then a screwring on top is tightened to prevent leakage. After the solution to be studied is introduced with a syringe through a small hole in the side of the cell, a sealing plug is screwed into the barrel.

In Figure 1 is shown the top view of a four-cell rotor containing a counterbalance and three kinds of cells. The counterbalance is constructed with two D-shaped holes which provide reference edges for the image corresponding to distances of 5.7 and 7.3 cm from the center of the rotor. A large variety of cell centerpieces are available for different purposes. Usually the walls are constructed so as to lie along radii from the rotor center. (For other shapes there are convective disturbances in the solution caused by density inversions arising from sedimentation of solute molecules against or away from the walls.) Two single-sector cells are shown with different angular openings, and the third cell contains two sectors which can be filled with two different solutions. Usually one is the solution containing the solute of interest and the other is the solvent.

Absorption Optical System. During an ultracentrifuge experiment the solute, if denser than the solvent, sediments toward the bottom of the cell, thereby generating a concentration gradient. (There are many types of experiments; the two most common types will be described later.) The instrument is constructed with two separate optical systems that record the concentration gradient during an experiment. One of these, the absorption optical system, is especially useful in biochemistry for the study of proteins and nucleic acids which have chromophores which absorb visible or uv light.

Since the detector system can only measure the light intensity, the concentration c is determined from the Beer-Lambert law, $A = \log Io/I = Ecl$, where A is the absorbance, I is the light intensity after passage through the solution of length l, Io is the intensity through solvent, and E is the extinction coefficient for that particular wavelength of light.

In the absorption optical system the cell is illuminated by monochromatic light obtained from a lamp with a filter or with a monochromator. (Additional details of this part of the system will not be given here.) The remainder of the system is shown in Figure 2. The light passes through the cell and then through a narrow slit (not shown) parallel to a radius through the center of the rotor. The light continues through a condensing lens which converges the light to a narrower beam for passage through the camera lens. The camera lens-condensing lens combination focuses an image of the cell onto a suitable detector, which provides the radial distribution of light intensity in the cell. The radial absorbance profile is obtained from a combination of the intensity profiles from a solution and a solvent cell.

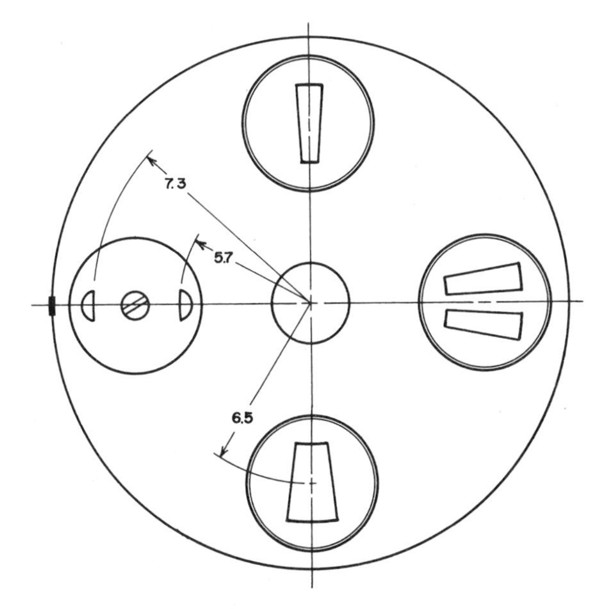

Figure 1. Schematic drawing of a four-cell rotor, top view

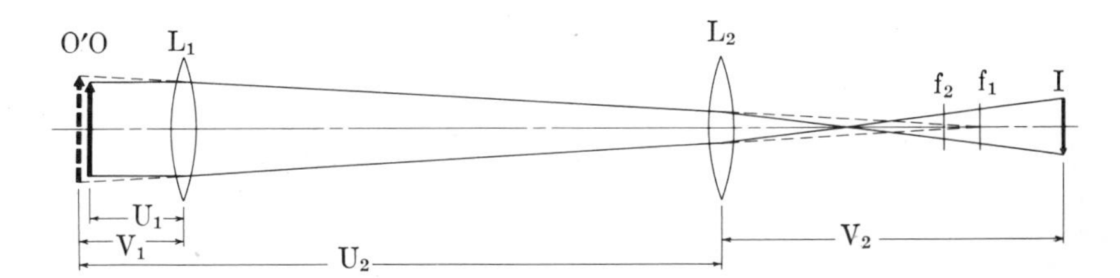

Figure 2. Scale drawing of camera lens system as used with OMA. (The vertical direction is enlarged about 8 times for clarity.) The system has been turned through 90°; the actual light path is vertical. L_1 is the condensing lens, $f = 69.25$ cm at 260 nm. L_2 is the camera lens, $f = 21$ cm. $U_1 = 8.25$ cm, $V_1 = 9.37$ cm, $U_2 = 54.7$ cm, $V_2 = 29.2$ cm. The thickness of the cell in the direction of the optical path is usually 1.2 cm.

Film and Photomultiplier Detector Systems. In the original ultracentrifuge built by Svedberg and co-workers (3,4) and also in the commercial instrument, the light intensity pattern was recorded on film, requiring a densitometer to obtain the absorption profile. Schachman and co-workers (5,6) constructed a mechanically scanned photomultiplier system in the early 1960's. In addition to a commercial version now available (7), a number of other systems with computer controlled gathering of data have been constructed (8, 9, 10, 11, 12).

Vidicon Detector Systems. It was obvious to many workers that the use of a television camera tube as the light detector would offer a number of advantages over the photomultiplier tube. The viewing of the image in real time would aid in aligning the optical system and also in decision making during an experiment.

Lloyd and Esnouf (13) constructed a vidicon-based system of their own design for the ultracentrifuge, but it had a number of drawbacks. Any refinements to their system have not appeared in publication.

When the commercial OMA (Model 1205, Princeton Applied Research Corporation, Princeton, NJ) became available, we recognized its potential as a replacement for the photomultiplier detector. The vidicon detector surface was divided into 500 channels, the image could be seen on a cathode ray tube (CRT) monitor in real time, the intensity profile was available in digital form, the profile could be time-averaged for any desired number of video scans, and the final profile was stored in internal memory for transfer to an external output device. Not only had a considerable amount of work gone into its development and the verification of performance, but its potential for use for a variety of physical techniques would ensure the construction of enough units to support further development of the system. Moreover the need for low-light-level detectors for other purposes would lead to further improvements in detector devices.

Our first work with the OMA demonstrated that, with a modified optical system easily constructed, absorbance data could be obtained that were as good as those from existing photomultiplier systems (1). However, there were drawbacks. Even though the Model 1205F uv-sensitive vidicon detector head was used, our medium pressure Hg arc lamp with interference filters did not provide sufficient uv light in the 250-280 nm range to make up for the 1% duty cycle of a cell in a spinning rotor. It was unlikely that any simple monochromator system could provide sufficient light. Moreover it was necessary to obtain the intensity profile from a solution and solvent cell spun successively, a time-consuming process.

Before an OMA-based system could be considered as a potential replacement for the photomultiplier scanner, it was necessary to extend the wavelength capability to the 250-280 nm range and to find a method of examining cells individually in a multicell rotor. One way of solving these problems was to use an intense pulsed light source, such as a Xe arc or a laser, but such systems were expensive and did not have the reproducibility of pulse amplitude suitable for time-averaging.

The manufacturer of the OMA already had available a detector head with an SIT vidicon (Model 1205D), which is an image intensifier stage coupled directly to a silicon vidicon tube. With appropriate accelerating voltages applied to the photocathode, a gain of signal strength up to 1500 times could be achieved. Moreover it had been demonstrated that the intensifier stage could be gated on and off by the application of flat-topped pulses from a suitable pulsed power supply. The only drawback to the SIT vidicon was that light of wavelength lower than 350 nm was not transmitted through the fiber optics faceplate. They overcame this problem by placing a very thin fluorescent film against the faceplate to convert the uv light to higher wavelengths for passage through the faceplate. The film did not significantly affect operation for light of wavelengths above 350 nm, but it provided sufficient conversion efficiency, about 10%, to make the SIT vidicon considerably more sensitive than the uv vidicon.

Once preliminary experiments with a pulsed SIT vidicon system had demonstrated that it performed satisfactorily in the desired uv region and that it could be successfully gated to examine individual cells in a multicell rotor, we constructed an interface-controller for automatic operation of the OMA with single- or double-sector cells in multicell rotors (2). The cell location in the rotor and the start and stop of the gate pulse is obtained from a phase-lock loop circuit. A mark on the rotor interrupts a light beam reflected from the rotor to a photocell, providing a reference pulse for each rotation. The time between each pulse is divided into 3600 parts irrespective of the rotor speed. Appropriate switches are used to select the cell hole in the rotor and the pulse width, in terms of the angle, for single- or double-sector cells. Additional details concerning the controls for automatic data gathering and the performance of the system are published elsewhere (2).

When 8-bit microprocessor-based computers became available, we decided that such a computer, even though slower than minicomputers, would be adequate to operate the OMA and our interface controller with the ultracentrifuge. We now have in the system an Altair 8800 computer with 28K of memory (MITS, Albuquerque, NM), a hard-wired arithmetic board and two minifloppy disk drives (North Star, Berkeley, CA), a 700 ASR Terminal (Texas Instruments, Dallas, TX), and a 7202A Graphic Plotter (Hewlett-Packard, Palo Alto, CA). Appropriate software, written in Basic, has been developed to collect intensity data from the OMA automatically and also to treat and plot the data at the end of the experiment. Details of the system and software will be published elsewhere. We also have an improved illumination system with a 200 W Hg-Xe arc lamp and a Model H-20 monochromator with a holographic grating (Jobin-Yvon, Metuchen, NJ) (14).

Performance of the System

The manufacturer provides specifications for the performance of the OMA, including linearity of counts as a function of intensity and the geometric distortion and channel-to-channel crosstalk of the vidicon. However, the user needs methods for verifying the performance of his OMA operating with his system. This information is needed both for designing correction schemes if distortion is found and for determining whether further improvements in the system are needed. Ideally the methods should be simple so that the testing can be performed on a routine basis.

Obtaining the greatest possible accuracy in molecular weight determinations and polydispersity analyses requires the greatest possible accuracy in the absorbance profile. As a starting target we would be satisfied with an accuracy of 0.001 absorbance units in the range from 0 to 1 absorbance units. Further effort to achieve greater accuracy would be warranted only when the target level was reached.

During the development of our OMA-based detector system, we performed a number of experiments checking the performance by measuring the absorbances of uniform solutions spun in the ultracentrifuge. It was observed that the flat absorbance profiles for the hundreds of points for each cell varied only by about 0.002 absorbance units and a plot of the average absorbance for each cell vs. the concentration was linear from 0 to 1 absorbance units and even higher (1,2). However, such a demonstration with uniform solutions does not prove that the correct absorbance profile is obtained from a cell with a concentration gradient.

Not only can errors in absorbance measurements arise from non-linearity in the detector circuitry, but distortion in the linearity of the position of channel detector elements can lead to a corresponding distortion of the measured intensity profile. The geometric distortion of the SIT vidicon, as stated in the specification sheet supplied by the OMA manufacturer, is typically 2 channels between channels 100 and 400 for a 2.5 mm high image centered on the tube. This distortion is sufficient to require correction of data obtained for experiments with steep concentration gradients in our system.

During the development of our OMA-based detector system we performed a number of tests aimed at verifying the correct behavior of various components. With the completion of the entire system, it was important to evaluate its performance by the examination of images obtained from objects with known dimensions and solutions of known sedimentation behavior.

Before beginning these studies, the optical system was aligned according to the usual procedures (15) and the detector head electronics were adjusted following the procedures given in the Operating and Service Manual supplied by the manufacturer.

For the SIT vidicon the line-scan amplitude is reduced to give a 5 by 12.5 mm scanning pattern and adjusted so as to center the image on the tube face. Adjustment of the symmetry control is especially important. Misadjustment will cause a distortion in the intensity profile of a knife-edge image; at the bottom it will appear rounded or it will fall below the zero intensity level.

The image pattern presented to the face of the SIT vidicon is about 12 mm in the horizontal direction, corresponding to the radial dimension of the cell, and about 1 mm in the vertical direction, representing a blurred image of the defocused stationary slit above the rotor. For each revolution of the rotor the vidicon is pulsed for both the reference counterbalance hole and for the desired cell sector (Figure 1), resulting in an image with a long rectangle (from the cell) with a small rectangle on both ends (from the two counterbalance holes).

Ruled Line Target. For the measurement of pincushion distortion, we decided to examine a ruled line target. It turned out that the intensity profiles obtained for these measurements were also useful for evaluation of the distortion caused by the pulsing of the SIT vidicon and also for measurement of channel-to-channel crosstalk.

The manufacturer of the ultracentrifuge provides a ruled disk that when placed in a suitable holder in a stationary rotor at the plane corresponding to half-way through the cell, serves both as a target for focusing the camera lens and as a series of lines of known spacing for determination of the optical magnification factor. The disk, constructed of glass with blackened, etched lines 1 mm apart, was not suitable for our purposes, since it could not transmit uv light and also because there were small blemishes at the edges of the lines.

With the aid of Micrometrology (Dallas, TX) we constructed a quartz disk with a ruled pattern. A 10-times enlarged pattern was cut with a blade into Rubylith using a coordinatograph with an accuracy better than 0.001 in. A photograph, reduced exactly 10 times, was obtained, and the image was transferred from the photograph to a quartz disk using photoresist technology. The final pattern consisted of 35 transparent lines, 0.080 mm wide and spaced exactly 0.500 mm apart on an opaque background. The edges were sharply defined, with only an occasional blemish.

Behavior of Pulsed SIT Vidicon. Before proceding with the experiments involving the pulsed SIT vidicon, it is necessary to discuss the effect of pulsing the tube on the image. The signal gain of the SIT vidicon is determined by the photocathode voltage, which can be regulated with an adjustment potentiometer. When an image is examined continuously, the correct voltage for the focusing grid of the intensifier stage is supplied by the circuit, with no adjustment required when the gain is changed. Operated in the pulsed mode, the intensifier stage requires an optimal pulse voltage which varies with the photocathode voltage. As the voltage of the pulse is changed in either direction from its optimal value, the sharpness of the image deteriorates and the magnification of the image changes.

During the rise and fall periods of the pulse duration, the intensifier voltage is incorrect, resulting in a deterioration in the fidelity of the final image, since it will contain a series of images which progressively change in sharpness and size. The magnitude and the characteristics of the deterioration in the image, accumulated during the pulse, depend upon the duration of the rise and fall periods relative to the total pulse time. Presumably the deterioration in the image can be reduced to a negligible level by using a pulse generator with rise and fall times very short compared to the total pulse time.

Procedure for Examination of Ruled Disk. Since the lines on the ruled disk are straight and not concentric arcs about the center of the rotor, the sharpest image of the lines is obtained with a stationary rotor. The disk in its holder was placed in the rotor, which was coupled to the drive. The correct orientation of the lines, perpendicular to a radius of the rotor, was accomplished by rotating the disk holder to give the sharpest line edges as examined on the monitor in real time (see Figure 3). The camera lens was focused to produce the sharpest line images.

Determination of Optimum Pulse Voltage for the SIT Vidicon. A number of procedures for the determination of the optimal pulse voltage were evaluated. Comparison of a series of accumulated patterns obtained at different voltages proved to be no more sensitive than examination of the image in real time as the voltage was changed. Since the magnification of the image changes with voltage, the greatest sensitivity was achieved by 1) finding the line near the center of the pattern from the ruled disk which did not move as the voltage was changed and 2) moving the vidicon relative to the image until this line was centered between two channels. The center line image, magnified horizontally and vertically, was examined as the voltage was changed; at the optimal voltage, the vertical size was maximum and the minima between the line images were the lowest and the flattest.

For the particular gain setting (about 700) that we used, the pulse voltage which gave the sharpest line images for the ruled disk was about 700 V, as measured with a Model 465 oscilloscope (Tektronix, Inc., Beaverton, OR) using a 100X probe. The voltage was about the same whether using the Model 1211 (Princeton Applied Research Corp., Princeton, NJ) or the Model 340 (Velonex, Santa Clara, CA) high voltage pulse generator.

Deterioration of Image Caused by Pulsing the SIT Vidicon. When we began measuring the pincushion distortion with the ruled disk, we had assumed that a pulse width of 10 μsec obtained from

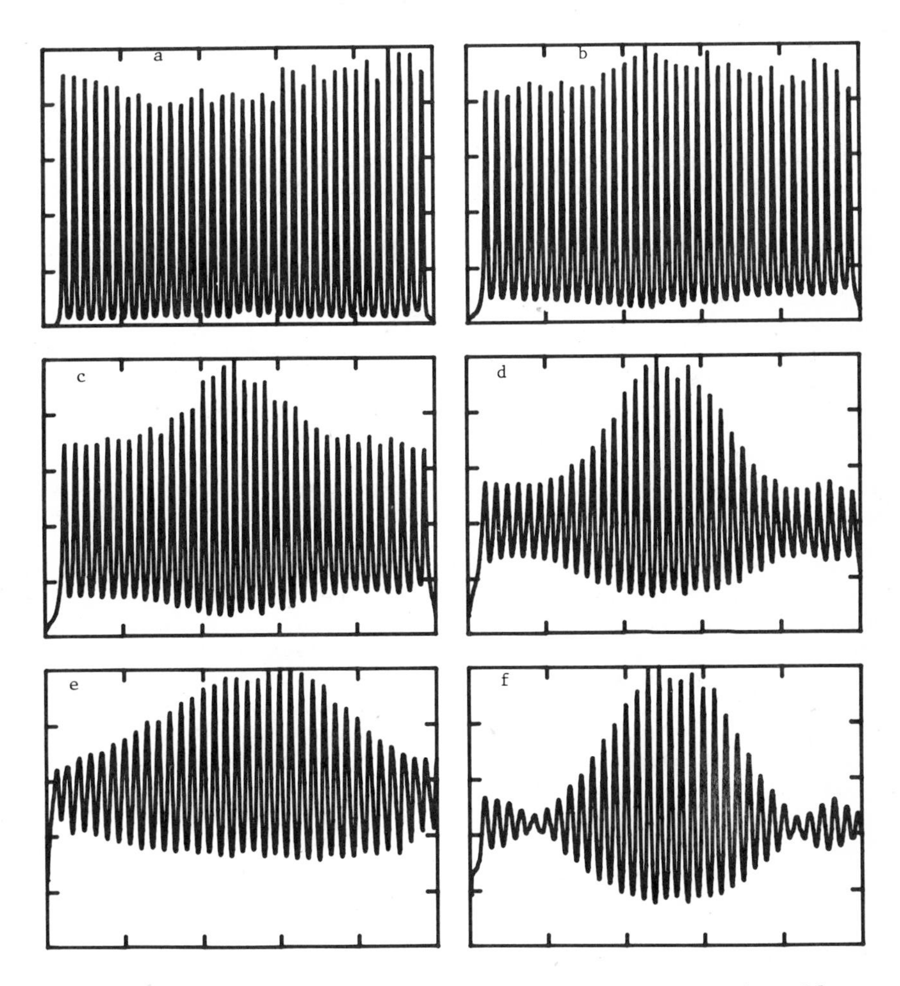

Figure 3. Intensity patterns from ruled disk obtained with varying pulse widths. Ordinate, relative intensity from 0 to 1; abscissa, channel number from 0 to 500. (a) unpulsed; (b) 10 μsec; (c) 5 μsec; (d) 2 μsec; (e) 1 μsec; (f) 1 μsec but changed from 700 to 800 V.

the Model 1211 pulse generator would be sufficient to render negligible the contribution (1%) of the defocused image accumulated during the 50 nsec rise and fall periods of the pulse. When it was found that the line images from the pulsed SIT vidicon were not as sharp as those from the vidicon operated in the continuous mode, a more detailed study of the effect of pulse width on image quality was undertaken.

For these studies the ruled disk was placed in the rotor and adjusted as described earlier. The lamp position was adjusted to give the most uniform illumination possible at a wavelength of 265 nm. The pulse frequency, 578 Hz, was equivalent to a rotor speed of 33,467 rpm. For each pulse width, a sufficient number of scans were accumulated to give between 80,000 and 90,000 counts maximum. For the shorter pulse widths, the entrance slit of the monochromator was widened to increase light throughput. The accumulated patterns for the ruled disk were corrected for nonuniform illumination and nonuniform response of the vidicon with a normalizing pattern obtained when the rotor was turned to an open hole. The number of scans for the latter pattern was reduced to give about the same maximum number of counts. The intensity of each channel of the ruled disk pattern was divided by the intensity of the same channel of the open pattern obtained at the same pulse width. The resulting relative intensity pattern was normalized by multiplying by a constant so as to give a value of 1 for the channel with the maximum relative intensity.

The relative intensity patterns obtained from this study are shown in Figure 3. Compared to the unpulsed pattern (a), the line images from the 10 μsec pulsed pattern (b) are less sharp. The minima in the center are elevated and the elevation increases progressively on both sides away from the center. Enlarged portions of the sides and center of the patterns are shown in Figure 4a and b. These patterns are correctly shown as bar graphs to emphasize that each channel segment gives an average of the light striking it. The lines for the unpulsed SIT vidicon are symmetrical across the pattern. For the pulsed SIT vidicon the lines in the center are symmetrical, but the lines away from the center become progressively rounded at the bottom on the side facing away from the center.

Since a 1% contribution of changing defocused images (based upon the relative times of the rise and fall periods of the pulse to the total duration) would produce only a small effect on the final pattern, one can only conclude that inside the intensifier stage there exists a defocused state that is considerably longer than the 100 nsec combined rise and fall times measured outside the tube. Moreover the progressive distortion away from the center of the pattern is what one would expect from a substantial contribution of images of greater magnification caused by reduced voltages during the rise and fall of the voltage inside the intensifier stage.

More information as to the actual duration of the defocused

time period can be obtained by examination of patterns obtained for shorter pulses. At 5 μsec (Figure 3c) the progressive deterioration of lines away from the center increases. At 2 μsec (d) the envelope of maxima and manima narrows more rapidly away from the center, then remains flat. At 1 μsec (e) the pattern changes its appearance, with increased deterioration away from the center. At 1 μsec, increasing the pulse voltage from 700 to 800 V improves the sharpness of the lines in the center, but the lines away from the center deteriorate progressively then appear to improve slightly at the edges of the pattern (f). The envelope minima and maxima appear to converge, meet (or crossover, perhaps), then diverge again in a manner suggestive of a phase inversion, and the spacing of the line images is discontinuous at the crossover regions. Moreover the positions of the crossovers changed with pulse magnitide and width.

There are at least two kinds of changes in the appearance of the patterns as the pulse width is decreased, which suggests that more than one process is involved as the voltages of the photocathode rise and fall at the beginning and end of the pulse. We did not investigate the defocused condition any farther, as there were two ways of eliminating the defocused portion of the image.

With the ultracentrifuge the SIT vidicon can be gated outside the cell opening, thereby limiting the defocused state to periods of darkness while providing correct focusing for the cell opening. However, properly focused images of the ruled disc are still needed to provide the magnification factor and a measure of the pincushion distortion for ultracentrifuge patterns.

For both pulse generators that we have examined, the shape of the pulse edges, as shown on the oscilloscope screen, remains the same as the pulse width is progressively increased. One can hypothesize that a correct pattern for the focused state might be obtained from two pulses of different length, but both sufficiently long to allow the intensifier stage to reach the conditions for correct focus. It is likely that the contribution of the rise and fall periods to the final image would be the same for both pulses. By subtracting the image of the shorter pulse from that of the longer pulse, one would obtain a correctly focused difference image corresponding to the central portion of the longer pulse.

This hypothesis was tested by combining the images obtained for different widths shown above to obtain difference images. even though the procedure for data gathering was not fully satisfactory. Only the relative intensity patterns, not the individual disk and air patterns, had been recorded on the diskettes. Moreover since the rotor had been moved to record disk and air patterns for each pulse width, there was no assurance that the disk had always been returned to its original position, even though a reference mark on the rotor and a stationary pointer had been used as alignment aids. Finally a variety of slit widths had been used for the monochromator.

To obtain a difference pattern from the normalized patterns, it was necessary to reduce the magnitude of the pattern for the shorter pulse to a size corresponding to the relative length of the pulses; this was accomplished by multiplying the intensities for the shorter pulse by the ratio of the pulse widths. Difference patterns for 10-5, 10-3, 5-3 and 3-2 μsec (not shown) were of a quality similar to the pattern obtained from the continuous SIT vidicon, with minima near the zero level. However, the 2-1 μsec difference pattern was unsatisfactory, with the line maxima progressively decreasing in intensity away from the center. In Table I are listed the magnification factors obtained for the difference patterns and the 1 μsec pattern (1-0 μsec) from the least squares straight line through the centers of the 12 lines in the center of the pattern. The increase in magnification for the 2-1 and 1 μsec patterns suggests that during the time periods encompassing the first and last microsecond of the pulse, the SIT vidicon is in a defocused state. The contribution from these periods is sufficient to warp patterns obtained from pulses 3-10 μsec long and even longer. In spite of the deficiencies in the data gathering, this study demonstrates that the defocused portion of a pattern can be removed by the use of appropriate difference patterns.

TABLE I

Magnification of Difference Patterns

Difference Pattern	Magnification Factor Channels/mm
10-5 μsec	26.69
10-3 μsec	26.68
5-3 μsec	26.56
3-2 μsec	26.65
2-1 μsec	27.19
1-0 μsec	28.39

Since the study described above was performed with a borrowed Model 1211 pulse generator, we deemed it advisable to examine patterns obtained with our Model 340 Velonex pulse generator to see if it exhibited the same behavior. The experimental procedures were changed to avoid the problems described above and two new parameters were investigated. The wavelength was changed to 405 nm. The line images should be sharper, since more of the light is transmitted directly, thereby avoiding the randomization of the entrance angle caused by wavelength conversion within the scintillation film. Even though relative intensity patterns had been obtained earlier for 5 voltages encompassing 650-750 V, it was possible that difference patterns would provide more information as to the effect of voltage on image quality. Therefore difference patterns were obtained for 725 V, the voltage that gave the sharpest pattern for the Velonex pulser, and also at 700 and 750 V.

After adjusting the illumination of the cell for 405 nm light the camera lens was moved to refocus the ruled disk. With the ruled disk in the same position, patterns for 8.96 and 4.48 μsec pulse widths were obtained at the three voltages mentioned above. Since the voltage of the Velonex pulse generator increased slightly when the pulse width was reduced, a slight adjustment of the voltage control was required to maintain the same voltage for the shorter pulse. Moreover the voltage across the pulse was not constant; it was arbitrarily decided to adjust the height of the shorter pulse, as observed on the oscilloscope screen, to match the first half of the longer pulse. For each pattern sufficient scans were accumulated to bring the maximum counts to between 90,000 and 100,000 counts, but the monochromator slit was not touched. After the six patterns for the ruled disk were obtained, six patterns were obtained for air with the same sequence of voltages and pulse widths. For each image, the intensities were divided by the number of scans. Then for each of the three voltages the difference in the images for the disk at the two pulse widths was divided, channel by channel, by the difference in the images for air. Then the relative difference patterns were normalized as before to give a maximum value of 1.

The line images for the patterns obtained at the two pulse widths were distorted as was shown in Figure 3. However, the quality of the line images in the normalized difference pattern for 725 V (Figure 4c) were as good as those obtained for the unpulsed SIT vidicon. There is only a small amount of increased curvature at the minima on the side of the lines away from the center. The difference patterns for 700 and 750 V (not shown) were more rounded at the minima between the lines, but careful examination provided no improved criteria for their use in determining the optimum focus voltage.

Even though the intensity profile of a line or knife-edge image is distorted by pulse shape and pincushion distortion, one would expect the profile obtained from an image with nearly uniform illumination to be considerably less affected. The normalized air patterns obtained at 725 V for the two pulse widths (not shown) were the same, except for small differences at the sides of the pattern.

A comparison of the difference pattern for the pulsed SIT vidicon (Figure 4c) and the pattern for the unpulsed SIT vidicon (a) reveals that the minima between the lines are closer to the zero level for the former pattern. Since we had changed the wavelength from 265 to 405 nm to investigate the effect of the fluorescent film on channel-to-channel crosstalk, it seemed likely that the increased sharpness of the lines for the difference pattern was due to this change. To confirm this conclusion and also to verify that the improved methodology gives good difference patterns in a reproducible fashion the ruled disk and air patterns

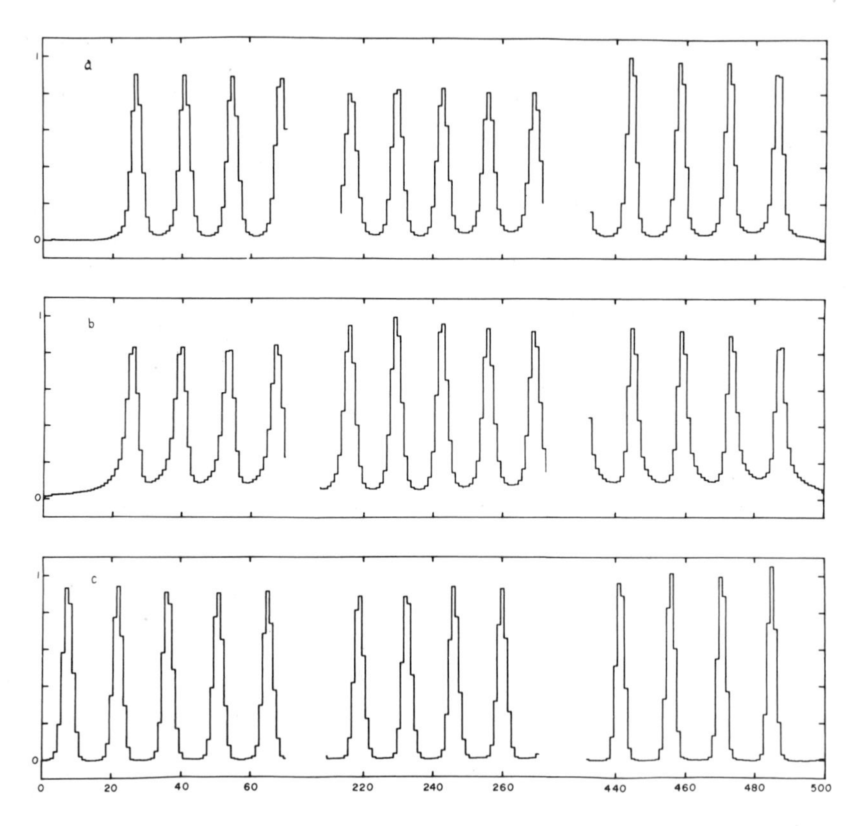

Figure 4. Magnified line images for ruled disk at sides and center of image. (a) unpulsed; (b) 10 μsec pulse; (c) difference pattern for 8.96–4.48 sec.

were obtained for the two pulse widths at 725 V using light at 265 nm. The normalized difference pattern (not shown) closely resembled the pattern for the unpulsed SIT vidicon (Figure 4a) with raised minima, thereby verifying that the fluorescent film slightly increased the channel-to-channel crosstalk.

Pincushion Distortion. The major aim of the study involving the ruled disk was the measurement of the distortion of the image introduced by the intensifier stage of the SIT vidicon, which is known to be of the "pincushion" type. Since the spacing of the lines on the disk is accurate to 1 μm, the distortion is easily measured, in principle, by plotting the channel number of the peak position of the line image against the distance of that line from the first line. The measurements from the disk can be translated to distances from the center of the rotor by comparison with the channel numbers obtained from the reference edges of the counterbalance cell (Figure 1).

Knowing the size of the image on the faceplate of the SIT vidicon, one could also measure the distortion in terms of the distance from the center of the tube. Based on early measurements with film placed at the image plane, we know that the image has a magnification of about 0.5. Since experiments are performed at a variety of wavelengths, requiring a change in camera lens position with a change in magnification, we are concerned only with the final magnification of the electronic image compared to the distance in the cell. The "Frame Scan" potentiometer is frequently adjusted to move the image of the reference holes to positions near the outer edges of the pattern; a magnification factor is then obtained with the ruled disk. Thus, for our purposes the measurement of distortion relative to distances on the faceplate serves no purpose.

The patterns obtained from the study of distortion caused by pulsing were examined for radial distortion. Since the line images are not necessarily symmetrical and most of the light for each line is spread over 8 to 10 channels, a problem arises concerning the definition of the line center. Based upon an approximation to a gaussian shape, $y = \exp(-x^2)$, we chose to fit the log of the intensities for each group of points to a cubic equation. The use of a cubic equation permitted a better approximation to the asymmetric profile. The position of the line was determined by calculating the x position where the slope, determined from the first derivative, was 0. (A different procedure, not tried, would be to sum the intensities and to find the fractional channel number that would place half the light intensity on both sides of that number.)

Examination of many plots of image line position vs. actual line position revealed that the center 11 to 13 points were nearly linear, with the other points, upon moving on either side away from the center, deviating progressively from a straight line. To best demonstrate the distortion, the positions for the 12 lines in the center were fit with a least mean squares straight line, then the difference between the measured line positions and the positions calculated by extending the straight line was calculated. Three such plots for the unpulsed SIT vidicon and the difference plots obtained for 725 V with illumination at 265 and 405 nm are shown in Figure 5. The x dimension has been converted to distances in the cell measured from the center of the rotor. The deviation approaches 0.02 cm at the extremities, which corresponds to 4 channel numbers. The pattern deviates more on the right, indicating that the frame scan is not centered with respect to the faceplate, an adjustment that could easily be made.

It should be emphasized that these plots represent the combined distortion caused by the camera lens and the SIT vidicon. The plots could be used to correct data obtained from ultracentrifuge experiments.

For some experiments only the 6.7 to 7.2 cm region of the cell is actually used. Thus a 10 μsec pulse pattern was obtained with the vidicon moved a distance corresponding to 125 channels, so as to place its center over the region of interest. The plot of deviation *vs*. channel number, for this image, was the same as that obtained for the centered image, indicating that the distortion arose entirely from the SIT vidicon.

Channel-to-Channel Crosstalk. In one of the brochures supplied by the manufacturer of the OMA the channel-to-channel crosstalk for the SIT vidicon is stated in these terms: with a 10 μm line centered on a channel, more than 60% of the signal amplitude is centered in that channel and more than 98% of the signal is in that channel and the two adjacent channels. Some of the patterns obtained from the ruled disk studies were examined to see if they were suitable for the measurement of crosstalk.

The lines on the ruled disk are 80 μm wide in the radial direction; at the plane of the SIT vidicon faceplate, they are reduced to half that width, or about 40 μm. The width of an OMA channel element is 25 μm. Thus one can make an estimate of crosstalk by centering a line between two channels. The relative intensities for such a line are normalized so that the sum has a value of 2. The normalized relative intensity for one of the center channels is $f_0 + f_1$; for the next three channels it is $f_1 + f_2$, $f_2 + f_3$, and f_3, respectively, where f_0 refers to the fraction of signal in the center channel, and f_1, f_2, and f_3 are the fractions for the successive channels on both sides. The sum, $f_0 + 2(f_1 + f_2 + f_3)$, should be 1.

The calculated f values for the unpulsed pattern at 265 nm and the difference pattern at 405 nm are given in Table II. The crosstalk for the first pattern was higher; in fact an f_4 value should have been included. The higher values are due to the effect of the fluorescent film. We have no way of determining whether a 10 μm line centered on a channel would give the same values with our system as the values given by the manufacturer

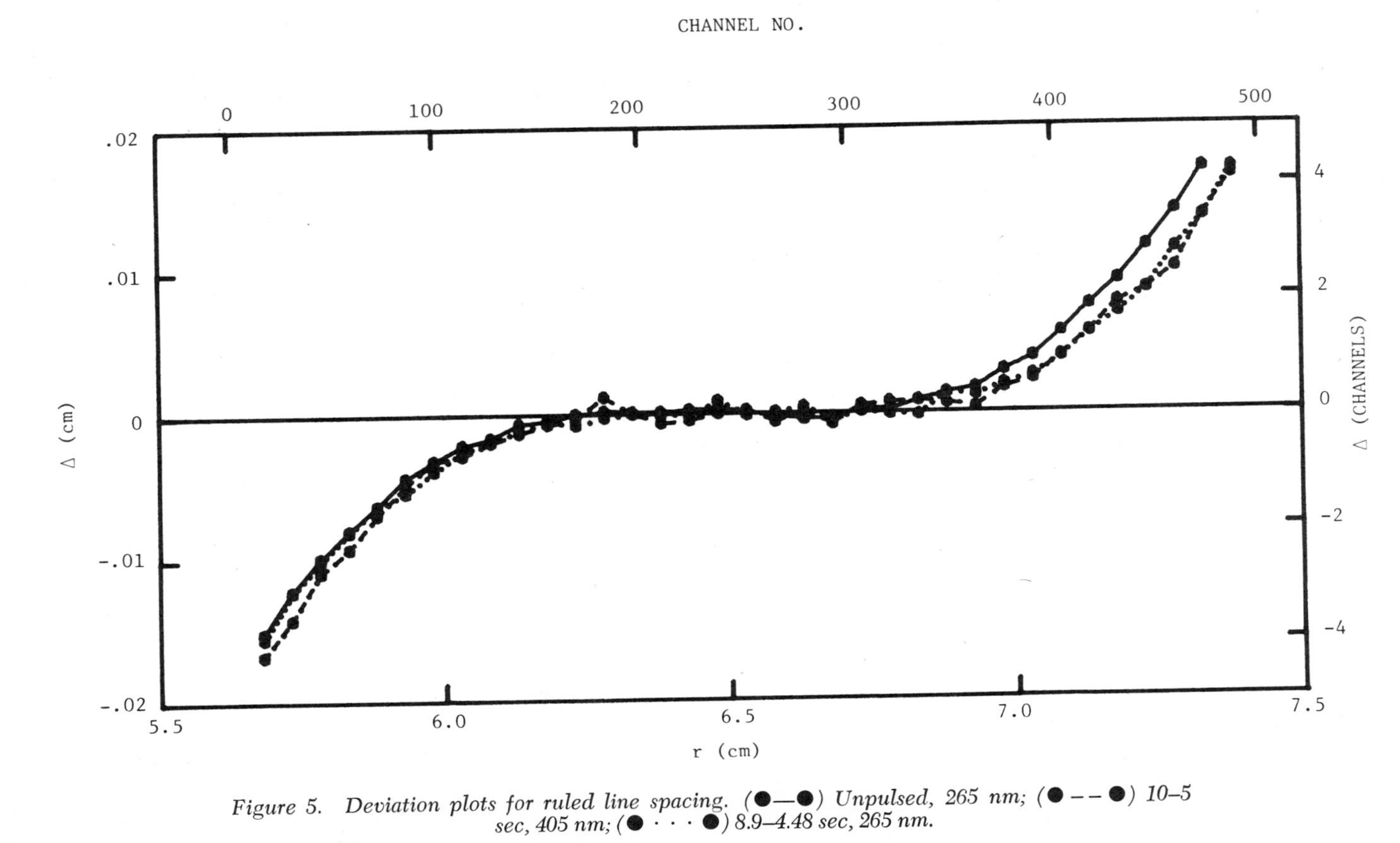

Figure 5. Deviation plots for ruled line spacing. (●—●) *Unpulsed, 265 nm;* (● – – ●) *10–5 sec, 405 nm;* (● · · · ●) *8.9–4.48 sec, 265 nm.*

for their system. Since our optical system is more complicated, it is possible that our higher values arose from reflection of light from the disk and/or lens surfaces. Nevertheless, we can check, when necessary, to see whether a correction for crosstalk with our values would change significantly the measured intensities.

TABLE II

Channel-to-Channel Crosstalk

	Unpulsed Image at 265 nm	Difference Pattern at 405 nm[a]
f_0	0.248	0.324
f_1	0.227	0.236
f_2	0.091	0.081
f_3	0.057	0.020

[a] Average of 3 line measurements

Accuracy of Measurement of Absorbance Gradients. As stated earlier, we set as a starting target the ability of our OMA system to measure concentration gradients corresponding to the absorbance range from 0 to 1 with an accuracy of 0.001 absorbance units. The assessment of the performance of the system requires the measurement of the intensity profile for an optical density wedge with a precisely known gradient.

The classical way of assessing the behavior of an ultracentrifuge optical system has been to measure the sedimentation behavior of solutes, usually proteins. In one type of experiment, called sedimentation velocity, a uniform solution is spun in a rotor at a high speed, and the shape of the boundary is examined as it moves toward the bottom of the cell. The shape of boundary, while resembling an integrated gaussian curve, is distorted by a number of effects difficult to assess, including diffusion, deviation from ideal behavior, inhomogeneity of centrifugal field, shape of cell, and even convection.

The usual method, then, is to perform a sedimentation equilibrium experiment, in which a solution containing a solute of known behavior is spun at a much lower speed until the concentration gradient remains invariant with time. The distribution of solute for an ideal, two-component system should correspond to the equation, where c is the concentration of solute with

$$\frac{d \ln c}{d r^2} = \frac{M(1 - \overline{V}\rho)\omega^2}{2RT}$$

molecular weight M and partial specific volume $\overline{V}$, r is the radius from the center of the rotor, ω is the angular velocity, R is the gas constant, T is the absolute temperature, and ρ is the density of the solvent.

The behavior of the optical system is assessed by plotting ln c (absorbance in this case) vs. r^2. The plot should be linear and the molecular weight calculated from the known partial specific volume and the other constants should agree closely with the known value, typically within 1 or 2%.

The results from a recent experiment with the oxidized disulfide form of coenzyme A are shown in Figure 6. Five double-sector cells, each containing solution and solvent, were placed in a six-cell rotor, which was allowed to spin overnight in order to achieve equilibrium. The absorbance profiles for light at 265 nm were recorded, adjusting the number of scans so as to give about 300,000 counts for the lower concentration region.

The plots for ln A vs. Δr^2 (Figure 6) are linear, with the expected amount of scatter for the absorbance range 0.3-0.8. The agreement of the slopes (0.2323, 0.2368, 0.2325 and 0.2369 with an average value of 0.2349 cm^{-2}) is satisfactory.

An exact value of $\bar{V}$ is not known, but we have obtained a value of 0.556 ml/g from preliminary sedimentation equilibrium measurements in mixtures of H_2O and D_2O (16). A value of 0.563 ml/g was estimated from known atomic and molar volumes (17,18). These values for $\bar{V}$ gave molecular weights of 1480 and 1500, respectively, in good agreement with the known molecular weight of 1532 for the acid form of oxidized coenzyme A. We have also obtained good molecular weight values for sperm whale myoglobin.

Even though one can obtain good agreement between the measured and calculated light intensity profiles for sedimentation equilibrium experiments, this method has drawbacks for the routine assessment of the performance of the optical system. There is not commercially available a standard solute with guaranteed purity and certified sedimentation behavior. Moreover each experiment requires a correction baseline obtained from the cells spun with both sectors filled with solvent. Since a time period of 8 hr or more is required to achieve equilibrium, it becomes a formidible task to investigate the effect of a number of parameters.

We turned to the possibility of using an optical density wedge to provide a light intensity gradient. For sedimentation velocity experiments, the wedge should have a range from 0 to about 1.5 absorbance units over a distance of about 1.3 cm, the normal span of an ultracentrifuge cell. For sedimentation equilibrium experiments a suitable wedge would range from 0 to 1.2 absorbance units over a distance of 3-4 mm. The wedge should transmit uv light. The wedge could be either held stationary or spun in an appropriate holder in a rotor. It is unlikely that such small wedges are commercially available. They could be specially constructed, but, before use, their density profile would have to be measured with a densitometer of proven accuracy using a very narrow slit. Such wedges would be difficult to make.

We decided to test the feasibility of spinning a geometrical

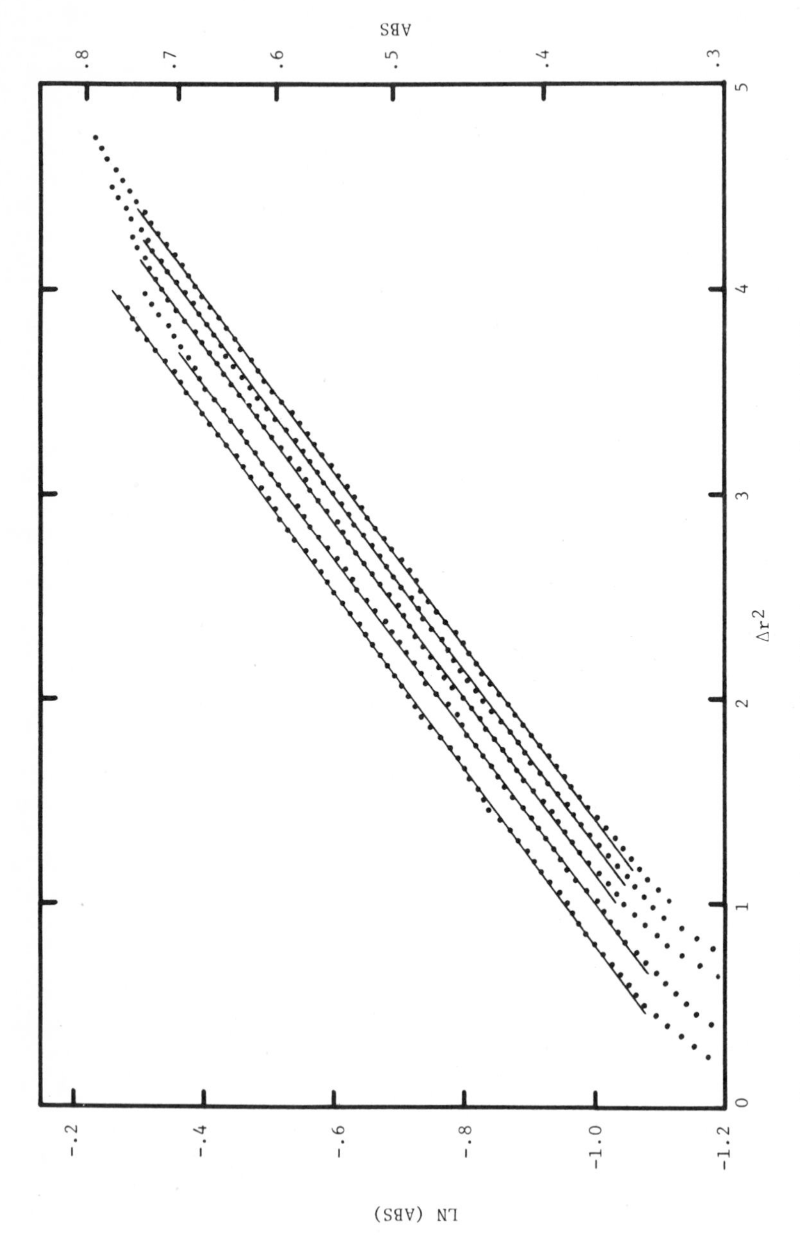

Figure 6. Sedimentation equilibrium of oxidized coenzyme A. Speed, 40,000 rpm; temperature, 20.0°; wavelength, 265 nm; solvent, 0.05M potassium phosphate, pH 6.8.

shape to provide a light flux gradient in the radial direction. A special mask pattern was transferred to a quartz window of a centrifuge cell using the same procedure described above for the ruled disk. On the mask were two, 1° sector openings, one of which tapered to a point over the range corresponding to 6.7 to 7.10 cm. Centered between them were three radial reference lines. The edges of the two openings were measured with a Nikon Model 6c shadowgraph to an accuracy of 1.25 μm, and it was found that the equations for the edges agreed extremely well with those calculated. The mask was spun in a cell filled with water. On the first attempt the light intensity profile agreed closely with that calculated from the geometry of the two profiles. However, with the entire system improved, recent measurements with the spinning mask showed a larger deviation between the two profiles. No improvement was observed when the focus plane was changed from the one-half plane of the cell to the mask plane, which was on the lower surface of the window. Changing the mask window to the top of the cell, with the camera lens focused on the mask, offered no improvement.

We are baffled as to the cause of the discrepancy between the calculated and measured intensity curves. The mathematics of the calculated curve needs to be refined to include the width of the slit above the rotor, which we had assumed to be negligible. Perhaps the effect of changing the slit width and the focus plane in the cell should be examined. Based on the good results obtained from sedimentation equilibrium experiments, we believe that the SIT vidicon, OMA electronics, and our software controlling the gathering of data are all behaving properly, but perhaps there are still problems to be solved.

Conclusions

In general, we are satisfied with the performance of our OMA-based light detector system for the absorption optical system in the ultracentrifuge. Many of the problems that we had to solve were inherent in the optical system and the cells, but were hidden to users with photomultiplier detector systems. Other problems associated with the SIT vidicon have been satisfactorily solved. We intend to examine the problem of the mask in the spinning rotor. We also intend to construct a quartz disk with lines that are arcs about the center of the rotor. Placed in a special holder at a plane equivalent to the mid-plane in a normal cell, it would provide radial magnification and correction information for any experiment.

We are looking, with anticipation, to the development of improved solid-state detectors with increased sensitivity in the uv region and no distortion.

Acknowledgment

This work was supported by the Medical Research Service of the Veterans Administration and USPHS NIH grant HL #14938.

Literature Cited

1. Richards, E.G., and Rockholt, D., Arch. Biochem. Biophys. (1973) 158, 864.
2. Rockholt, D.L., Royce, C.R., and Richards, E.G., Biophysical Chem. (1976) 5, 55.
3. Svedberg, T., and Rinde, H., J. Am. Chem. Soc. (1924) 46, 2577.
4. Svedberg, T., and Pederson, K., "The Ultracentrifuge." The Clarendon Press, Oxford (1940). Reprinted, the Johnson Reprint Corp., New York (1959).
5. Hanlon, S., Lamers, K., Lauterbach, G., Johnson, R., and Schachman, H.K., Arch. Biochem. Biophys. (1962) 99, 157.
6. Lamers, K., Putney, F., Steinberg, I.A., and Schachman, H.K., Arch. Biochem. Biophys. (1963) 103, 379.
7. Chervenka, C.A., Fractions, Spinco Division of Beckman Instruments, Inc., Palo Alto, CA. (1971).
8. Crepeau, R.H., Edelstein, S.J., and Rehman, M.J., Analyt. Biochem. (1972) 50, 213.
9. Williams, Jr., R.C., Biophysical Chem. (1976) 5, 19.
10. Spragg, S.P., Burnett, W.A., Wilcox, J.K., and Roche, J., Biophysical Chem. (1976) 5, 43.
11. Cohen, R., Cluzel, J., Cohen, H., Male, P., Moigner, M., and Soulié, C., Biophysical Chem. (1976) 5, 77.
12. Wei, G.J., and Deal, Jr., W.C., Arch. Biochem. Biophys. (1977) 183, 605.
13. Lloyd, P.H., and Esnouf, M.P., Analyt. Biochem. (1974) 60, 25.
14. Rockholt, D.L., and Richards, E.G., Fed. Proc. (1976) 35, 1457.
15. Schachman, H.K., Gropper, L., Hanlon, S., and Putney, F., Arch. Biochem. Biophys. (1962) 99, 175.
16. Richards, E.G., and Rockholt, D.L., Fed. Proc. (1978) 37, 1710.
17. Cohn, E.J., and Edsall, J.T., eds., "Proteins, Amino Acids and Peptides." Reinhold Publishing Corp., New York (1943).
18. McMeekin, T.L., Groves, M.L., and Hipp, N.J., J. Am. Chem. Soc. (1949) 71, 3298.

RECEIVED February 7, 1979.

INDEX

INDEX

F

G

H

I

J

K

L

M

R

S

W